CLINICAL CHEMISTRY
IN
DIAGNOSIS AND TREATMENT

Clinical Chemistry
in
Diagnosis and Treatment

JOAN F. ZILVA
M.D., B.Sc., F.R.C.P., M.R.C.Path., D.C.C. (Biochem.)

*Senior Lecturer in Chemical Pathology, Westminster
Medical School, London; Honorary Consultant in Chemical
Pathology, Westminster Hospital, London*

and

P. R. PANNALL
M.B., B.Ch. (Witwatersrand), F.F.Path. (S.A.)., M.R.C.Path.

*Senior Lecturer in Chemical Pathology,
University of the Orange Free State Medical School;
Senior Specialist in Chemical Pathology, National Hospital,
Bloemfontein; Formerly Registrar in Chemical Pathology,
Westminster Hospital, London*

(*Reprint*)

LLOYD-LUKE (MEDICAL BOOKS) LTD
49 NEWMAN STREET
LONDON
1973

FIRST EDITION 1971
Reprinted   1972
Reprinted   1973

PRINTED AND BOUND IN ENGLAND BY
THE WHITEFRIARS PRESS LTD
LONDON AND TONBRIDGE
ISBN 0 85324 095 7

FOREWORD

THIS book aims at giving, within a single cover, all the relevant bio-chemical and pathological facts and theories necessary to the intelligent interpretation of the analyses usually performed in departments of Clinical Chemistry or Chemical Pathology. The approach is firmly based on general principles and the authors have gone to great trouble to ensure that the development of ideas is logical and easy to follow. A basic knowledge of medicine and of elementary biochemistry is assumed but, given this, the reader should be able to understand even the more involved metabolic inter-relationships without undue difficulty and should thereafter be in a strong position to apply this knowledge in medical practice.

I have appreciated very much the opportunity of reading this book during its preparation and feel that it represents a distinctly novel approach to the interpretation of biochemical data. In my opinion it could be read with advantage by all the categories of reader mentioned in the preface, and moreover I believe that they will enjoy the experience.

N. F. MACLAGAN.

January, 1971

PREFACE

THIS book is intended primarily for medical students and junior hospital staff. It is based on many years practical experience of undergraduate and postgraduate teaching, and of the problems of a routine chemical pathology department. It is written for those who learn best if they understand what they are learning. Wherever possible, explanations of the facts are given: if the explanation is a working hypothesis (like, for instance, that for the ectopic production of hormones) this is stressed, and where no explanation is known, this is stated. Our experience of teaching and our discussions with students have led us to believe that many of them are willing to read a slightly longer book if it gives them a better understanding than a shorter one. Electrolyte and acid-base balance have been discussed in some detail because, in our experience, these are the most common problems of chemical pathology met with by junior clinicians and ones in which there are often dangerous misunderstandings. Some subjects, such as the porphyrias and conditions of iron overload, are discussed in greater detail than is necessary for undergraduate examinations: however, the incidence of these is high in some areas of the world, and an elementary source of reference seemed to be needed.

We have tried to stress the clinical importance of an understanding of the subject: by including in the chapter Appendices some details of treatment, difficult to find together in other books, we hope that this one may appeal to clinicians as well as to students. Two chapters are included on the best use of a laboratory, including precautions which should be taken in collecting specimens and interpreting results. As we have stressed, pathologists and clinicians should work as a team, and full consultation between the two should be the rule. The diagnostic tests suggested are those which we have found, by experience, to be the most valuable. For instance, in the differential diagnosis of hypercalcaemia we find the steroid suppression test very helpful, phosphate excretion indices fallible and tedious to perform and estimation of urinary calcium useless.

Our own junior staff have found the drafts helpful in preparing for the Part 1 examination for Membership of the Royal College of Physicians, as well as for the primary examination for Membership of the Royal College of Pathologists, and our Senior Technicians are using it to study for the Special Examination for Fellowship in Chemical Pathology of the Institute of Medical Laboratory Technology. We feel that those studying for the primary examination for the Fellowship of the Royal College of Surgeons might also make use of it. It could provide a groundwork for study for the final examination for the Membership of the Royal College of Pathologists in Chemical Pathology, and for the Mastership in Clinical Biochemistry.

Initially each chapter should be worked through from beginning to end. For revision purposes there are lists and tables, and summaries of the contents of each chapter. The short sub-indices in the Table of Contents should facilitate the use of the book for reference.

Appendix A lists some analogous facts which we hope may help understanding and learning. The list must be far from complete, and the student should seek other examples for himself.

We wish to thank Professor N. F. Maclagan for his unfailing encouragement and his helpful advice and criticisms. We are also indebted to a great many other people, foremost amongst whom we should mention Dr. J. P. Nicholson who has read and commented on the whole book, and Professor M. D. Milne, Professor D. M. Matthews, Mr. K. B. Cooke and Dr. B. W. Gilliver for helpful advice and criticism on individual chapters. Many registrars and senior house officers in the Department, in particular Dr. Krystyna Rowland, Dr. Elizabeth Small, Dr. Nalini Naik and Dr. Noel Walmsley, have been closely involved in the preparation of the book and have provided invaluable suggestions and criticisms. Students, too, have read individual chapters for comprehensibility, and we would particularly like to thank Mr. B. P. Heather, Mr. J. Muir and Miss H. M. Merriman for helpful comments. Mr. C. P. Butler of the Westminster Hospital Pharmacy was most helpful during the preparation of the sections on therapy. Mrs. Valerie Moorsom and Mrs. Marie-Lise Pannall, with the help of Mrs. Brenda Sarasin and Miss Barbara Bridges, have borne with us during the typing of the drafts and the final manuscript. The illustrations were prepared by Mr. David Gibbons of the Department of Medical Photography and Illustration of the Westminster Medical School.

Finally, we should like to thank the publishers for their co-operation and understanding during the preparation of this book.

May, 1971

J.F.Z.
P.R.P.

CONTENTS

FOREWORD v

PREFACE vii

ABBREVIATIONS USED IN THE BOOK xxv

I THE KIDNEYS: RENAL CALCULI . . . I

The Kidneys, 1
  Normal Renal Function
    Glomerular Filtration
    Tubular Function
      Homeostasis of Solute
      Homeostasis of Water
  Chemical Pathology of Kidney Disease
    Glomerular Dysfunction
      Reduced Glomerular Filtration Rate
      Nephrotic Syndrome (Increased Glomerular
        Permeability)
    Tubular Dysfunction
    Generalized Renal Failure
  Investigation of Renal Function
  Biochemical Principles of Treatment of
    Renal Dysfunction

Renal Calculi, 18

Summary, 21

Appendix, 23

II SODIUM, POTASSIUM AND WATER METABOLISM . 25

Water and Electrolyte Balance, 26
  Intake and Output
  Assessment of State of Hydration

Distribution of Water and Electrolytes in
the Body, 29
Distribution of Electrolytes
Osmotic and Colloid Osmotic Pressure
Distribution of Water Across Cell Walls
Distribution of Water Across Blood Vessel Walls

Clinical Features of Water and Sodium
Disturbances, 33
Disturbances of Sodium Concentration
Disturbances of Fluid Volume

Control of Electrolyte and Water Metabolism, 34
Control of Electrolytes
Control of Water
Interrelationship Between Sodium and Water
Homeostasis

Disturbances of Sodium and Water
Metabolism, 38
Predominant Water Depletion
Predominant Sodium Depletion
Predominant Excess of Water
Predominant Excess of Sodium

Disturbances of Potassium Metabolism, 48
Excessive Loss of Potassium
Changes in Plasma in Potassium Depletion
Plasma Potassium Levels

Biochemical Basis of Treatment, 52
Sodium and Water
Potassium

Summary, 53

Appendix, 55

III   ACID-BASE BALANCE : BLOOD GAS LEVELS .   .   59

Acid-Base Balance, 59

Definitions
Acid-Base Homeostasis
General
Tissue Cells
Extracellular Fluid
Erythrocytes and Lungs
The Kidneys
Sodium, Potassium and Glomerular Filtration
Rate in Acid-Base Homeostasis
Chloride in Acid-Base Homeostasis

Disturbances of Acid-Base Balance

Acidosis
Hydrogen Ion Excess with Normal
Homeostasis
Failure of Homeostatic Mechanisms
Renal
Respiratory
Mixed Respiratory and Non-Respiratory
Acidosis
Bicarbonate Depletion
Effect of Acidosis on Potassium
Metabolism
Alkalosis
Pyloric Stenosis
Potassium Depletion
Respiratory Alkalosis

Assessment of Acid-Base Balance

Blood Gas Levels, 84

Summary, 86

Appendix, 88

IV   ADRENAL CORTEX   89

Chemistry of Adrenal Steroids, 89

Physiology of Adrenal Steroids, 89
Glucocorticoids
Mineralocorticoids
Androgens

Disorders of the Adrenal Cortex, 92
Cushing's Syndrome (Hyperadrenalism)
Addison's Disease (Hypoadrenalism)

Investigation of Adrenocortical Function, 94
Steroid Analyses in Common Use
Causes and Diagnosis of Cushing's Syndrome
Causes and Diagnosis of Addison's Disease

Secondary Adrenal Hypofunction, 100
Disorders and Investigation of the
Hypothalamic-Pituitary-Adrenal Axis
Corticosteroid Therapy

Congenital Adrenal Hyperplasia, 104

Summary, 107

Appendix, 109

V   PITUITARY AND OVARIAN HORMONES   .   .   112

General, 112
Principles of Control of Pituitary Hormone
Secretion
Measurement of Pituitary Hormones

Growth Hormone, 115
Physiology
Acromegaly and Gigantism

Prolactin, 117

Adrenocorticotrophic Hormone (ACTH), 117

Thyroid Stimulating Hormone (TSH), 118

The Pituitary Gonadotrophins, 118
  Physiology and Menstrual Cycle

Deficiency of Pituitary Hormones, 120
  Panhypopituitarism
  Isolated Pituitary Hormone Deficiency

Summary, 123

VI   DISORDERS OF CARBOHYDRATE METABOLISM   .   125

General, 125
  Chemistry
  Digestion and Absorption

Glucose Metabolism, 126
  Pathways
  Maintenance of Blood Glucose Concentrations
    Hormonal Control
    Physiological Interaction of Hormones
      Ingestion of Glucose
      Fasting
      Stress
    Ketosis
    Glycosuria

Disturbances of Carbohydrate Metabolism, 133
  Measurement of Blood Glucose
  Hyperglycaemia and Diabetes Mellitus
    Nature and Causes
    Pathophysiology and Clinical Features
    Diagnosis
    Glucose Tolerance Test
    Diabetic Ketosis
    Hyperosmolar Coma
    Principles of Treatment of Diabetes

Hypoglycaemia
  Causes
  Insulinoma
  Hypoglycaemia in Adults
  Hypoglycaemia in Children
  Treatment of Hypoglycaemia
  Glycogen Storage Disease

Reducing Substances in the Urine, 149

Summary, 151

Appendix, 153

VII   THYROID FUNCTION   156

  Introduction, 156

  Chemistry, Metabolism and Function, 156

  Disorders of the Thyroid Gland, 159
    Hyperthyroidism
    Hypothyroidism
    Euthyroid Goitre

  Thyroid Function Tests, 162
    Radio-Iodine Uptake Tests
    Measurement of Circulating Thyroid
      Hormone
    Tests Based on Peripheral Action

  Summary, 172

  Appendix, 174

VIII   DISEASES   OF   CALCIUM,   PHOSPHATE   AND
       MAGNESIUM METABOLISM   175

  Calcium Metabolism, 175
    Total Body Calcium
    Plasma Calcium

Clinical Effects of Disorders of Calcium
Metabolism

Effects of Excess Ionized Calcium

Effects of Reduced Ionized Calcium

Effects of High Parathyroid Hormone Levels
on Bone

Diseases of Calcium Metabolism

Diseases Associated with High Parathyroid
Hormone Levels

Inappropriately High Parathyroid
Hormone Levels

Primary Hyperparathyroidism

Tertiary Hyperparathyroidism

Ectopic Production of Parathyroid
Hormone

Secondary Hyperparathyroidism

Diseases Associated with Low Circulating
Parathyroid Hormone Levels

Hypoparathyroidism

Secondary Suppression of Parathyroid
Hormone Secretion by Hypercalcaemia

Diseases of Bone not Affecting Plasma
Calcium Levels

Differential Diagnosis

Differential Diagnosis of Hypercalcaemia

Differential Diagnosis of Hypocalcaemia

Biochemical Basis of Treatment

Magnesium Metabolism, 195

Summary, 196

Appendix, 198

IX   INTESTINAL   ABSORPTION: PANCREATIC   AND
GASTRIC FUNCTION   202

Normal Digestion, 203

Normal Absorption, 203
  Lipid
  Carbohydrate
  Protein
  Vitamin B_{12}
  Electrolyte and Water
  Calcium and Magnesium
  Iron

Malabsorption Syndromes, 209
  Generalized Malabsorption
  Differential Diagnosis of Generalized Intestinal
    and Pancreatic Malabsorption
  Post-Gastrectomy Syndrome
  Tests of Exocrine Pancreatic Function and
    Acute Pancreatitis
  Failure of Absorption of Specific Substances
  Differential Diagnosis of Steatorrhoea

Gastric Function, 219

Summary, 221

Appendix, 223

X   PLASMA PROTEINS AND IMMUNOGLOBULINS   .   227

Plasma Proteins, 227
  General
    Functions
    Total Protein Levels
  Indirect Tests of Altered Plasma Proteins
    Flocculation Tests
    ESR

  Fractionation of Plasma Proteins
    Electrophoresis
    Immunoelectrophoresis

Alteration of Plasma Protein Fractions in
Disease
Albumin
α Globulins
β Globulins
γ Globulins
Electrophoretic Patterns

Immunoglobulins, 236
General
Structure
Classification and Nomenclature
Physiology
Bence-Jones Protein
Disorders of Immunoglobulin Synthesis
Myelomatosis
Macroglobulinaemia
Heavy Chain Disease
Cryoglobulinaemia
Essential Paraproteinaemia
Assessment of Paraproteinaemia
Hypogammaglobulinaemia

Summary, 246

Appendix, 248

XI   PLASMA LIPIDS AND LIPOPROTEINS   .   •   •   249

Introduction, 249

Terminology and Classification, 249
Chemical Classification
Fatty Acids
Triglycerides
Phospholipids
Cholesterol
Lipoproteins
Ultracentrifugation

Metabolism and Functions of Lipids, 253
  Triglycerides and Fatty Acids
  Cholesterol
  Phospholipids
  Role of Liver in Fat Metabolism

Abnormalities of Plasma Lipids, 258
  Hyperlipaemia
  Patterns of Hyperlipoproteinaemia
  Diagnosis of Hyperlipaemia
  Hypolipoproteinaemia

Summary, 262

XII   LIVER DISEASE AND GALL STONES   .   .   .   263

  Liver Disease, 263
    Outline of Functions of the Liver
    Bile Pigment Metabolism
    Disorders of Bile Pigment Metabolism and the
      Classification of Jaundice
    Biochemical Tests in Liver Disease
      Basic Pathological Processes in Liver Disease
      Scope of Tests Used in Liver Disease
      Biochemical Changes in Individual Liver
        Diseases and the Selection of Tests
    Congenital Hyperbilirubinaemia
    Drugs and the Liver

  Bile and Gall Stones, 279

  Summary, 281

  Appendix, 283

XIII PLASMA ENZYMES IN DIAGNOSIS   .   .   .   285

  General, 285

Causes of Altered Plasma Enzyme Levels, 286
  Aminotransferases (Transaminases)
  Lactate Dehydrogenase
  Creatine Phosphokinase
  Amylase
  Alkaline Phosphatase and 5'-nucleotidase
  Acid Phosphatase
  Aldolase
  Isocitrate Dehydrogenase

Enzyme Patterns in Disease, 293
  Myocardial Infarction
  Liver Disease
  Malignant Disease
  Haematological Disorders

Cholinesterase and Succinylcholine Sensitivity, 295

Chemical Pathology of Muscle Disease, 296

Summary, 297

Appendix, 298

XIV DISORDERS OF PURINE AND URIC ACID
    METABOLISM   299

Hyperuricaemia and Gout, 299
  Normal Urate Metabolism
  Causes of Hyperuricaemia
  Dangers of Hyperuricaemia
  Primary Hyperuricaemia and Gout
  Secondary Hyperuricaemia

Hypouricaemia, 306

Summary, 306

XV DISORDERS OF IRON METABOLISM . . . 307

Normal Iron Metabolism, 307
Distribution of Iron in the Body
Iron Balance
Iron Transport

Factors Affecting Plasma Iron Levels, 311
Physiological Factors
Pathological Factors

Transferrin and Total Iron Binding Capacity, 312
Physiological Changes
Pathological Changes

Percentage Saturation of TIBC, 313

Investigation of Anaemia, 315

Iron Therapy, 316

Iron Overload, 316

Summary, 321

XVI THE PORPHYRIAS 323

Biosynthesis and Chemistry of Porphyrins, 323

Normal Porphyrin Metabolism, 325

Screening Tests in Porphyria, 325

Disorders of Porphyrin Metabolism, 325
Classification of the Porphyrias
Hepatic Porphyrias
Acute Intermittent Porphyria
Porphyria Variegata
Acquired Cutaneous Hepatic Porphyria
Hereditary Coproporphyria
Erythropoietic Porphyrias
The Nature of the Porphyrias
Other Causes of Excessive Porphyrin Excretion

Table of Abnormalities in Porphyria, 330

Summary, 331

Appendix, 332

XVII INBORN ERRORS OF METABOLISM . . . 333

General Discussion, 333
Clinical Importance of Inborn Errors of
Metabolism
Patterns of Inheritance

Diseases Due to Inborn Errors of Metabolism, 337
Aminoaciduria
Abnormalities of Transport Mechanisms
Cystinuria
Hartnup Disease
Overflow Aminoaciduria
Maple Syrup Urine Disease
Disorders of Aromatic Amino-Acid
Metabolism
Phenylketonuria
Alkaptonuria
Albinism
Disorders of Carbohydrate Metabolism
Galactosaemia
Disorders of Erythrocyte Metabolism
Glucose-6-phosphate Dehydrogenase
Deficiency
Methaemoglobinaemia
Inherited Deficiencies of Carrier Proteins
Wilson's Disease

Summary, 346

Appendix, 348

XVIII VITAMINS 351

Classification of Vitamins, 351

Fat Soluble Vitamins, 351
Vitamin A
Vitamin D
Vitamin K
Vitamin E

Water Soluble Vitamins, 355
The B Complex
Thiamine
Riboflavin
Nicotinamide
Pyridoxine
Biotin and Pantothenic Acid
Folic Acid and Vitamin B_{12}
Ascorbic Acid (Vitamin C)

Summary, 363

Appendix, 364

XIX PREGNANCY AND ORAL CONTRACEPTIVE THERAPY 365

Assessment of Foeto-Placental Function, 365
Urinary Oestriol
Urinary Pregnanediol
Heat-Stable Alkaline Phosphatase

Metabolic Effects of Pregnancy and Oral
Contraceptive Therapy, 366
Carbohydrate Metabolism
Carrier Proteins
Thyroxine Binding Globulin
Cortisol Binding Globulin
Transferrin
Caeruloplasmin
Lipoproteins

Other Proteins
Plasma Folate Levels
Liver Function Tests
Hormone Secretion

Summary, 370

XX ENDOCRINE EFFECTS OF TUMOURS . . . 371

The Carcinoid Syndrome, 371

Catecholamine Secreting Tumours, 374
Phaeochromocytoma
Neuroblastoma

Hormonal Effects of Tumours of Non-Endocrine
Tissue, 376
Mechanism of Ectopic Hormone Production
Hypercalcaemia
Hyponatraemia
Hypokalaemia
Polycythaemia
Hypoglycaemia
Gynaecomastia
Hyperthyroidism
Carcinoid Syndrome

Summary, 382

XXI THE CEREBROSPINAL FLUID 384

Examination of the CSF, 384
Taking the Sample
Appearance
Protein Content
Glucose Content
Chloride Content

Procedure for Examination of CSF, 388

Summary, 388

XXII   CHEMICAL PATHOLOGY AND THE CLINICIAN   .   389

Introduction, 389

Request Forms, 389

Collection of Specimens, 392
Blood
Urine
Faeces

Labelling Specimens, 397

Sending the Specimen to the Laboratory, 399

Summary, 399

XXIII   INTERPRETING RESULTS   401

Is the Result Normal? 401
Normal Ranges
Physiological Differences
Differences Between Laboratories

Is the Abnormality of Diagnostic Value? 403
Relationship Between Plasma and Cellular Levels
Relationship Between Extracellular
    Concentrations and Total Body Content
Non-Specific Abnormalities

Has There Been a Clinically Significant Change? 404
Reproducibility of Laboratory Estimations
Physiological Variations

Consultation with the Laboratory Staff, 405

Summary, 406

APPENDIX A   407

INDEX   411

Acid Phos.	Acid Phosphatase
ACTH	Adrenocorticotrophic Hormone
ADH	Antidiuretic Hormone ("Pitressin": Vasopressin)
ALA	δ Aminolaevulinic Acid
Al.AT	Alanine Aminotransferase (= SGPT)
Alk. Phos.	Alkaline Phosphatase
A.P.	Alkaline Phosphatase
Asp.AT	Aspartate Aminotransferase (= SGOT)
BEI	Butanol Extractable Iodine
BJP	Bence-Jones Protein
BMR	Basal Metabolic Rate
BSP	Bromsulphthalein
CBG	Cortisol-Binding Globulin (Transcortin)
CoA	Coenzyme A
CPK	Creatine Phosphokinase
CRF	Corticotrophin Releasing Factor
CSF	Cerebrospinal Fluid
DIT	Di-iodotyrosine
DNA	Deoxyribonucleic Acid
DOC	Deoxycorticosterone
DOPA	Dihydroxyphenylalanine
DOPamine	Dihydroxyphenylethylamine
DPN	Diphosphopyridine Nucleotide (= NAD)
EDTA	Ethylene Diamine Tetraacetate (Sequestrene)
EM Pathway	Embden-Meyerhof Pathway (Glycolytic Pathway)
ESR	Erythrocyte Sedimentation Rate
FBS	Fasting Blood Sugar
FFA	Free Fatty Acids (= NEFA)
FSH	Follicle Stimulating Hormone
FTI	Free Thyroxine Index
GFR	Glomerular Filtration Rate
GH	Growth Hormone
GOT	Glutamate Oxaloacetate Transaminase (= ASD AT)
G-6-P	Glucose-6-Phosphate
G-6-PD	Glucose 6-Phosphate Dehydrogenase
GPT	Glutamate Pyruvate Transaminase (= Al.AT)
GTT	Glucose Tolerance Test
HBD	Hydroxybutyrate Dehydrogenase
HDL	High Density Lipoprotein
5HIAA	5-Hydroxyindole Acetic Acid
HMMA	4-Hydroxy-3-Methoxymandelic Acid (= VMA)
5HT	5-Hydroxytryptamine (= Serotonin)
5HTP	5-Hydroxytryptophane

ICD	Isocitrate Dehydrogenase
ICSH	Interstitial Cell Stimulating Hormone (= LH)
LATS	Long Acting Thyroid Stimulator
LDH	Lactate Dehydrogenase
LDL	Low Density Lipoprotein
LH	Luteinising Hormone (= ICSH)
MIT	Mono-iodotyrosine
MSH	Melanocyte Stimulating Hormone
NAD	Nicotinamide Adenine Dinucleotide (= DPN)
NADP	Nicotinamide Adenine Dinucleotide Phosphate (= TPN)
NEFA	Non-Esterified Fatty Acids (= FFA)
5'NT	5' Nucleotidase
11-OHCS	11-Hydroxycorticosteroids ("Cortisol")
17-OHCS	17-Hydroxycorticosteroids (17-oxogenic steroids)
OP	Osmotic Pressure
PA	Pernicious Anaemia
PBG	Porphobilinogen
PBI	Protein Bound Iodine
P.P. factor	Pellagra Preventive Factor (nicotinamide: niacin)
PRPP	Phosphoribosyl Pyrophosphate
PTH	Parathyroid Hormone (Parathormone)
RNA	Ribonucleic Acid
RU	Resin Uptake (of T_3 or T_4)
SG	Specific Gravity
SGOT	Serum Glutamate Oxaloacetate Transaminase (= Asp AT)
SGPT	Serum Glutamate Pyruvate Transaminase (= Al.AT)
SHBD	Serum Hydroxybutyrate Dehydrogenase
T_3	Tri-iodothyronine
T_4	Thyroxine (Tetra-iodothyronine)
TBG	Thyroxine Binding Globulin
TCA cycle	Tricarboxylic Acid Cycle (= Krebs' Cycle)
TIBC	Total Iron Binding Capacity (usually measure of transferrin (siderophilin))
TP	Total Protein
TPN	Triphosphopyridine Nucleotide (= NADP)
TSH	Thyroid Stimulating Hormone (Thyrotrophin)
VLDL	Very Low Density Lipoprotein
VMA	Vanillyl Mandelic Acid (= HMMA)
Z–E syndrome	Zollinger-Ellison Syndrome

Chapter I

THE KIDNEYS : RENAL CALCULI

THE KIDNEYS

THE kidneys excrete waste products of metabolism and are the most important organs in the maintenance of normal body homeostasis. The renal tubules reabsorb some metabolically important substances, such as glucose, from the glomerular filtrate, secrete other substances into it, and exchange ions across the cell wall (for instance potassium and hydrogen in exchange for sodium ions). It should be remembered that, although the renal tubular cells are of the greatest importance from the point of view of homeostasis, many of these processes occur in other cells of the body, including those of the intestinal mucosa. The normal functioning of these cells in the kidney depends on an adequate volume of glomerular filtrate with which the exchanges can occur (and therefore on normal glomerular function), on concentrations of ions in tubular cells which are representative of those of the body as a whole (for example, potassium and hydrogen ions), and on the presence of such hormones as antidiuretic hormone (ADH) and aldosterone, and integrity of the feed-back mechanisms controlling them. If all these factors are normal the kidney retains just as much of each constituent as the body requires.

The kidney also produces erythropoietin—a hormone which stimulates erythropoiesis in the bone marrow. The student is referred to textbooks of haematology for further details.

NORMAL RENAL FUNCTION

Glomerular Filtration

The normal glomerular filtrate contains all plasma constituents, except protein and protein-bound substances, at concentrations identical with those in plasma, if the effect of the difference in protein concentration is allowed for (compare the distribution of electrolytes across blood vessel walls, p. 30).

Glomerular filtration is a passive process. Changes in the blood supply to the glomerulus, or reduction of the permeability of the membrane, affect the volume, but not the composition of the filtrate: however, the composition of urine passing into the bladder may vary with an alteration of filtration rate if very abnormal volumes of filtrate are presented to tubular cells. Increased permeability of the glomerulus may lead to proteinuria.

Tubular Function

Many substances are dealt with actively by the tubular cells, while others are reabsorbed passively. *Passive transport* can be explained by the presence of physicochemical gradients. For instance, a hydrostatic pressure gradient accounts for glomerular filtration and in the tubules water will move passively from an area of relatively low to relatively high osmotic pressure, or solute will move in the opposite direction: ions can also move along an electrochemical gradient produced by reabsorption of charged ions (for instance, active reabsorption of cation may be accompanied by passive reabsorption of anion). For such movements to take place the cell wall must be permeable to the substances concerned, and selective permeability may explain preferential absorption of one ion or another. Passive reabsorption requires no metabolic energy. Cell death may affect passive reabsorption by alteration of permeability of the cell walls.

Active transport can occur against physicochemical gradients and this process requires energy supplied by oxygen and ATP, and is directly affected by cell death and enzyme poisons. Such types of exchange occur in all cells in the body (for instance the "sodium pump" p. 29) : in absorptive cells, such as those of the renal tubule and the intestinal mucosa, the process is one of passing substances through the cell from the lumen into the blood stream; in other cells transport is in the same direction on all sides of the cell, and substances pass in or out of the cell rather than through it.

Many substances, such as urea and hydrogen ion, can reach concentrations in the urine well above those in the blood. Whether this differential concentration is the result of reabsorption of water without the relevant solute (urea) or of secretion by the tubular cell (hydrogen ion), its maintenance depends on the relative impermeability of that part of the tubule distal to the site of concentration. If this breaks down high concentrations may not be reached.

We will now consider some of the more important urinary constituents dealt with by the renal tubular cells.

Glucose and amino-acids are normally almost completely reabsorbed by the proximal renal tubule, and fluid entering the descending limb of the loop of Henle is usually free of these constituents which can then be re-utilized in body metabolism. Glucose is a "threshold" substance: the tubular cells have a limited capacity to reabsorb it, and at concentrations in the filtrate of above approximately 180 mg/100 ml glucose is usually present in the urine. The maximum amount which the tubules can completely reabsorb (Tm) may be reduced due to tubular factors (see also p. 132).

Phosphate is also reabsorbed by an active process in the proximal tubule, but reabsorption is rarely complete. This reabsorption is inhibited by parathyroid hormone (PTH), and this action accounts for some of the changes in the plasma when PTH is circulating in excess (p. 177). The presence of phosphate in the urine provides some of its buffering power (p. 66).

Sodium.—(a) *Reabsorption.* About 70 per cent of the sodium in the glomerular filtrate is reabsorbed by an active process in the proximal tubule. This reabsorption is limited by the availability of chloride (see below).

(b) *Exchange with hydrogen ion.* Sodium reabsorption in exchange for hydrogen ion is linked with bicarbonate reabsorption, and is dependent on the presence of the enzyme carbonic anhydrase, present in cells throughout the renal tubule (see p. 65 for more detailed discussion).

(c) *Exchange with potassium ion.* Sodium is reabsorbed in exchange for potassium ion in the distal tubule. This exchange is stimulated by aldosterone.

Chloride.—Although an active mechanism for chloride reabsorption has been suggested, probably most of the chloride in the glomerular filtrate is reabsorbed passively in the proximal tubule along the electro-chemical gradient created by sodium reabsorption. Because sodium cannot be reabsorbed by mechanism (a) above without anion, and as chloride is the predominant anion in the glomerular filtrate, reabsorption of sodium is limited by the availability of chloride (p. 68).

Potassium.—(a) *Reabsorption.* Potassium is almost completely reabsorbed by an active process in the proximal tubule, and fluid entering the distal tubule is almost potassium free.

(b) *Exchange with sodium ion.* In the distal tubule potassium is secreted in exchange for sodium, and this process is stimulated by aldosterone. Hydrogen and potassium ions compete for this exchange.

Hydrogen ion.—Hydrogen ion is secreted throughout the tubule in exchange for sodium. Final adjustment takes place in the distal tubule. As potassium competes for this exchange, disturbances of acid-base balance can be initiated by abnormalities of potassium metabolism (p. 67).

Bicarbonate.—Bicarbonate is reabsorbed from the glomerular filtrate although the tubular cells are impermeable to it. It is converted to carbon dioxide when hydrogen ion is secreted into the urine, and the carbon dioxide diffuses passively into the tubular cell where it is reconverted to bicarbonate in the presence of carbonic anhydrase (p. 65).

Urea.—Urea diffuses passively into the blood from the proximal tubule as water reabsorption increases its concentration in the filtrate.

However, back diffusion is slight and in the distal tubule is very limited Urinary urea can reach concentrations well above those in blood.

Creatinine.—Creatinine, in man, is not reabsorbed but is secreted by the renal tubule in small amounts.

Water.—Water will be reabsorbed from the lumen of a tubule, provided that the wall is permeable to it, if the osmotic pressure in the adjacent tissue or blood is higher than that in the lumen. All reabsorption of water in the kidney probably occurs in this way: it does not directly require energy expenditure, but energy is required for the creation of the osmotic gradient.

(a) The proximal tubules pass through the renal cortex and their walls are freely permeable to water. Active reabsorption of sodium, glucose and other solute from the glomerular filtrate is accompanied by passive reabsorption of an osmotically equivalent amount of water. Blood flow is brisk in this area, and solute and water are removed rapidly. Since reabsorption of the two is almost simultaneous, the osmolarity of the urine throughout the proximal tubule and entering the descending limb of the loop of Henle is the same as that of blood. In other words, water reabsorption at this site is secondary to solute reabsorption, and although 70 per cent of water in the filtrate is reabsorbed in the proximal tubule, no adjustment of extracellular osmolarity takes place.

(b) Reabsorption of the remaining water is adjusted to the body's needs in the distal tubule and collecting ducts. If extracellular osmolarity is to be corrected the kidney must be able to vary the proportion of water to solute and produce urine that is either of higher or of lower osmolarity than that in the extracellular fluid. As we have seen, the proximal tubules cannot make this adjustment because water and solute reabsorption occur in parallel.

Three facts make this possible in the distal part of the distal tubule and collecting ducts.

(i) Water leaving the ascending limb of the loop of Henle and entering the distal tubule is usually hyposmolar.

(ii) The wall of the proximal part of the distal tubule is probably impermeable to water: that of the distal part and collecting ducts is only permeable when acted on by antidiuretic hormone (ADH). However great the osmotic gradient, water cannot be reabsorbed in the absence of ADH: hyposmolar urine will therefore be passed if ADH is absent.

(iii) The osmolarity of kidney tissue is higher in the medulla than in the cortex, and may reach very high levels at the tips of the papillae and of the vasa recta. The collecting ducts pass through the zones of increasing osmolarity in the medulla, and if ADH is present, water can leave them, pass into the vasa recta and thence into the general circulation. Urinary osmolarity can reach levels four to five times as high as that of plasma during conditions of maximal ADH secretion (p. 36).

It is generally accepted that the high medullary osmolarity, essential for water reabsorption in the distal tubules and collecting ducts, is created by *countercurrent multiplication*: this is made possible by the looped arrangement of the loops of Henle, or the vasa recta, or both. Although there is some difference of opinion about the details of the mechanism, the general principles of all theories are the same.

Let us consider one of the mechanisms by which this concentration could be made possible in general terms. For clarity we will isolate each step, but it must be remembered that the process is a continuous one.

Suppose that, in a loop (in the renal medulla), solute such as sodium can be actively pumped from the ascending limb to the descending limb. Fluid entering the descending limb from the cortex (whether urine in the loop of Henle or blood in the vasa recta) is isosmotic—that is, of the same osmotic pressure as that in the general circulation. This is normally a little under 300 m. osmoles/litre, and for ease of discussion we will use the figure 300 m. osmoles/litre.

1. Suppose that the loop has been filled, no pumping has taken place, and the fluid in the loop is stationary. Osmolarity throughout the loop and the adjacent medullary tissue will be at about 300 m. osmoles/litre.

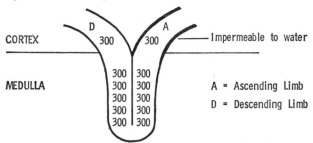

2. Suppose 1 m. osmole/litre of solute is pumped from limb A into limb D, the fluid column remaining stationary.

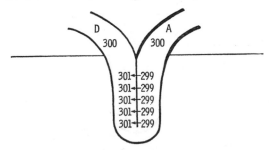

If this pumping were continued and there were no flow limb D would become very hyperosmolar and limb A equally hyposmolar, and if the outer walls of the loop were in osmotic equilibrium with surrounding tissue the latter would remain isosmolar, since an equal amount of water would move into limb D as moved out of limb A (or solute in the opposite direction).

3. However, let us suppose that the fluid flows so that each figure "moves two places".

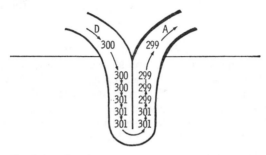

The thick wall of the distal part of limb A is impermeable to water.

4. As this happens more solute is pumped from limb A to limb D.

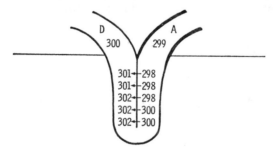

5. If the fluid again flows "two places", then the situation will be:

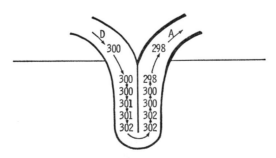

If these steps occur simultaneously and continuously the consequences would be:

(i) Increasing osmolarity in the tips of the loops and, if these are in osmotic equilibrium with all surrounding tissues, increasing osmolarity in the deeper layers of the medulla, and in the urine in the loops of Henle and the blood in the vasa recta.

(ii) Hyposmolar fluid leaving the ascending limb. In the loop of Henle urine entering the distal tubule could be hyposmolar either because this structure is responsible for the multiplication or because it is in osmotic equilibrium with the vasa recta, if these are the active structures. As the proximal part of the distal tubule is impermeable to water, hyposmolar urine would be passed in the absence of ADH: if ADH were present urine could be considerably concentrated as water is reabsorbed (ultimately into the vasa recta) along the osmotic gradient.

Relatively sluggish flow in the vasa recta allows the build up of medullary hyperosmolarity (compare the cortex).

Most workers believe the loops of Henle to be the "multipliers" and sodium to be the solute pumped. However, one group believes that the vasa recta are the important structures. Whatever the exact mechanism, it depends on active processes, which may be deranged when the tubules are damaged.

Osmotic diuresis.—Under physiological circumstances by far the largest contribution to the osmolarity of the glomerular filtrate comes from sodium salts, and active removal of sodium in the proximal tubule is followed by passive reabsorption of water. Suppose that another osmotically active substance is circulating in significant amounts, that this substance is freely filterable at the glomerulus, but that it cannot be reabsorbed either actively or passively to any significant extent in the proximal tubule. *Mannitol*, which cannot diffuse significantly through cell walls, is such a substance. As water reabsorption takes place with that of sodium the mannitol will become more concentrated, and its osmotic effect will inhibit further water diffusion. Since less water is reabsorbed a larger volume than usual will enter the loop of Henle and flow through the rest of the tubular system. Water reabsorption in the distal tubule and collecting duct has a limited capacity, and water diuresis will result. Moreover, as some sodium reabsorption occurs without water, the sodium concentration falls in the fluid in the distal part of the proximal tubule: back diffusion of sodium from blood along this concentration gradient opposes the action of the sodium pump. Sodium reabsorption is therefore impaired, although to a lesser extent than that of water. Note that urine leaving the proximal tubule is still isosmotic with blood, but that the contribution to the osmotic pressure of the tubular fluid from sodium is less than that in blood; the difference is made up by mannitol (in the absence of osmotic diuretics the sodium concentrations are the same in the proximal tubular lumen and in the blood). *Urea* can diffuse back to a limited extent in the proximal tubule, and *glucose* can be actively reabsorbed up to a "threshold" value. However, if these substances are filtered at very high concentrations the reabsorptive capacity is exceeded and they then act as osmotic diuretics (see p. 36).

Summarizing the functions of the kidney:

1. Excretion of most substances depends initially on normal permeability of the *glomerulus* (cortex), and on a hydrostatic pressure gradient between the blood flowing through it and the lumen of the glomerulus. If either of these factors is significantly reduced the tubules may not receive adequate amounts of material for "fine adjustment" to the body's needs.

2. The *proximal tubule* (cortex) reabsorbs many substances which can be re-utilized by the body almost completely (e.g. glucose and aminoacids). About 70 per cent of the sodium and water filtered at the glomerulus is reabsorbed at this site, the active process being reabsorption of sodium.

3. The *loop of Henle* (medulla) by means of countercurrent multiplication, creates the osmotic gradient which, in the presence of a normally functioning ADH feedback mechanism, enables hyposmolar or hyperosmolar urine to be formed according to the body's needs.

4. The *distal tubule* (cortex) makes the final adjustment of sodium, potassium and hydrogen ions, according to the body's needs, by means of exchange mechanisms.

5. Final adjustment of water excretion takes place in the *distal tubule* and the *collecting ducts* (medulla) under the influence of ADH, and is dependent on normal functioning of the loop of Henle.

CHEMICAL PATHOLOGY OF KIDNEY DISEASE

Although some diseases affect primarily the glomeruli and others the renal tubules, it is rare that disturbances of each of these are completely isolated from one another: the parts of the nephron are so closely associated anatomically, as well as being dependent on a common blood supply, that the end result of almost all renal disease is disturbance of the nephron as a whole. In most cases not all nephrons are equally affected, and while some may be completely non-functional, others may be quite normal, and yet others may have some functions disturbed to a greater extent than others. Some of the effects of chronic renal failure can be explained by this patchy distribution of disease (compare the effects of patchy pulmonary disease, p. 85).

However, in the initial stages some diseases affect either tubules or glomeruli predominantly and can occasionally be arrested or even reversed at this stage. It is probably easier to understand renal failure if these two types of lesion are isolated and discussed first.

Glomerular Dysfunction

Consequences of a reduced glomerular filtration rate.—If the GFR is reduced an abnormally small volume of filtrate is produced: its composition remains that of a plasma ultrafiltrate. Abnormally small amounts of all constituents of the filtrate are presented to the tubular cells, and as the flow is relatively sluggish, stay in contact with them for longer than normal.

1. The reduced volume of filtrate may, of itself, result in *oliguria*: this will only reduce the urine volume to less than 400 ml a day if the GFR is reduced to less than 30 per cent of its normal value. If the low GFR is due to factors that also cause maximal stimulation of ADH secretion water reabsorption in the collecting ducts will also be high, and *urine of high specific gravity* will be passed. This high specific gravity is due to the presence of substances not normally reabsorbed significantly by the tubular cells: the concentration of urinary urea and creatinine, for instance, will be high.

2. The total daily amount of *urea and creatinine* lost in the urine depends mainly on the amount filtered at the glomerulus during the same period, since tubular action on them is quantitatively insignificant in this context. The amount filtered at the glomerulus depends on plasma concentration and the GFR. If the rate of excretion falls below the rate of production the plasma levels will rise: as a higher plasma level results in a higher rate of excretion the concentration may equilibrate temporarily at this raised concentration. If, however, the rise in concentration cannot compensate for the fall in filtered volume, levels continue to rise.

Phosphate and urate are also liberated during catabolism. These can be reabsorbed in the proximal tubule, and reabsorption may be complete if the amount filtered is low. Here again, if production is not balanced by excretion (and in this case by anabolism), levels will rise.

3. Sodium reabsorption is almost complete in the proximal tubule, and less than normal is available for exchange with hydrogen and potassium ions. *Urinary sodium concentration* will be low, there will be systemic *acidosis* with a *low plasma bicarbonate* concentration and *potassium retention*. The tendency to hyperkalaemia is aggravated by shifts out of cells due to acidosis (p. 30). Thus the laboratory findings in advanced cases will be as follows:

In the blood:

Uraemia, high plasma creatinine concentration
Acidosis with a low plasma bicarbonate

A tendency to hyperkalaemia
Hyperuricaemia, hyperphosphataemia, hypocalcaemia (p. 183).

In the urine:
Oliguria
Urine of high specific gravity
High concentration of urea
Low concentration of sodium.

N.B. These urinary findings may be reversed if the dehydration is due to diabetes insipidus (p. 40) or to an osmotic diuresis (p. 41). Additional findings will depend on the cause of the low GFR.

Causes of reduced glomerular filtration rate.—As stated earlier, the relatively uncomplicated picture is usually seen only in the early stages of the disease. Later the nephron as a whole is affected.

1. Reduction in differential hydrostatic pressure in the glomerulus.
   (*a*) Reduced glomerular blood flow ("pre-renal uraemia"). Renal circulatory insufficiency due to:
      Low systemic blood pressure (haemorrhage, dehydration, "shock")
      Congestive cardiac failure
      Renal artery stenosis
      Acute tubular necrosis (primarily a tubular lesion)
   (*b*) Increased intraluminal pressure
      ? Acute tubular necrosis (primarily a tubular lesion)
      Obstruction of the ureters or urethra ("post-renal uraemia").

2. Disease of the glomerulus
      Acute glomerulonephritis
      Chronic glomerulonephritis.

1. (*a*) *Renal circulatory insufficiency* is probably the commonest cause of a low GFR with normal tubular function, and is most commonly due to haemorrhage or dehydration. If blood pressure (or, more accurately, renal blood flow) is restored within a few hours the condition is reversible: if the condition persists for longer periods of time the danger of ischaemic damage to the tubules increases, and when glomerular function is restored the picture of acute tubular necrosis manifests itself within a few days. If the low GFR is due to this cause the patient will be hypotensive and possibly clinically dehydrated and, in addition to the laboratory findings listed above, there may be haemoconcentration (p. 27). Uraemia due to renal dysfunction is aggravated if there is increased protein breakdown, due either to tissue damage or to the presence of blood in the gastro-intestinal tract: the liberated amino-acids

are converted to urea in the liver. Increased tissue breakdown also aggravates hyperkalaemia and acidosis.

In congestive cardiac failure circulation to the kidney may be sufficiently impaired to cause a mild uraemia: the clinical findings are those of the primary condition, and haemodilution is often present. In renal artery stenosis hypertension of renal origin is usually present.

In acute tubular necrosis it has been shown that renal blood flow, especially to the cortex, is reduced, and may account for some of the oliguria in this condition.

(b) *Increased intraluminal pressure* reduces the hydrostatic pressure gradient essential for normal filtration. In acute tubular necrosis there may be some obstruction to tubular flow due to oedema of the tissues, aggravating the oliguria due to reduced cortical flow. "Post-renal uraemia" may be due to obstruction by calculi, polyps or other neoplasms, strictures or prostatic hypertrophy. Long continued back pressure may lead to renal damage, with uraemia persisting after the relief of the obstruction.

2. *Glomerulonephritis* reduces the permeability of the glomerular membrane, but in chronic glomerulonephritis the tubules may also be involved in scarring. Fluid and sodium retention occur, and may be aggravated by injudicious fluid administration: in such cases there is haemodilution. In acute glomerulonephritis there is often a typical history of sore throat, and protein and red cells in small amounts are found in the urine. Proteinuria and occasional erythrocytes may also be found in the chronic condition.

Nephrotic Syndrome

Increased glomerular permeability occurs in the nephrotic syndrome, when most plasma proteins can pass the glomerulus and proteinuria of several grams a day occurs. Loss of plasma proteins results in a reduction of all fractions except the relatively high molecular weight α_2 and β lipoproteins (p. 236). Typically the plasma electrophoretic pattern in this condition shows a relatively high α_2 globulin, since the rise in β lipoprotein is rarely detectable by routine methods. The α_2 globulin level may even be high in absolute terms: this may be due to a non-specific increase in synthesis of liver proteins resulting from a feed-back from the low albumin level (p. 228), and further loss in the urine of all fractions except α_2 globulin. Typically the γ globulin level is low, but it may be raised if the syndrome is due to autoimmune disease. Plasma lipid and cholesterol concentrations are raised. Uraemia occurs only in the late stage of the disease, when many glomeruli cease to function. Loss of specific binding proteins in the urine (thyroxine binding globulin, and cortisol binding globulin, for instance) may cause low levels of total thyroxine, and cortisol in the blood and these may be misinterpreted.

Similarly, low albumin levels may cause hypocalcaemia with no change in the physiologically important ionized calcium concentration.

Tubular Dysfunction

Consequences of generalized tubular damage.—Even if the GFR is normal, damage to the tubular cells impairs the adjustment of the composition and volume of the urine.

1. The countercurrent mechanism may be impaired. Water reabsorption is reduced and large volumes of dilute urine are passed.

2. The tubules cannot secrete hydrogen ion and therefore cannot reabsorb bicarbonate normally and cannot acidify the urine.

3. Reabsorption of sodium and exchange mechanisms involving sodium are impaired and the urine contains a relatively high concentration of sodium. Failure of sodium reabsorption in the proximal tubule contributes to impairment of water reabsorption at this site.

4. Potassium reabsorption in the proximal tubule is impaired and potassium depletion may develop.

5. Reabsorption of glucose, phosphate and amino-acids is impaired and there is often glycosuria, phosphaturia and generalized amino-aciduria (acquired Fanconi syndrome). The plasma phosphate level may be low.

Uraemia occurs only if fluid and electrolyte depletion causes renal circulatory insufficiency, or in acute tubular necrosis (p. 13).

Thus the laboratory findings in advanced cases may be:

In the blood:

    Acidosis
    Hypokalaemia*
    Hypophosphataemia*
    Haemoconcentration (p. 27)

In the urine:

    Polyuria*
    Urine of high pH and low specific gravity*
        low concentration of urea*
        high concentration of sodium*

In most cases there is mild proteinuria, and casts are present in the urine.

Contrast those findings marked * with those of glomerular damage.

Causes of predominantly tubular damage.—In all these cases the glomeruli are involved in the later stages of the disease. A few examples only are given here.

1. Acute tubular necrosis.
   Prolonged renal circulatory insufficiency
   Proximal tubular necrosis due to various poisons (e.g. carbon
   tetrachloride)

2. Progressive damage to the tubules.
   Hypercalcaemia
   Hypokalaemia
   Hyperuricaemia
   Wilson's disease (copper, p. 345).
   Bence-Jones protein in myeloma (p. 241)
   Galactosaemia (p. 343)
   Various poisons, especially heavy metals
   Early pyelonephritis

3. Inborn errors of specific tubular functions. These are discussed in the relevant chapters and summarized in Chapter XVII.

1. *Acute tubular necrosis* (*acute oliguric renal failure, acute renal failure*) often follows the period when GFR is reduced because of renal circulatory insufficiency, and from the therapeutic point of view it is important to distinguish these two phases. The oliguria is probably not due to glomerular damage, but to reduced cortical blood flow: this may be aggravated by back-pressure on the glomeruli due to obstruction of flow in the tubules by oedema: at this stage many of the findings are those of a low GFR (uraemia, hyperkalaemia, acidosis with a low plasma bicarbonate, etc.). However, sodium reabsorption is impaired and urinary sodium concentration is relatively high. Water retention may lead to oedema with haemodilution if fluid intake is not restricted.

As cortical blood flow increases and as the tubular oedema resolves the findings approximate those of pure tubular lesions. Urinary output increases and the polyuria may cause water depletion. Electrolyte depletion may occur and the initial hyperkalaemia may be replaced by hypokalaemia. The blood urea concentration falls rapidly. Mild acidosis persists until late.

2. *Progressive damage to the tubular cells* is frequently due to precipitation of substances such as calcium in the renal tubules; prolonged potassium depletion causes vacuolation of the tubular cells. Many of the other substances listed under this heading can cause acute tubular necrosis if their concentration is high enough. In the early stages of these chronic conditions the picture may be that described under pure tubular lesions: for instance, cases of chronic hypercalcaemia can present complaining of polyuria, and are often found to have hypokalaemia. In the later stages the whole nephron is involved in scarring with impairment of glomerular function.

Pyelonephritis, while affecting the kidneys as a whole, has a predilection for the medulla. The ability to form a concentrated urine, and other tubular functions, are therefore lost early in the disease.

Generalized Renal Failure: Chronic Renal Failure

All the above conditions can progress to generalized disease of the nephron, giving the common picture of chronic renal failure. In addition many other diseases (for instance polycystic disease) affect the kidney as a whole.

In *chronic renal failure* individual nephrons will be affected to different degrees. As more are involved the rate of urea excretion falls and cannot balance the rate of production by catabolism: as a consequence the blood urea level rises, and the urea concentration in the filtrate of the normal nephrons rises. This may cause an osmotic diuresis in these nephrons, and in the early stages there may therefore be polyuria and a tendency to water depletion which may superimpose renal circulatory insufficiency on the other lesions: polyuria may also be the result of tubular without glomerular damage in some nephrons. If, however, water loss is replaced by intake urea excretion can continue through the remaining healthy nephrons at a high rate, until a new steady state is reached at a higher level of blood urea. If these subjects are kept well hydrated they may remain in a stable condition with a moderately raised blood urea for years. If, however, nephron destruction continues there will come a point where oliguria precipitates a steep rise in blood urea, and this stage is often terminal. Before assuming that the latter is the case, care should be taken to ensure that the sudden rise is not due to electrolyte and water depletion.

INVESTIGATION OF RENAL FUNCTION

Plasma urea and creatinine levels depend on the balance between their production and excretion.

Urea is the product of amino-acid breakdown in the liver and is therefore derived from protein, either in the diet or in body tissues: the rate of production is accelerated by a high protein diet, or by increased endogenous catabolism due to starvation or tissue damage. The capacity of the normal kidney to excrete urea is high, and in the presence of normal renal function only extremely high protein diets can cause rises of blood urea to levels above the normal range. In patients with gross increase in tissue catabolism (severe tissue damage or starvation) urea levels may rise above normal, especially as renal function is often mildly impaired in such cases. In spite of these reservations, a significantly high blood urea concentration almost certainly indicates impaired renal function (this is almost certainly so at levels above 80 mg/100 ml [B.U.N. above 39 mg/100 ml]): the probability is increased if a cause for renal dysfunction is present, or if there are protein, casts or cells in the urine. In the few cases when doubt remains, clearance studies (see below) or measurement of plasma creatinine may resolve it.

Plasma *creatinine* is little, if at all, affected by diet, as it is destroyed in the gut. Almost all the circulating creatinine is derived from metabolism of tissue creatine: although plasma levels would be expected to increase with increased tissue breakdown, they do so less than those of urea. In theory, therefore, creatinine would seem preferable to urea estimation as an index of renal function, and for this reason is used by many laboratories for this purpose. However, in spite of an improvement in the precision and speed of creatinine estimation with the advent of automated methods, the accuracy of that of urea is still significantly higher. (In a recent inter-laboratory survey the percentage variation of the creatinine value estimated on the same specimens was about twice that of urea). Which of these parameters is used is largely a matter of local choice.

If urea or creatinine levels are significantly raised, and especially if they are rising, if there is oliguria or a history suggestive of renal disease, or if there is proteinuria, and the urine contains protein, casts, cells or bacteria in significant amounts, they can usually be safely assumed to be due to renal impairment. For routine clinical purposes progress can be followed merely by measuring these concentrations in the plasma, because they parallel changes in renal clearance.

Differential Diagnosis of Oliguria with Uraemia

Oliguria with uraemia may be due to renal circulatory insufficiency, or to renal damage, and the treatment is radically different in these two cases. In most situations the clinical history and clinical examination

TABLE I

LABORATORY FINDINGS IN THE DIFFERENTIAL DIAGNOSIS
OF THE CAUSE OF OLIGURIA

	Renal circulatory insufficiency	Parenchymal damage
Urine microscopy, protein, etc.	−	+
Haemoconcentration	+	−
Urinary specific gravity osmolarity and urea concentration	↑	↓
Urinary Na concentration	↓	↑

will differentiate the two, but if doubt remains examination of the urine may help. The findings are summarized in Table I, and discussed more fully in the relevant sections.

Detection of Minor Degrees of Renal Damage

More than 60 per cent of the kidney must be destroyed before either plasma urea or creatinine levels are significantly raised (this is only valid for urea if the patient is taking a normal or low protein diet, and if there is no excessive protein catabolism, p. 14). Damage may be suspected for other reasons, such as evidence of renal infection, a previous episode of uraemia, or the finding of protein in the urine. If plasma urea or creatinine concentrations are normal more refined tests are useful: by the time they are abnormal presence of disease is not in doubt. This is a general principle which also applies, for example, to the detection of diabetes mellitus (p. 137) and liver damage (p. 271).

Renal concentrating ability.—This is a simple test and can be carried out on the ward. The ability to form a concentrated urine in response to water deprivation depends on normal tubular function (countercurrent multiplication), and on the presence of ADH. Failure of this ability is usually due to renal disease, but if there is any doubt the test can be repeated after administration of ADH (pitressin) (Appendix, p. 23).

Clearance tests of glomerular function.—Clearance tests measure the amount of blood which could theoretically be completely cleared of a substance per minute. This figure can be calculated if the amount excreted per minute is divided by its concentration in the blood: the amount excreted per minute can be calculated on a timed collection by multiplying the concentration of the substance in the specimen by the volume passed in the time, and dividing by the time in minutes. In the case of urea therefore:

Urea Clearance (ml/minute) =
$$\frac{\text{Urinary urea (mg/ml)} \times \text{Urine volume (ml)}}{\text{Blood urea (mg/ml)} \times \text{Time of collection (minutes)}}$$

If a true estimate of GFR is to be made a substance should be chosen which is excreted solely by glomerular filtration and is not reabsorbed or secreted by the tubules. *Inulin* is thought to be such a substance: inulin is not produced in the mammalian body and measurement of its clearance requires administration either by constant infusion to maintain its level in the blood steady during the period of the test, or by a single injection followed by serial blood sampling so that its concentration at the mid-point of urine collection can be calculated. Such exogenous clearances are not very practicable for routine use, and this objection applies to clearances of radioactive *vitamin B$_{12}$* and chromated ethylenediamine tetracetic acid (*EDTA*), which have also been claimed to be cleared by glomerular action only.

Substances produced in the body are usually present in a fairly steady circulating concentration for the period of the test, and blood need only be taken at the mid-point of the urine collection. Urea and creatinine clearances are commonly used for clinical purposes. Neither of these substances fulfils the criterion that they are not reabsorbed from or added to the glomerular filtrate by the tubular cells. *Urea* diffuses back into the blood stream from the proximal tubule, and urea clearance values are lower than those of inulin: *creatinine* is secreted in small amounts by the tubule and gives clearance values higher than those of inulin. Either clearance gives an approximation to the GFR adequate for clinical purposes, and although the estimation of urea is more accurate than that of creatinine, there is little to choose between them. It should be noted that the rate of protein breakdown, while it may affect levels of plasma urea, does *not* affect its rate of clearance by the kidney.

If urea clearance is chosen, care should be taken to inhibit the activity of urea splitting organisms which may be present in the urine by the use of mercury salts as a preservative. If such organisms are present, short periods of collection (for example, three collections of 1 hour) are preferable to a long one (for example, 24 hours).

The biggest error of any clearance method is in the timed urine collection.

It should be noted that clearance tests will give low values in the oliguric phase of acute tubular necrosis, or in "post-renal" uraemia, even if the glomeruli are unaffected.

Incidental Abnormal Findings in Renal Failure

In assessing the severity and progress of renal failure it is usual to estimate plasma urea or creatinine, electrolytes (especially potassium) and bicarbonate concentrations. Other abnormalities occur which, although not useful in diagnosis or assessment of renal dysfunction, may be misinterpreted if the cause is not recognized. Plasma *urate* levels rise in parallel with plasma urea, and a high level does not necessarily indicate primary hyperuricaemia (p. 301). Plasma *phosphate* levels also rise, and those of *calcium* fall (p. 183). In chronic uraemia secondary hyperparathyroidism may lead to bone disease with a high level of *alkaline phosphatase*. Hypocalcaemia should only be treated if there is evidence of bone disease (p. 194). *Anaemia* is commonly present, and is normocytic and normochromic in type: it does not respond to iron therapy.

Biochemical Principles of Treatment of Renal Dysfunction

Oliguric renal failure.—The oliguria of dehydration or haemorrhage, which is due to a reduction of glomerular filtration rate only, should be treated with the appropriate fluid (p. 56).

In acute tubular necrosis and other forms of oliguric renal failure due to parenchymal damage the aims are:

1. To restrict fluid and sodium, giving only enough fluid to replace that lost in the previous 24 hours (p. 27).

2. To provide adequate non-protein calories to prevent aggravation of uraemia and hyperkalaemia by increased endogenous catabolism.

3. To prevent dangerous hyperkalaemia (p. 55).

In chronic renal failure with polyuria the aim is to replace fluid and electrolytes lost. Sodium and water depletion may aggravate the uraemia.

Haemodialysis or peritoneal dialysis removes urea and toxic substances from the blood stream, and corrects electrolyte balance, by dialysing the patient's blood against fluid containing no urea, and normal plasma concentrations of electrolytes, *ionized* calcium and other plasma constituents. The blood is either passed through a dialysing membrane before being returned to the body, or the folds of the peritoneum are used as a dialysing membrane with their capillaries on one side, and suitable fluid injected into the peritoneal cavity on the other. A relatively slow reduction of urea concentration is preferable to a rapid one because of the danger of cellular overhydration when extracellular osmolarity falls abruptly (p. 32). Dialysis is used in cases of potentially recoverable acute oliguric renal failure, to tide the patient over a crisis, or as a regularly repeated procedure in suitable cases of chronic renal failure. It may also be used to prepare patients for renal transplantation, and to maintain them until the transplant functions adequately.

RENAL CALCULI

Renal stones are usually composed of normal products of metabolism which are present in the normal glomerular filtrate, often at concentrations near their maximum solubility: quite minor changes in urinary composition may cause precipitation of such constituents, whether in the substance of the kidney (see section on tubular damage, p. 13), as crystals or as calculi. Although this discussion concerns stone formation it should be remembered that crystalluria and parenchymal damage can occur under the same circumstances, and that the treatment of all such conditions is the same.

Conditions Favouring Calculus Formation

1. **A high urinary concentration** of one or more constituents of the glomerular filtrate.

(a) *A low urinary volume*, with normal renal function, due to restricted fluid intake or excessive fluid loss over long periods of time (this is particularly common in the tropics). This condition favours formation of most types of stone, especially if one of the other conditions listed below is also present.

(b) An abnormally *high rate of excretion* of the metabolic product forming the stone, due either to an increased level in the glomerular filtrate (secondary to high plasma concentrations) or to a failure of normal tubular reabsorption from the filtrate.

2. **Changes in pH** of the urine, which favour precipitation of different salts at different hydrogen ion concentrations.

3. **Urinary stagnation** due to obstruction to urine outflow.

Composition of Urinary Calculi

1. Calcium containing stones
    (a) Calcium oxalate   } with or without magnesium
    (b) Calcium phosphate   } ammonium phosphate.
2. Uric acid containing stones.
3. Cystine containing stones.
4. Xanthine containing stones.

Calculi composed of Calcium Salts

These account for 70 per cent or more of all renal stones. Precipitation of calcium is favoured by hypercalcuria, and the type of salt depends on urinary pH and on the availability of oxalate or phosphate. All patients presenting with renal calculi should have a plasma calcium estimation performed, and if this is normal it should be repeated at regular intervals.

Hypercalcaemia causes hypercalcuria if renal function is normal, and estimation of urinary calcium in such cases does not help in the diagnosis. The causes and differential diagnosis of hypercalcaemia are discussed on p. 187.

In many subjects with calcium containing renal calculi the serum calcium level is normal. It is in such cases that the estimation of the daily excretion of urinary calcium may be useful. The commonest cause of *hypercalcuria with normocalcaemia* is the so-called *idiopathic hypercalcuria*, a name which reflects our ignorance of the aetiology of the condition: because some of these cases may represent an early stage of primary hyperparathyroidism, plasma calcium estimations should be carried out at regular intervals, especially if the plasma phosphate level is low. Any *increased release of calcium from bone*, as in actively progressing osteoporosis (in which loss of matrix causes secondary decalcification) or in prolonged acidosis (in which ionization of calcium salts is increased) causes hypercalcuria, but rarely hypercalcaemia. Renal tubular acidosis (p. 72) not only increases the renal load of calcium but, because of the relative alkalinity of the urine, favours its precipitation in the kidney and renal tract.

An increased excretion of *oxalate* favours the formation of the very insoluble calcium oxalate, even if calcium excretion is normal. The source of the increased oxalate may be the diet: the very rare inborn error of oxalate metabolism, primary hyperoxaluria, should be considered if renal calculi occur in childhood.

It has already been mentioned that *alkaline conditions* favour calcium precipitation, and whereas calcium oxalate stones form at any urinary pH, a high pH favours formation of calcium phosphate: this type of stone is particularly common in chronic renal infection with urease containing (urea splitting) organisms (for example, *Proteus vulgaris*), which convert urea to ammonia.

A significant proportion of cases remain in which there is no apparent cause for the calcium precipitation.

Calcium containing calculi are usually *hard and white*. They are *radiopaque*. Calcium phosphate stones are particularly prone to form "staghorn" calculi in the renal pelvis, easily visualized by straight x-ray.

Treatment of calcium containing calculi.—This depends on the cause. Excretion of calcium should be reduced

(*a*) By treating the primary condition (especially hypercalcaemia);

(*b*) If this is not possible, by reducing intake of calcium in the diet, and possibly by decreasing calcium absorption by administration of oral phosphate (p. 200);

(*c*) By reducing the concentration of urinary calcium by maintaining a high fluid intake (unless renal failure is present).

Uric Acid Stones

These account for about 10 per cent of all renal calculi, and are sometimes associated with *hyperuricaemia* (with or without clinical gout). Precipitation is favoured in an *acid urine*. In a large proportion of cases no predisposing cause can be found.

Uric acid stones are usually *small, friable* and *yellowish-brown* in colour. They are *radiotranslucent*, but may be visualized on an intravenous pyelogram.

Treatment of hyperuricaemia is discussed on p. 304. If the plasma uric acid concentration is normal fluid intake should be kept high, and the urine alkalinized. A low purine diet (p. 304) may help to reduce uric acid production and therefore excretion.

Cystine Stones

These are rare. In normal subjects the concentration of urinary cystine is well within its solubility. In severe cases of the inborn error cystinuria (p. 338) the solubility may be exceeded and the patient may present with renal calculi. Like uric acid, cystine is more soluble in alkaline than acid urine and the principles of treatment are the same as for uric acid stones. Penicillamine can also be used in therapy (p. 339).

Xanthine Stones

These are very uncommon and may be the result of the rare inborn error, xanthinuria (p. 306). Xanthine stones following the use of xanthine oxidase inhibitors, such as allopurinol, have not been reported.

SUMMARY

THE KIDNEYS

1. Normal renal function depends on a normal glomerular filtration rate (GFR) and normal tubular function.

2. In most cases of renal disease glomerular and tubular dysfunction coexist.

3. A low GFR leads to:
   Uraemia and retention of other nitrogenous end products and of phosphate.
   Acidosis.
   Hyperkalaemia.
   Oliguria.

4. A low GFR with normal tubular function is most commonly due to renal circulatory insufficiency. It can also be the result of obstruction to urinary outflow, or of glomerular damage.

5. In the nephrotic syndrome the glomerulus is more permeable than normal to proteins.

6. Tubular damage leads to:
   Acidosis.
   Hypokalaemia.
   Hypophosphataemia.
   Polyuria.

7. In acute tubular necrosis there is a reduced GFR (see p. 13) and the findings are usually those associated with this.

8. The differentiation between the oliguria of a primary glomerular lesion with normal tubular function and of acute tubular necrosis is best made on clinical grounds and by examining the urine (Table I).

9. In most cases plasma urea or creatinine levels parallel changes in renal clearance and are adequate for diagnosing and following up cases

of renal disease. Tubular function may be tested by assessing the ability of the kidney to concentrate urine.

10. Clearance tests are valuable if a minor degree of renal damage is suspected in spite of a plasma urea or creatinine level within the "normal" range.

RENAL CALCULI

1. The formation of renal calculi is favoured by:

(a) A high urinary concentration of the constituents of the calculi. This may be due to oliguria, or a high rate of excretion of the relevant substances.

(b) A pH of the urine which favours precipitation of the constituents of the calculi.

(c) Urinary stagnation.

2. Calcium containing calculi account for 70 per cent or more of all renal stones. They are most commonly idiopathic in origin but hypercalcaemia, especially that of primary hyperparathyroidism, should be excluded as a cause.

3. Uric acid stones account for a further 10 per cent of renal calculi. Rare causes are cystinuria and xanthinuria.

FURTHER READING

DE WARDENER, H. E. (1967). *The Kidney*, 3rd edit. London: J. & A. Churchill.

APPENDIX TO CHAPTER I

URINE CONCENTRATION TEST

In the normal subject restriction of water intake for a period of hours results in maximal stimulation of ADH secretion (p. 36). ADH acts on the collecting ducts, water is reabsorbed and a concentrated urine is passed. If the counter-current multiplication mechanism is impaired (p. 5) maximal water reabsorption cannot take place, and if ADH levels are low the effect is similar.

If the feed-back mechanism is intact ADH levels are sufficient to produce maximal effect. Under these circumstances administration of exogenous ADH will not improve renal concentrating power. If, however, the primary disease is diabetes insipidus with normal tubular function, administration of ADH will convert this to normal.

Procedure

The patient is allowed no food or water after 6 p.m. on the night before the test.

On the day of the test:—

7 a.m.—The bladder is emptied, and the *specimen discarded.*

8 a.m.—The bladder is emptied. The specific gravity (or osmolarity) of this specimen is measured. If this reading is above 1·022 (or 800 m. osmoles/litre) the test may be terminated: if it is below 1·022 the specific gravity of urine passed at 9 a.m. should be measured.

Interpretation

A maximum specific gravity of below 1·022 indicates impaired renal concentrating power, either due to tubular disease or to diabetes insipidus. In most cases it is clear which of these possibilities is implicated. Where this is still in doubt the pitressin test may be carried out.

PITRESSIN TEST

The above procedure is followed, but 5 units of the oily suspension of vasopressin (pitressin) tannate is injected intramuscularly at 7 p.m. on the evening before the test. If the failure to concentrate is due to tubular disease this will not be improved by the pitressin: if it is due to diabetes insipidus the urine will now be concentrated normally.

Caution.—1. Hydrometers are frequently inaccurate. It should be checked that the specific gravity of distilled water reads 1·000 (the hydrometer is usually calibrated at room temperature): if it does not, a suitable correction should be made.

2. The hydrometer should be floating freely when the reading is taken. If it touches the wall of the container false values will be obtained. The procedure should be carried out by someone experienced with it.

Urinary urea concentration may be a more valuable estimation. If an osmometer is available, measurement of urinary osmolarity gives more precise results.

3. Sugar, protein, and contrast media used in intravenous pyelography contribute to both urinary specific gravity, and, to a lesser extent, to osmolarity. In the presence of glycosuria and proteinuria high readings are not necessarily indicative of normal renal function. Under such circumstances estimation of urinary urea concentration may be valuable.

Chapter II

SODIUM, POTASSIUM AND WATER METABOLISM

SODIUM and potassium are present in most of the salts in the body. In the ionized form sodium is predominantly in the extracellular fluid; quantitatively significant but relatively metabolically inert sodium is present in bone salts. Potassium, on the other hand, is a predominantly intracellular cation, and only about 2 per cent of that in the body is in the extracellular fluid.

Sodium is the most abundant extracellular cation, and for this reason it (and its associated anions) accounts for most of the osmotic activity of the extracellular fluid. The clinical symptoms of disturbances of sodium concentration are due to changes in osmolarity. The concentration of any ion in solution depends on both the absolute amount of the ion and the amount of water, and it is not surprising to find a close link between the homeostatic mechanisms for sodium and for water.

The clinical signs of water deficiency, when electrolyte concentration is unchanged, are due to an inadequate circulating volume.

Like calcium and magnesium (pp. 179, 195), the very low extracellular concentration of potassium ions is important for normal neuromuscular activity and cardiac action.

Sodium and potassium are both alkali metals. In spite of the differences in body distribution, disturbances of one are usually associated with disturbances of the other, and the transport mechanisms of the two across all cell walls are linked.

Anions cannot exist without associated cations, and disturbances of sodium and potassium metabolism are often accompanied by those of chloride and bicarbonate and, to a lesser extent, of other anions such as phosphate. Hydrogen is another monovalent cation, and its concentration (and therefore the pH) can often be altered in similar circumstances: for instance, the hydrogen ion competes with the potassium ion for exchange with sodium across cell walls. The separation of the contents of this chapter from that on acid-base balance (Chapter III) is arbitrary, and for ease of discussion only. A clinical situation should be assessed with all these factors in mind.

WATER AND ELECTROLYTE BALANCE

A 70 kg man contains approximately 45 litres of water and 3000 mEq each of potassium and metabolically active sodium. Maintenance of this total amount depends on the balance between intake and loss. Water and electrolytes are taken in food and drink, and are lost in urine, faeces and sweat: in addition, about 500 ml of water is lost daily in expired air.

LOSS THROUGH THE KIDNEYS AND INTESTINAL TRACT

Renal loss of electrolytes and water depends on the balance between that filtered at the glomerulus and that reabsorbed during passage through the tubules, and therefore on normal glomerular and tubular function. *Faecal loss* is mainly dependent on the balance between the electrolytes and water secreted in bile, saliva and gastric, pancreatic and intestinal juices, and reabsorbed during passage through the intestine: the contribution from oral intake is small. This loss therefore depends on the integrity of the intestinal epithelial cells, and on the time for which intestinal contents are in contact with them. Intestinal hurry or loss of secretions from the upper gastro-intestinal tract by vomiting or through fistulae are important causes of electrolyte and water depletion.

It is a sobering thought that approximately 200 litres of water and 30,000 mEq of sodium are filtered through the glomerulus, and a further 10 litres of water and 1,500 mEq of sodium are secreted into the intestinal tract each day. In the absence of homeostatic mechanisms for reabsorption, the whole of the extracellular water and sodium could be lost in about 2 hours. It is, therefore, not surprising that failure of these mechanisms causes such extreme disturbances of water and electrolyte balance. Normally 99 per cent of this initial loss is reabsorbed, and net daily losses amount to about 1·5 to 2 litres of water and 100 mEq of sodium in the urine and 100 ml and 15 mEq in faeces.

LOSS IN SWEAT AND EXPIRED AIR

Normal daily water loss by these two routes amounts to about 900 ml. Although antidiuretic hormone (ADH) and aldosterone have some effect on the composition of sweat, this is relatively unimportant, and sweat loss is primarily controlled by body temperature. Respiratory water loss depends on respiratory rate, and control of this bears no relation to the body requirements for water. Normally loss by these routes is unimportant for electrolyte and water homeostasis, and is corrected by changes in renal and intestinal loss. However, as sweat and respiratory losses cannot be significantly controlled to meet sodium and water requirements, they may contribute considerably to abnormal balance when homeostatic mechanisms fail, or in the presence of gross deficiency of intake.

ASSESSMENT OF ELECTROLYTE AND WATER BALANCE

Although it is easy to measure the intake of water and electrolytes of patients receiving liquid feeds (either oral or intravenous), it is less easy to do so when a solid diet is being taken. Fortunately, accurate measurement is rarely necessary in such cases.

Renal loss is also easy to measure but that in formed faeces, sweat and expired air ("insensible loss") is more difficult to assess and may be important when homeostatic mechanisms have failed, in the presence of abnormal losses by extrarenal routes, in unconscious patients and in infants (see p. 41). The aim should be to ensure that such subjects are normally hydrated, and then to keep them "in balance". The latter involves accurate assessment of losses so that they may be quantitatively replaced. The medical attendant has the difficult task of imitating normal homeostasis without the aid of the sensitive and interlinked mechanisms of the body.

ASSESSMENT OF THE STATE OF HYDRATION

Assessment of the state of hydration of a patient depends on observation of his clinical state, and on laboratory evidence of haemoconcentration or haemodilution. It must be stressed that both these methods are crude, and that quite severe disturbances of water balance can occur before they are obvious clinically or by laboratory methods.

In extracellular dehydration (other than that due to haemorrhage), water and often electrolytes are lost from the vascular compartment, and the concentration of large molecules and of cells rises: there is therefore a rise in all plasma protein fractions, in haemoglobin levels, and in the haematocrit reading (*haemoconcentration*). Conversely, in overhydration these concentrations fall (*haemodilution*). These findings, of course, may also be affected by pre-existing abnormalities of protein or red cell concentrations.

The problem of assessing hydration can be a difficult one, but can usually be resolved if the history, clinical and laboratory findings are all taken into account.

ASSESSMENT OF FLUID BALANCE

By far the most important measurement in assessing changes in day to day fluid balance is that of intake and output. "Insensible loss" is usually assumed to be about 900 ml per day, but this must be balanced against "insensible" production of about 500 ml water daily by metabolism. The *net* "insensible loss" is therefore the difference between these two—about 400 ml a day. A normally hydrated patient, unable to control his own balance, should be given this basic volume of fluid daily with, in addition, the volume of measured losses (urine, vomitus, etc.) during the preceding 24 hours. If he is thought to be abnormally hydrated fluid intake should be adjusted until hydration is restored. Inevitably the intake for any day must be calculated from the output in the preceding 24 hours. This is adequate when the patient starts in a normal state of hydration.

It should be remembered that a pyrexial patient may lose a litre or more of fluid in sweat, and that if he is also overbreathing respiratory water loss can be considerable. In such cases the allowance of 400 ml daily for insensible loss may not be enough.

Many very ill patients are incontinent of urine, and measurement of even this volume may be impossible. Changes in body fluid may be assessed by daily weighing, since 1 litre of water weighs 1 kg. Over short periods of time changes in solid body weight will be small, and alteration in weight can be assumed to be due to changes in fluid balance. Unfortunately, very ill patients may be unable to sit in weighing chairs. Some hospitals have weighing beds, in which the patient is weighed with the bed and the bedclothes. In this situation, care must be taken to keep the weight of the bedclothes constant.

Assessment of fluid balance in severely ill patients may present grave problems. Every attempt must be made to make *accurate* measurements of fluid intake and loss. In most circumstances carefully kept fluid charts and daily weighing are of even more importance than frequent plasma electrolyte estimations. Inaccurate charting is useless, and may be dangerous.

ASSESSMENT OF SODIUM BALANCE

If fluid balance is accurately controlled *in a normally hydrated patient* plasma sodium concentrations are the best means of assessing sodium balance. As we shall see later, the proviso of normal hydration is important, and plasma electrolyte values *alone* should never be used to assess the need for therapy. They must be correlated with the history and the present state of hydration.

ASSESSMENT OF POTASSIUM BALANCE

Potassium is a predominantly intracellular ion, and its balance is difficult to assess from extracellular levels. For further discussion of this problem see p. 29.

Measurement of daily electrolyte losses in urine and fistula fluid may occasionally be of value in severe disturbances: these may then be replaced. However, as discussed above, if hydration is controlled, plasma sodium levels indicate the state of sodium balance and plasma levels of potassium should be kept normal whatever the state of its balance.

Radioisotopic methods can be used to measure the amounts of sodium, potassium and water in the body. Such methods are expensive and time-consuming and rarely give more information than can be gained by a critical assessment of the clinical state and routine laboratory findings. Moreover, the estimations take about 24 hours to complete, and require the patient to be in a steady state. The estimations are therefore impractical just when most needed, and have little place in routine use.

DISTRIBUTION OF WATER AND ELECTROLYTES IN THE BODY

In mild disturbances of water and electrolyte metabolism the total amount of these in the body is of less importance than their distribution within it.

DISTRIBUTION OF ELECTROLYTES

The body has two main fluid compartments of very different electrolyte composition. The compartments are:

1. **The intracellular compartment,** in which *potassium* is the predominant cation.

2. **The extracellular compartment,** in which *sodium* is the predominant cation.

The extracellular fluid can be subdivided into:

(*a*) The interstitial fluid which is of very low protein concentration.

(*b*) The intravascular fluid (plasma) which contains protein.

Distribution of Electrolytes Between Cells and Extracellular Fluid

The intracellular concentration of sodium is less than a tenth of that n the extracellular fluid (ECF), while that of potassium is about thirty times as much. In absolute amounts about 95 per cent of the metabolically active sodium in the body is outside cells, and about the same proportion of potassium is intracellular. The cell walls are physically freely permeable to both sodium and potassium, and these differential concentrations are maintained in the body at the cost of energy produced by glucose metabolism and ATP (the so-called "sodium pump"): this active process is also necessary for sodium-potassium exchange in renal tubular and intestinal epithelial cells. *If this energy process is interfered with* (for instance, in diabetes mellitus when glucose is not metabolized normally, and in anoxia when ATP is not produced by the tricarboxylic acid cycle) sodium and potassium diffuse passively across cell walls, increasing extracellular potassium. Conversely, if glucose metabolism is increased by insulin the reverse process occurs and this may be used in the emergency treatment of hyperkalaemia (p. 55). In *acidosis* hydrogen ions replace potassium in the cells and hyperkalaemia may occur. In *potassium depletion* sodium-potassium exchange across cell walls maintains extracellular levels until cellular levels are very low. Under all these and many other circumstances measurement of plasma potassium gives little information about total body potassium.

Because glucose metabolism is necessary to maintain the differential concentration of sodium and potassium across cell walls (including erythrocytes), false plasma electrolyte results may be obtained if whole blood is allowed to stand *in vitro* until glucose is used up (p. 396).

In most circumstances the shift of potassium across cell membranes is accompanied by a shift of sodium in the opposite direction, but the *percentage* change in extracellular sodium levels will be much less than that of potassium. A simplified example will demonstrate this. Let us assume extra- and intracellular volumes to be equal, the plasma sodium to be 140 mEq/litre and potassium 4·0 mEq/litre, with reversal of these concentrations inside cells. An exchange of 4·0 mEq/litre of sodium for potassium across the cell wall would double the plasma potassium concentration (a very clinically significant change) while only reducing the plasma sodium concentration to 136 mEq/litre. *Extracellular* levels are the physiologically important ones, and these shifts affect potassium more than sodium.

Other ions tend to move across cell walls with sodium and potassium. The hydrogen ion has already been mentioned and, for instance, magnesium and phosphate are predominantly intracellular, and chloride extracellular ions. The distribution of all these, and of bicarbonate, will be affected by the same conditions as those mentioned.

Distribution of Electrolytes Between Plasma and Interstitial Fluid

The vascular wall, unlike that of the cell, is freely permeable to small ions *in vivo* as well as *in vitro*. Plasma contains protein in significant concentration and interstitial fluid does not. Electrolyte concentrations are therefore higher in the latter to balance the osmotic effect of the electrolyte and protein concentration inside vessels. The difference is small and clinically insignificant, and for practical purposes one can assume that plasma electrolytes are representative of those in the extracellular fluid as a whole.

DISTRIBUTION OF WATER IN THE BODY

A little over half the body water is inside cells. Of the extracellular water about 15–20 per cent is in the plasma. The remainder makes up the extravascular, extracellular interstitial fluid.

The distribution of water across cell walls depends on the *in vivo* effective osmotic difference between intra- and extracellular fluid: that across blood vessel walls is determined by the balance between the *in vivo* effective osmotic pressure of plasma and the net outward hydrostatic pressure. Correct interpretation of plasma electrolyte results depends on a clear understanding of these factors.

Concept of Effective Osmotic Pressure

In the present context the net movement of water across a semipermeable membrane depends on the differences in *molar* concentration (number of molecules per unit volume) of non-diffusible ions between the two sides of the membrane. With monovalent ions such as sodium and potassium the number of milliEquivalents per litre is the same as that of millimoles per litre, and the usual clinical units of measurement indicate their molarity. However, results of protein estimations are usually expressed in g/100 ml, and for comparison on a molar basis we must divide the figure by the molecular weight of the protein. Given the same concentration in g/100 ml, the lower the molecular weight the higher the molar concentration (to put it another way, there are more small than large molecules per g).

Osmotic pressure (OP) is expressed in milliosmoles/litre (in the present context this is numerically equal to the number of millimoles/litre). If the separating membrane were permeable only to water, only the difference in osmolarity on the two sides determines the osmotic drive. However, if it is permeable to smaller molecules as well as water the effective OP depends on the concentration gradient of molecules too large to pass through the membrane. The *effective osmotic pressure*, therefore, depends both on the relative permeability of the membrane and on the difference in molarity between the two sides.

The *total osmotic pressure* is usually measured by the depression of freezing point below that of pure water. This figure depends on molar strength, and is therefore a measure of the OP of a solution in contact with a membrane permeable only to water. It must be clearly differentiated from the effective *in vivo* osmotic pressure.

The *oncotic pressure* or *colloid osmotic pressure* is a term used to describe the effective OP across blood vessel walls, which are permeable to electrolytes but not to larger molecules. It is almost entirely due to plasma proteins.

It should be understood that we are talking about *net* movement of water across membranes. If the OP on the two sides of a membrane is equal water can still diffuse across it, but movement in the two directions is quantitatively the same.

Distribution of Water Across Cell Walls

There is a negligible difference in hydrostatic pressure across cell walls, and distribution of water depends almost entirely on the difference in osmotic pressure on the two sides. The wall is physically impermeable to protein and, because of the "sodium pump", is effectively impermeable to sodium and potassium *in vivo*. Normally the total intracellular OP (due predominantly to potassium and its associated anions, and, to a much smaller extent, to cellular proteins) equals that of the interstitial fluid (made up predominantly of sodium and its associated anions). There is therefore little net movement of water, and cellular hydration remains constant.

Changes of intake and output affect extracellular concentrations first. Osmotically, changes in sodium (and chloride) *concentration* are the most important. A rapid reduction of this reduces extracellular OP: before readjustment of electrolytes can occur across the cell wall water moves from the lower to the higher osmotic region, causing cellular overhydration. Conversely, a rapid increase in extracellular sodium concentration causes cellular dehydration, and the symptoms of hypo- and hypernatraemia are due to changes in cellular hydration. Rapid changes are much more dangerous than gradual ones, as electrolytes can only diffuse slowly to minimize hydration changes.

In the presence of uraemia and hyperglycaemia urea and glucose contribute significantly to extracellular osmolarity. These diffuse fairly rapidly into cells, but if the extracellular concentration is lowered very rapidly (e.g. during haemodialysis or treatment of diabetic coma) cellular overhydration may occur. Cerebral oedema, on the other hand, may be treated by rapid infusion of hyperosmolar solutions such as urea and dextrose.

Distribution of Water Across Blood Vessel Walls

The maintenance of blood pressure depends on retention of intravascular water at a pressure higher than that of the interstitial fluid.

Unlike the cell walls, those of blood vessels are freely permeable to electrolytes even *in vivo*. The smallest molecule normally present in significant amounts which cannot diffuse readily through the wall is albumin. Any molecule from this size upwards will exert an osmotic effect across the wall, and as albumin (which is the plasma protein with the lowest molecular weight) is present in by far the highest molar concentration, it is osmotically the most important of the proteins. The effective OP of plasma across the blood vessel wall is called the oncotic or colloid osmotic pressure to distinguish it from the total OP measured by freezing point depression.

Because proteins are not present to any significant extent in interstitial fluid the osmotic effect tends to draw water into the blood vessels.

This is opposed *in vivo* by the net hydrostatic pressure (the blood pressure minus the pressure of the interstitial fluid). In the absence of oncotic pressure the plasma water would be lost rapidly into the interstitial space. Albumin is the most important factor maintaining the oncotic pressure, and any condition associated with low plasma albumin levels results in net movement of water from the vascular lumen. The homeostatic mechanisms brought into play cause retention of water by the kidneys and hence maintenance of blood pressure; however, more water then leaves the blood vessels, with the formation of oedema.

CLINICAL FEATURES OF WATER AND SODIUM DISTURBANCES

We are now in a position to explain the immediate clinical consequences of water and sodium disturbances. These depend on changes in extracellular osmolarity and hence in cellular hydration (sodium) and changes in circulating volume (water). Clinical features of potassium depletion are discussed on p. 52.

CLINICAL FEATURES OF DISTURBANCES OF SODIUM CONCENTRATION

Almost all the immediate clinical features of disturbances of sodium metabolism are due to changes in its *extracellular concentration* and therefore its osmolarity.

Gradual changes, by allowing time for electrolyte exchange across cell walls, may produce little clinical effect until they are extreme.

Hyponatraemia causes cellular overhydration. The clinical effect of overhydration of cerebral cells is to cause *headache, confusion* and, later, *fits*. Passage of water into cells reduces the apparent change in extracellular sodium concentration and aggravates any extracellular water depletion.

Hypernatraemia causes cellular dehydration and this causes thirst. Again, the effect of dehydration on cerebral cells is to cause mental confusion and, later, coma. Passage of water from cells reduces the change in extracellular sodium concentration by dilution.

Rapid changes in the volume of cerebral cells may cause tearing of small blood vessels, with cerebral haemorrhages ranging from petechiae to major cerebral catastrophes. It is most important to bear this in mind during treatment.

CLINICAL FEATURES OF DISTURBANCES OF FLUID VOLUME

If the extracellular osmolarity is unchanged the clinical features of disturbances of water metabolism are due to changes in circulating volume.

Water deficiency causes hypovolaemia. If cellular hydration is not altered by changes in effective osmolarity across cell membranes clinical signs of "dehydration" and thirst may be absent. *Hypotension and collapse* follow, and death may result from circulatory insufficiency. Laboratory findings are those of *haemoconcentration* with a raised plasma protein concentration and haematocrit. Because renal perfusion is poor, glomerular filtration rate may fall and there may be *uraemia* and other signs of nitrogen retention.

Water excess, in the absence of changes in effective OP across cell walls, causes *hypertension* and overloading of the heart with *cardiac failure. Oedema* occurs when albumin levels are low, because the reduced oncotic pressure together with increased intravascular hydrostatic pressure cause passage of water into interstitial fluid. Laboratory findings are characteristic of *haemodilution* and, unless there is renal failure, the blood urea level tends to be low.

We shall refer back to these clinical features when we come to discuss syndromes associated with electrolyte and water disturbances. In the meantime we shall look more carefully at the control of electrolyte and water metabolism, as an understanding of this is also necessary to understand the sequence of events in disease states.

CONTROL OF ELECTROLYTE AND WATER METABOLISM

Electrolytes and water follow the general rule that total body amounts are normally controlled secondarily to extracellular concentrations.

CONTROL OF ELECTROLYTES

Intake of electrolytes is probably not actively controlled. The most important factor controlling loss is the mineralocorticoid hormone, aldosterone.

Aldosterone

Aldosterone is secreted by the zona glomerulosa of the adrenal cortex (p. 91). It affects sodium-potassium exchange across *all* cell walls. We shall concentrate on its effect on renal tubular cells, but we should bear in mind that it also affects faecal sodium loss, and the distribution of electrolytes in the body.

In the kidney tubule aldosterone increases sodium reabsorption from the glomerular filtrate in exchange for potassium. The net result in the body is retention of sodium and loss of potassium. In the presence of high levels of circulating aldosterone *urinary sodium concentrations are low.*

Many factors have been implicated in the feed-back control of aldosterone secretion. Such factors as local electrolyte concentration in the adrenal and the kidney are probably of little clinical or physiological importance compared with the effect on the adrenal of the renin-angiotensin system.

The Renin-Angiotensin System

Renin is a proteolytic enzyme secreted by a cellular complex situated near the renal glomeruli (and therefore called the juxtaglomerular apparatus). In the blood stream it acts on a renin substrate (an α_2 globulin) to form *angiotensin I*. This is further split by a circulating peptidase to *angiotensin II*. This peptide hormone has two actions:

1. It acts directly on blood vessel walls, causing vasoconstriction. It therefore helps to maintain blood pressure.

2. It stimulates the cells of the zona glomerulosa to secrete aldosterone.

The most important stimulus to renin production seems to be reduced renal blood flow (possibly changes in the mean blood pressure in renal vessels are the actual stimuli). Poor renal blood flow is often associated with an inadequate systemic blood pressure and the two effects of angiotensin II ensure that this is corrected:

1. Vasoconstriction raises the blood pressure before the circulating volume can be restored.

2. Sodium retention occurs due to the action of aldosterone: as we shall see later, this will usually be accompanied by water retention with restoration of the circulating volume.

We may make an oversimplified statement based on the effect and control of aldosterone secretion. Aldosterone causes sodium retention. The stimulus to it is renin, which is controlled, effectively, by circulating blood volume, Therefore, *blood volume controls sodium retention.*

Non-Aldosterone Factors Affecting Renal Sodium Excretion

Aldosterone is probably the most important factor affecting sodium excretion. However, renal factors such as changes in *glomerular filtration rate* (GFR) and *tubular function* may be important in pathological conditions. In glomerular failure the volume of filtrate is small and the amount of filtered sodium proportionately reduced. The flow is sluggish. In the presence of aldosterone sodium will be reabsorbed more completely than usual. Conversely a higher glomerular filtration rate may cause a sodium diuresis. A further hormonal factor controlling sodium excretion has been postulated: this is the *natriuretic hormone* or "third factor" (the GFR is the "first factor" and aldosterone the "second factor"). This hormone, which is said to be secreted in response to an expansion of plasma volume, may inhibit sodium reabsorption in the proximal tubule. It has been suggested that it fails to be secreted in oedematous states.

In certain inborn errors of renal tubular function the kidneys cannot respond to aldosterone; this may also be the case in the recovery phase of acute tubular necrosis, and with tubular damage of any kind: for instance, prolonged hypokalaemia in primary aldosteronism may prevent maximal tubular response to aldosterone.

In the later discussion we will assume the renin-aldosterone mechanism to be of overriding importance in the control of sodium excretion.

CONTROL OF WATER

Intake of water is controlled by thirst. The hypothalamic thirst centre responds to increased osmolarity in the blood circulating through it (or, more accurately, to the osmotic difference between this and the cells of the centre), and therefore to the sodium concentration. This occurs whether or not the fluid volume is normal.

Loss of water is also controlled via the hypothalamus in response to osmolarity changes. Increased plasma osmolarity (and therefore sodium concentration) stimulates secretion of antidiuretic hormone (ADH). The mechanism is very sensitive and a rise of osmotic pressure of only 2 per cent quadruples ADH output, while a similar fall cuts it off completely. Such changes (of about 3 mEq/litre of sodium) may *not* be obvious using relatively crude laboratory methods.

Antidiuretic hormone is a peptide produced by the hypothalamus and secreted by the posterior pituitary gland. By increasing the permeability of distal renal tubular cells it increases passive water reabsorption along the osmotic gradient produced by the countercurrent mechanism (p. 5). Under its influence a *concentrated urine of high specific gravity is passed.*

Water intake and loss are both controlled by plasma osmolarity. Plasma osmolarity depends largely on its sodium concentration. We have already pointed out that fluid volume controls sodium retention. We can now make the further simplified statement that *sodium concentration controls the amount of water in the body.*

Non-ADH Factors Affecting Water Excretion

The distal tubule has a limited capacity for reabsorption of water, even in the presence of a maximal amount of ADH: thus if a large volume reaches this site water diuresis will occur.

The glomerular filtrate may contain high concentrations of osmotically active substances which are not completely reabsorbed during passage through the proximal tubules and loop of Henle: these inhibit water and, to a lesser extent, sodium reabsorption in the proximal tubule (p. 7) and a larger volume than normal reaches the distal tubule. This is the basis of action of osmotic diuretics such as mannitol and, to a lesser extent, urea and hypertonic glucose. Patients being fed intravenously, or who, because of tissue damage, are breaking down larger than usual quantities of protein and producing excessive amounts of urea from the released amino-acids, may become dehydrated even in the presence of adequate amounts of ADH (p. 41).

As in the case of sodium and aldosterone, such non-ADH effects are usually relatively unimportant.

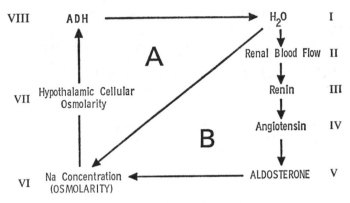

FIG. 1.—Cycle of sodium and water homeostasis.

INTERRELATIONSHIP BETWEEN SODIUM AND WATER HOMEOSTASIS

Let us now look more closely at the simplified statements made above concerning the control of ADH and aldosterone secretion. We said that, effectively, sodium controls ADH secretion and water controls aldosterone secretion. But ADH secretion controls water loss and aldosterone controls sodium loss. The homeostasis of sodium and water is interdependent and this simplified scheme is shown in Fig. 1. The thirst mechanism is not shown here but it should be remembered that an increase of osmolarity not only reduces water loss but increases thirst and therefore intake. The diagonal line which divides the rectangle into two triangles, A and B, indicates that changes in hydration can also directly alter sodium concentration.

We shall refer to this scheme repeatedly while explaining changes occurring in pathological states. The reader should bear in mind that it is a simplified scheme and does not allow for the effect of fluid shifts across cell walls on extracellular concentrations and volume.

DISTURBANCES OF SODIUM AND WATER METABOLISM

Disturbances of sodium and water metabolism are most commonly due to excessive losses from the body. Sometimes inadequate intake contributes to the deficiency. In the presence of normal homeostatic mechanisms excessive intake is rarely of clinical importance.

Disturbances can also be due to abnormal amounts of the homeostatic hormones, aldosterone and ADH, or to failure of the end organs, particularly the kidney and intestine, to respond to them.

WATER AND SODIUM DEFICIENCY

Pure water and pure sodium deficiency are rare. However, conditions in which either is lost in excess of the other are relatively common. Predominant sodium depletion is almost always accompanied by some water depletion and *vice versa*. Potassium depletion and acid-base disturbance commonly accompany one another.

TABLE II

APPROXIMATE SODIUM CONCENTRATIONS IN BODY FLUIDS (mEq/litre)

Plasma	Gastric	Biliary and pan-creatic	Small intes-tinal	Ileal	Ileostomy (new)	Diarrhoea	Sweat
140	60	140	110	120	130	60	60

Predominant Water Depletion

This syndrome is due to loss of water in excess of loss of sodium. This is usually the result of the loss of fluid containing a lower concentration of sodium than that of plasma, or to deficient water intake. Sweat and gastric juice contain concentrations of sodium much lower than those in plasma (see Table II); in diabetes insipidus, during an osmotic diuresis, or in the rare inborn error associated with failure of the renal tubules to respond to ADH, urine of low sodium concentration is passed. As hyperosmolarity due to predominant water loss causes thirst, clinical effects are only seen if water is not available or cannot be taken in adequate quantities.

The clinical situations associated with predominant water loss are:

1. Water deficiency in the presence of normal homeostatic mechanisms.
  (i) Excessive fluid loss—(*a*) Loss of excessive amounts of sweat.
                    (*b*) Loss of gastric juice.
                    (*c*) Loss of fluid stools of low sodium content (usually in infantile gastro-enteritis).

(ii) Deficiency of fluid intake—Inadequate water supply, or mechanical obstruction to its intake.

2. Failure of homeostatic mechanisms for water retention.
   (i)   Deficiency of ADH (diabetes insipidus).
   (ii) Failure of renal tubular cells to respond to high levels of ADH (Nephrogenic diabetes insipidus).
   (iii) Inadequate response to thirst mechanism (for example in comatose patients).

In most clinical states associated with predominant water depletion more than one of these factors is responsible.

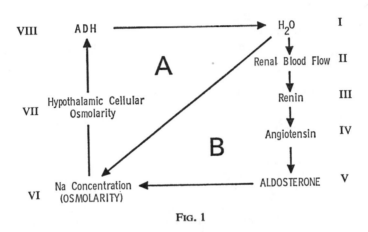

FIG. 1

1. Predominant water depletion with normal homeostatic mechanisms.— The reader should refer to Fig. 1 during the following explanation.

Triangle B—Immediate Effects:
   (a) Loss of water in excess of sodium increases the plasma sodium concentration (diagonal line I–VI).
   (b) Loss of water reduces renal blood flow and stimulates aldosterone production (I–V). Sodium is retained and the rise in plasma sodium is aggravated (V–VI).

Triangle A—Compensatory Effects:
Increased plasma osmolarity stimulates:
   (a) Thirst, increasing water intake if water is available and the patient can respond to it (not shown on diagram).
   (b) ADH secretion (VI–VIII). Urinary volume falls (VIII–I) and water loss is minimized.

If adequate amounts of water are available depletion is rapidly corrected. In the absence of intake, or in the presence of continued loss by extrarenal routes, the mechanisms in Triangle A cannot function and homeostasis breaks down. Hypernatraemia is therefore an early finding in water depletion: it is important to realize that it may be present before clinical signs of dehydration are obvious.

The clinical signs are those of:
1. Hypernatraemia.
2. Later, water deficiency.
3. ADH secretion leading to oliguria.

The findings are:
1. Haemoconcentration.
2. Hypernatraemia.
3. Low urinary sodium (in response to high aldosterone levels).
4. Mild uraemia.
5. A urine of low volume, high specific gravity and high urea concentration (due to the action of ADH).

2. Failure of homeostatic mechanisms for water retention.—*Diabetes insipidus* may be due to pituitary or hypothalamic damage caused by head injury or during hypophysectomy, or to invasion of the region by tumour. It may be idiopathic in origin.

Hereditary nephrogenic diabetes insipidus is a rare inborn error of renal tubular function in which ADH levels are high but the tubules cannot respond to it (compare pseudohypoparathyroidism, p. 184): the newborn infant passes large volumes of urine and rapidly becomes dehydrated. Urinary loss is difficult to assess at this age, and the cries of thirst may be misinterpreted. During the *recovery phase of acute tubular necrosis* or when, for instance, hypercalcaemia *damages the renal tubules*, there may also be failure to respond to ADH.

The reader should refer again to Fig. 1 and to the immediately preceding section.

The first stage is identical with that described in the previous section. Because Triangle A is not functioning (*b*) cannot occur, and the point is soon reached at which intake cannot adequately replace loss.

The clinical signs and findings are those described in the previous section, with the exception that there is polyuria, not oliguria, and that the urine is of low specific gravity and concentration. These findings are the result of ADH deficiency. If any doubt remains as to the diagnosis, water may be deliberately withheld (see Appendix to Chapter I). In the absence of ADH, or when the tubules fail to respond to it, concentration of urine fails to occur. In the case of true ADH deficiency a concentrated urine will be passed if exogenous ADH (pitressin) is given. In nephrogenic diabetes insipidus maximal amounts of ADH are already circulating, and administration of it will not influence water reabsorption.

The unconscious patient.—The syndrome of predominant water depletion with hypernatraemia is seen most commonly in the unconscious or confused patient or in the infant with gastro-enteritis or pneumonia. In such subjects there is usually more than one cause of water depletion.

1. They are often pyrexial. Loss of hypotonic *sweat* is increased.

2. They may be *overbreathing* because of pneumonia, acidosis or brain stem damage. Water loss is increased.

3. They may be given hypertonic intravenous infusions, either to provide nutrient (dextrose or amino-acids) or to produce osmotic diuresis in cases of poisoning (thus increasing the urinary loss of poison). There may be tissue damage and hence breakdown of protein to urea. All these factors will cause an *osmotic diuresis* overriding the effect of ADH.

4. There may be true *diabetes insipidus* due to head injury.

5. The subject cannot respond to hyperosmolarity by drinking.

In the presence of factors 3 and 4 a high urine volume contributes to dehydration (and is *not* an indication of "good" hydration) and the extent of loss may not be realized if the subject is incontinent. Homeostatic mechanisms may not be capable of responding to hyperosmolarity (4 and 5) and hypernatraemia is an early finding. It may occur before clinical signs of dehydration are evident and is dangerous because of the resulting cellular dehydration.

Predominant Sodium Depletion

No normal body fluids contain significantly higher concentrations of sodium than those in plasma (see Table II, p. 38). In the presence of normal homeostatic mechanisms the commonest cause of predominant sodium depletion is loss of sodium and water followed by replacement with fluids of low sodium concentration. This is most commonly iatrogenic but may occur if patients have lost sodium in diarrhoea, vomiting or sweat, and then drink a large volume of water.

The clinical conditions accompanied by predominant sodium deficiency are:

1. Sodium deficiency in the presence of normal homeostatic mechanisms.

(a) Vomiting
(b) Diarrhoea   } Followed by replacement with
(c) Loss through fistulae } fluids low in sodium.
(d) Excessive sweating

2. Failure of homeostatic mechanisms for sodium retention.
  (a) Addison's disease (absence of aldosterone)
  (b) "Pseudo" Addison's disease (failure of the renal tubules to respond to aldosterone). This is very rare.

1. Predominant sodium depletion with normal homeostatic mechanisms.—
The reader should refer to Fig. 1.

Triangle A. Immediate effects and emergency compensation.
  (a) Sodium concentration tends to fall, cutting off ADH secretion (VI–VIII).
  (b) Water is lost in the urine (VIII–I).
  (c) Osmolarity is restored to normal (Diagonal line I–VI).

This is the emergency mechanism (Triangle A), preventing shift of water across cell membranes at the expense of water loss.

Triangle B. Compensatory Mechanisms.
  (a) Loss of water stimulates aldosterone secretion (I–V).
  (b) Sodium is retained (V–VI) and the initial sequence of events in Triangle A is reversed. Sodium and water are restored to normal.

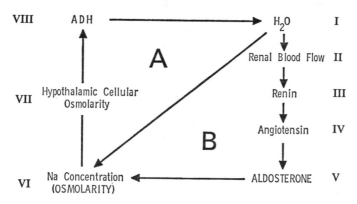

FIG. 1

In the presence of continuing sodium deficiency the homeostatic mechanisms of Triangle B cannot function effectively. Osmolarity is maintained at the expense of continued water loss. Only when this is extreme will hyponatraemia occur.

Clinical signs are:
  1. Those of water deficiency.
  2. *Late*, those of hyponatraemia.

The findings are those of:

1. Haemoconcentration.
2. Renal circulatory insufficiency with mild uraemia.
3. *Late* hyponatraemia.
4. Low urinary sodium concentration (due to aldosterone secretion).

2. Failure of homeostatic mechanisms for sodium retention.—Addison's disease with hypoaldosteronism is by far the most important cause of this type of disturbance. During the recovery phase of acute tubular necrosis large amounts of sodium can be lost in urine, and an inborn error known as pseudo-Addison's disease does occur.

The reader should again refer to Fig. 1 and to the immediately preceding section.

The first stage is identical with that described in the preceding section. The homeostatic mechanisms of Triangle B are not functioning, so that the second stage cannot occur. Osmolarity is maintained until late by water loss. The clinical and laboratory findings are those described in the preceding section except that, because of the absence of aldosterone, *urinary sodium concentration is high.*

WATER AND SODIUM EXCESS

In the presence of normal homeostatic mechanisms an excess of water and electrolytes is of relatively little importance, because the excess is rapidly corrected. These syndromes are commonly associated with failure of homeostatic mechanisms.

Predominant Excess of Water

Water overloading occurs in two circumstances in which normal homeostasis has failed.

1. In renal failure, where fluid of low sodium concentration has been replaced in excess of that lost. Fluid balance should be carefully controlled in such patients.

2. In the presence of "inappropriate" ADH secretion (the term "inappropriate" is used in this book to describe continued secretion of a hormone under conditions in which it should normally be cut off). ADH is one of the peptide hormones which can be manufactured by malignant tissue of non-endocrine origin (see Chapter XX for a further discussion). "Inappropriate" secretion (possibly from the pituitary itself) occurs in a variety of other conditions, including infections. Such ADH production is not under feed-back control and therefore continues to be produced in circumstances in which its secretion should be completely cut off (in the presence of low extracellular osmolarity). This

fact is evidenced by the production of a concentrated urine in the presence of a dilute plasma.

If we refer again to Fig. 1 we will see how excessive intake is normally corrected.

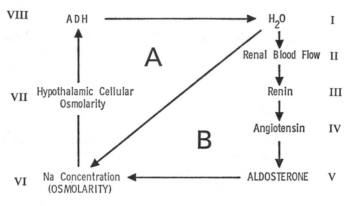

FIG. 1.

Triangle B. Immediate effects.
  (a) Excess water tends to lower plasma sodium (diagonal arrow), (I–VI).
  (b) Increased renal blood flow cuts off aldosterone production, increasing urinary sodium loss and therefore further decreasing plasma sodium (V–VI).

Triangle A. Compensatory effects.
  ADH is cut off (VI–VIII) and large volumes of dilute urine are passed (VIII–I).

When renal glomerular function is poor, or in the presence of "inappropriate" ADH secretion (which is not subject to feed-back control), Triangle A is out of action. The second stage cannot take place.

The clinical consequences are:
  1. Those of water excess.
  2. If overhydration is rapid, those of hyponatraemia.

Typically these patients may be remarkably well clinically with very low plasma sodium concentrations. This contrasts with the clinical state in true sodium depletion, when hypotension leads to collapse.

The findings are:
1. Haemodilution.
2. Hyponatraemia.

If the cause is glomerular failure there will be uraemia. If it is due to "inappropriate" ADH secretion the plasma urea level will tend to be low.

Predominant Excess of Sodium

Predominant sodium excess is most commonly due to an "inappropriate" secretion of excess aldosterone or other mineralocorticoids in Cushing's syndrome, or in Conn's syndrome (primary aldosteronism), or to excessive stimulation of a normally functioning adrenal in secondary aldosteronism. Cushing's syndrome is described more fully on p. 92.

Primary aldosteronism (Conn's syndrome).—Primary aldosteronism, or excess aldosterone secretion not subject to feed-back control, is most commonly due to a benign aldosterone secreting adenoma of the adrenal cortex.

The reader should refer again to Fig. 1.
1. Excess aldosterone causes urinary sodium retention (V–VI).
2. The increased sodium concentration stimulates ADH secretion. VI–VIII) and water retention (VIII—I).
3. Water retention tends to return plasma sodium concentrations to normal (diagonal arrow, I–VI).
4. Triangle B is out of action and aldosterone secretion cannot be cut off. This tends to maintain plasma sodium levels at or near the upper end of the normal range.
5. Continued action of aldosterone causes sodium retention at the expense of potassium loss, and potassium depletion occurs.

The clinical features are:
1. Those of water excess (p. 34). Patients are hypertensive but rarely oedematous.
2. Those of hypokalaemia (p. 52).

Findings are:
1. Hypokalaemia (due to excess aldosterone).
2. A high plasma bicarbonate (for explanation see p. 79).
3. A plasma sodium in the high normal range or just above it.
4. A low urinary sodium in the early stages. However, sodium excretion may rise later, possibly because of hypokalaemic tubular damage (p. 13), and consequent unresponsiveness to aldosterone, or because of secretion of natriuretic hormone (p. 35) in response to the expanded plasma volume.

Hypokalaemic alkalosis occurs in potassium depletion from any cause. However, the association of these findings in a patient without an obvious cause (such as administration of purgatives or diuretics) for potassium loss and with hypertension should suggest the diagnosis of primary aldosteronism. Further suggestive evidence would be the finding of high aldosterone with low renin levels (in all cases of *secondary* aldosteronism *both* are high). Unfortunately these estimations are research procedures and are unavailable in most routine laboratories.

Secondary aldosteronism: Oedema.—Any of the conditions already described in the sections on water and sodium depletion, in which aldosterone secretion is stimulated following reduction in renal blood flow could, strictly, be called secondary aldosteronism. The term is more commonly used to indicate the conditions in which, because the initial abnormality is not corrected, long-standing increased aldosterone secretion itself produces abnormalities.

Aldosterone is secreted following stimulation of the renin-angiotensin system by a low renal blood flow. This may occur, either because of local abnormalities in renal vessels, or because of a reduced circulating volume.

Secondary aldosteronism, in the usually accepted sense of the word, occurs in the following conditions:

1. Redistribution of extracellular fluid, leading to a reduction of plasma volume in the presence of normal or high total extracellular fluid volume. These conditions are due to a reduced plasma oncotic pressure, and are therefore associated with low plasma albumin levels. Oedema is present. Such conditions are:

(*a*) Liver disease.
(*b*) Nephrotic syndrome.
(*c*) Protein malnutrition.

2. Damage to the renal vessels, reducing renal blood flow. These conditions are usually not associated with oedema:

(*a*) Essential hypertension.
(*b*) Malignant hypertension.
(*c*) Renal hypertension (e.g. renal artery stenosis).

3. Cardiac failure. In this case two factors may cause low renal blood flow. Firstly the cardiac output may be low, with poor renal perfusion pressure. Secondly, high intravascular hydrostatic pressure on the venous side of the circulation may cause redistribution of fluid and oedema.

The mechanisms in Fig. 1 are brought into play:

1. Reduced renal blood flow stimulates aldosterone secretion (I–V).
2. Sodium retention stimulates ADH secretion (V–VIII) and therefore water retention (VIII–I).

Intravascular volume is temporarily restored, but in conditions with hypoalbuminaemia or in cardiac failure more fluid passes into the interstitial fluid and the cycle restarts. A vicious circle is set up in which circulating volume can only be maintained by water retention and oedema results. In oedematous secondary aldosteronism failure of secretion of natriuretic hormone in response to an expanded plasma volume (p. 35) is also said to contribute to the sodium and water retention. In non-oedematous states hypertension occurs.

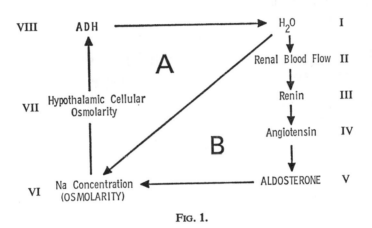

Fig. 1.

This cycle should only stimulate water retention in parallel with sodium retention. However, many of these patients have hyponatraemia. The reasons for this are not clear, but from the therapeutic point of view it must be remembered that in the presence of oedema the total amount of sodium in the body is high, even if there is hyponatraemia (see Table IV).

Hypokalaemia may be present, but is a less common finding than in primary aldosteronism. Again the reason is not clear, but may be due to a redistribution of potassium between cells and extracellular fluid. Hypokalaemia is, however, more readily precipitated by diuretic therapy in secondary hyperaldosteronism than in normal subjects.

The clinical features of these cases are those of the primary condition.

The findings are:
1. A normal or low plasma sodium concentration.
2. A low urinary sodium excretion.
3. Findings due to the primary disease, e.g. hypoalbuminaemia, uraemia, etc.

THE DIAGNOSTIC VALUE OF URINARY SODIUM CONCENTRATION

It will be noticed that urinary sodium excretion is low when aldosterone secretion is high. In the absence of primary aldosteronism this finding indicates low renal blood flow. Similarly, except in Addison's disease, high urinary sodium excretion indicates high renal blood flow. The estimation gives no information about the state of body sodium stores. In most cases the state of hydration and sodium metabolism can be assessed by noting the clinical picture and plasma findings. Only in the rare cases in which doubt still remains or in the differential diagnosis of renal tubular and glomerular lesions (p. 15) is urinary sodium estimation indicated.

DISTURBANCES OF POTASSIUM METABOLISM

Plasma potassium levels are a very poor indication of total body amounts of the ion, because of its predominantly intracellular location.

Potassium depletion results from excessive loss from the body, and is relatively common. True body overload is extremely rare. Homeostatic mechanisms for correction of potassium levels are poor, and are usually subordinated to sodium homeostasis.

TABLE III

APPROXIMATE POTASSIUM CONCENTRATIONS IN BODY FLUIDS (mEq/litre)

Plasma	Gastric	Biliary and pancreatic	Small intestinal	Ileal	Ileostomy (new)	Diarrhoea	Sweat
4	10	5	5	5	15	40	10

Excessive loss may occur:

1. **In intestinal secretions.**—Continued *vomiting* or *diarrhoea*, or loss through *intestinal fistulae*, especially in *ileostomy fluid*, may cause severe potassium loss. Habitual purgative takers may present with potassium depletion and are sometimes reluctant to admit to this habit. From the table above it will be seen that fluid from new ileostomy and diarrhoea stools are particularly rich in potassium, but a constant drain of any of these secretions causes depletion. This loss is often aggravated by loss in the urine (see below).

2. **In urine.**—(*a*) Failure to reabsorb potassium in renal tubular failure (p. 12).

(*b*) When the amount of sodium available for exchange with potassium in the distal tubule is increased. *Thiazide diuretics* inhibit sodium reabsorption in the proximal tubule and more is therefore available for exchange in the distal tubule; *infusion of sodium salts* has the same action as thiazide diuretics.

(*c*) When secretion of hydrogen ion in exchange for sodium in the renal tubule is inhibited (p. 3) more potassium is excreted. This occurs in *renal tubular acidosis*, when hydrogen ion transport is deficient, and in the presence of *carbonic anhydrase* inhibitors. It also occurs in *cellular alkalosis*, when hydrogen ions are not available in adequate amounts in the renal tubular cells for normal exchange (p. 77).

(*d*) With *excessive amounts of aldosterone* or other adrenal steroids, when sodium reabsorption and potassium secretion are increased. This occurs in primary or secondary aldosteronism and in Cushing's syndrome. The water depletion accompanying loss of intestinal secretions causes secondary aldosteronism and urinary potassium loss, thus aggravating the primary potassium depletion.

(*e*) When potassium is lost from the cells, even when the kidneys are functioning normally, for instance, in *diabetes mellitus*.

CHANGES IN PLASMA IN POTASSIUM DEPLETION

Sodium ions can be exchanged for those of both hydrogen and potassium in all body cells. In potassium depletion, potassium ions pass from the cells to the ECF, leaving an intracellular cation deficit. Sodium ions can replace this only to a limited extent because of the action of the "sodium pump", and the remaining deficit is made up by diffusion of hydrogen ions into cells. This results in extracellular alkalosis and intracellular acidosis; because of the renal action there is a raised plasma bicarbonate level (see p. 79). If other causes for a raised plasma bicarbonate (such as respiratory failure) are absent, and especially if circumstances known to cause potassium depletion are present (for instance, diuretic therapy), this finding is a sensitive indication of cellular potassium depletion, even in the absence of hypokalaemia.

PLASMA POTASSIUM LEVELS

Hypokalaemia is usually the result of potassium depletion, although potassium depletion is not always accompanied by hypokalaemia. It can occur, without potassium depletion, if there is a shift into cells, such as in the rare Familial Periodic Paralysis.

Hyperkalaemia occurs when the rate of potassium leaving cells is greater than its rate of excretion. This occurs in *anoxia* and in *acidosis* of any kind, but particularly in the presence of a *low glomerular filtration rate* (when sodium is unavailable for exchange with potassium in the distal tubule; p. 9). It can also result from aldosterone deficiency due

TABLE IV

HYPOTHETICAL NUMERICAL EXAMPLES TO ILLUSTRATE CONDITIONS ASSOCIATED WITH NORMAL AND ABNORMAL PLASMA SODIUM CONCENTRATIONS

	Example	ECF (litres)	E.C. Na (mEq)	Plasma Na (mEq/litre)	Haemoconc. Dilution	Clinical Features	Principle of Treatment
Normonatraemia (Equivalent Na and H$_2$O changes)							
Normal	—	20	2,800	140	None	—	—
Na + H$_2$O depletion	Early Addison's disease	15 ↓	2,100 ↓	140	Conc.	Water deficiency (p. 34)	Treat cause Isosmolar saline
Na + H$_2$O excess	Non-oedematous secondary aldosteronism	30 ↑	4,200 ↑	140	Dil.	Water excess (p. 34)	Treat cause Restrict Na + H$_2$O
Hyponatraemia (Relative H$_2$O excess)							
H$_2$O excess	Inappropriate ADH secretion	25 ↑	2,800	112 ↓	Dil.	Water excess (p. 34) Hyp-osmolarity (p. 33)	Restrict H$_2$O

Na depletion	Diarrhoea with H₂O replacement	*20*	*2,240* ↓	*112* ↓	None	Hyp-osmolarity (p. 33)	Give hyperosmolar saline.
Na + H₂O excess	Oedematous secondary aldosteronism (commonest form)	30 ↑	3,360 ↑↑	112 ↓	Dil.	Water excess (p. 34) Hyp-osmolarity (p. 33)	Restrict Na and H₂O Diuretics.
Na + H₂O depletion	Late Addison's disease	15 ↓	1,680 ↓	112 ↓	Conc.	Water deficiency (p. 34) Hyp-osmolarity (p. 33)	Give steroids + normosmolar or hyperosmolar saline.
Hypernatraemia (Relative Na excess) H₂O depletion	Unconscious patient	*18* ↓	*2,800*	*155* ↑	Mild conc.	Hyper-osmolarity (p. 33)	Give hyposmolar fluid *slowly*
Sodium excess	Excessive intake usually in infants (*Very* rare)	*20*	*3,100* ↑	*155* ↑	None	Hyper-osmolarity (p. 33)	Remove Na by dialysis

Values in first line taken as "normals" to which others are related. "Normal" values in italics throughout.
No account has been taken of shifts of fluid across cell walls which would slightly reduce changes in plasma sodium levels.
Note especially relatively slight reduction in volume associated with hypernatraemia.

to *Addison's disease*. It may be the result of over-enthusiastic *potassium therapy*, particularly if renal function is poor.

CLINICAL FEATURES OF DISTURBANCES OF POTASSIUM METABOLISM

The clinical features of disturbances of potassium metabolism (like those of, for example, sodium and calcium) are due to changes in extra-cellular concentration of the ion.

Hypokalaemia, by interfering with neuromuscular transmission, causes *muscular weakness* and *hypotonia*.

Intracellular potassium depletion causes extracellular alkalosis (see p. 79). This reduces ionization of calcium salts (p. 176) and in long-standing potassium depletion of gradual onset the presenting symptom may be muscle *cramps* and *tetany*. This syndrome is accompanied by high plasma bicarbonate levels.

Prolonged potassium depletion causes lesions in renal tubular cells, and this may complicate the clinical picture.

Severe hyperkalaemia always carries the danger of cardiac arrest. Both hypokalaemia and hyperkalaemia cause characteristic changes in the electrocardiogram.

BIOCHEMICAL BASIS OF TREATMENT OF ELECTROLYTE AND WATER DISTURBANCES

TREATMENT OF SODIUM AND WATER DISTURBANCES

It cannot be stressed too strongly that treatment should not be based on plasma sodium concentrations alone. Correct treatment of, for example, hyponatraemia depends on a knowledge of the state of hydration and renal function of the patient, involves assessment of the history, clinical findings, laboratory findings indicating haemoconcentration or haemodilution, and the level of blood urea. In a few circumstances it is also useful to know the urinary sodium and urea concentrations and specific gravity. The cause of the disturbance should be sought and treated.

Table IV uses hypothetical values to illustrate the various combinations of disturbances of sodium and water metabolism and their treatment. Solutions available for intravenous use are given in the Appendix. These rules can only be a guide to treatment in often complicated clinical situations. They may, however, help to avoid some of the more dangerous errors of electrolyte therapy.

When homeostatic mechanisms have failed, and especially in renal failure, normal hydration should be maintained according to the principles outlined on p. 27.

TREATMENT OF POTASSIUM DISTURBANCES

Abnormalities of plasma potassium should be corrected whatever the state of the total body potassium. However, an attempt should be made to assess the latter so that sudden changes in plasma potassium (for instance, during treatment of diabetic coma) can be anticipated. Treatment should be controlled by frequent plasma potassium estimations.

Hyperkalaemia.—Treatment of hyperkalaemia is based on three principles. In severe hyperkalaemia the first two principles are used:

1. Very severe hyperkalaemia can cause cardiac arrest. Calcium and potassium have opposing actions on heart muscle, and the immediate danger can be minimized by infusion of calcium salts (usually as gluconate) (see Appendix). This allows time to institute measures to lower plasma potassium.

2. Plasma potassium can be reduced rapidly (within an hour) by increasing the rate of entry into cells. Glucose and insulin speed up glucose metabolism and the action of the "sodium pump" (see Appendix). For purely practical reasons this treatment (which involves intravenous infusion) cannot be continued indefinitely, but its use allows long-term treatment to be instituted.

3. In moderate hyperkalaemia a slower acting method can be used. Potassium can be removed from the body at a rate higher than or equal to that at which it is entering the extracellular fluid by using oral ion exchange resins. These are unabsorbed and exchange potassium for sodium or calcium ions. It will be seen that plasma potassium is maintained at the expense of body depletion. This potassium may have to be replaced later.

Hypokalaemia or evidence of cellular potassium depletion should be treated by giving potassium. If hypokalaemia is mild, potassium supplements should be given orally until plasma potassium and bicarbonate levels return to normal. If severe hypokalaemia exists in a patient unable to take oral supplements, or with severe diarrhoea (which may be aggravated by potassium in the intestine) intravenous potassium should be given cautiously (see Appendix). A close watch should be kept on plasma potassium levels.

SUMMARY

1. Homeostatic mechanisms for sodium and water are interlinked, Potassium often takes part in exchange mechanisms with sodium.

2. Distribution of fluid between cells and extracellular fluid depends on osmotic differences between the intra- and extracellular fluid. Changes in this are mainly due to changes in sodium concentrations.

3. Distribution of fluid between the intravascular and interstitial

compartments depends on the balance between the hydrostatic pressure and the effective plasma osmotic pressure: the latter depends largely on albumin concentration.

4. Aldosterone secretion is the most important factor affecting body sodium.

5. Aldosterone secretion is controlled by the renin-angiotensin mechanism which responds to changes in renal blood flow.

6. ADH secretion is the most important factor affecting body water.

7. ADH secretion is controlled by plasma osmolarity. Plasma osmolarity depends mainly on sodium concentration.

8. Clinical effects of disturbances of water and sodium metabolism are due to:

(a) Changes in extracellular osmolarity, dependent largely on sodium concentration.

(b) Changes in extracellular volume.

9. Clinical disturbances of potassium metabolism are due to its action on neuromuscular transmission, and on the heart.

FURTHER READING

CHRISTENSEN, H. N. (1964). *Body Fluids and the Acid-Base Balance.* Philadelphia: W. B. Saunders.

APPENDIX TO CHAPTER II

POTASSIUM CONTAINING PREPARATIONS

1 g of potassium chloride contains 13 mEq of potassium.

For Intravenous Use

For use in serious depletion, or where oral potassium cannot be taken or retained. In most cases oral potassium is preferable. Intravenous potassium should be given with care, especially in the presence of poor renal function, and the following rules should be observed:

1. Intravenous potassium should not be given in the presence of oliguria unless the potassium deficit is unequivocal and severe.

2. Potassium in the intravenous fluid should not exceed 40 mEq/litre.

3. Intravenous potassium should not be given at a rate of more than 20 mEq/hour.

1. *Potassium Chloride Injection B.P.*

20 mEq of potassium and chloride in 10 ml.
This can be added to a bottle containing other intravenous fluid.

2. *Potassium Chloride and Dextrose Injection B.P.C.*

5 per cent dextrose with 40 mEq/litre of potassium and chloride.
This is hyperosmolar.

For Oral Use

1. Potassium Chloride Tablets B.P.—6·5 mEq K and Cl per tablet.
2. Potassium Effervescent Tablets B.P.—6·5 mEq K per tablet.
3. "Slow K" (Ciba)—8 mEq K and Cl per tablet.

TREATMENT OF HYPERKALAEMIA

Emergency Treatment

1. Calcium chloride (or gluconate). A 10 per cent solution is given intravenously with ECG monitoring. This treatment antagonizes the effect of hyperkalaemia on heart muscle, but does not alter potassium levels.

2. Glucose 50 g with 48 units of soluble insulin intravenously. This lowers plasma potassium by increasing entry into cells.

Long Term Treatment

Resonium A: 20–60 g a day by mouth in 20 g doses, *or*
                 10–40 g in a little water as a retention enema every 4–12 hours. This removes potassium from the body.

TABLE V

SOME SODIUM CONTAINING FLUIDS FOR INTRAVENOUS ADMINISTRATION

	Electrolyte Content (mEq/litre)				Dextrose (g/100 ml)	Ca (mg/100 ml)	Osmolarity
	Na	K	Cl	HCO₃			
1. Saline							
"Normal" (physiological) saline.	154	—	154	—	—	—	Isosmolar
Twice "Normal"	308	—	308	—	—	—	Hyperosmolar
Half "Normal"	77	—	77	—	—	—	Hyposmolar
Fifth "Normal"	31	—	31	—	—	—	Hyposmolar
2. Dextrose Saline							
	77	—	77	—	2·69	—	Isosmolar
	31	—	31	—	4·3	—	Isosmolar
	77	—	77	—	5·0	—	Hyperosmolar
	154	—	154	—	5·0	—	Hyperosmolar
	154	—	154	—	10·0	—	Hyperosmolar
3. Sodium Bicarbonate							
1·4%	167	—	—	167	—	—	Isosmolar
2·8%	334	—	—	334	—	—	Hyperosmolar
8·4%	1000	—	—	1000	—	—	Hyperosmolar
4. Complex Solutions							
Ringer's Solution	147	4·2	156	—	—	8·8	Isosmolar
Darrow's Solution	122	35·8	104	53 (as lactate)	—	—	Isosmolar
Hartmann's Solution	131	5·4	112	29 (as lactate)	—	—	Slightly hyposmolar
Sodium lactate 1/6 molar	167	—	—	167 (as lactate)	—	7·2	Slightly hyperosmolar

Amino-acid solutions

"Amigen"	35	18	Hyperosmolar
"Aminosol 3·3%"	53	0·15	Hyperosmolar
"Aminosol 10%"	160	0·5	Hyperosmolar
"Trophysan 5"	6	8	Hyperosmolar

TABLE VI

SODIUM FREE DEXTROSE SOLUTIONS FOR INTRAVENOUS ADMINISTRATION (USUALLY USED TO PROVIDE CALORIES)

Dextrose Concentration g/100 ml	Osmolarity	Calories/litre
5	Isosmolar	205
10	Hyperosmolar	410
20	Hyperosmolar	820
40	Hyperosmolar	1640

TABLE VII

OTHER HYPEROSMOLAR SOLUTIONS (USUALLY USED AS OSMOTIC DIURETICS)

	Concentration g/100 ml	Calories/litre
Mannitol	10	0
	20	0
Urea	4	0 (But may also contain fructose 10% giving 410 calories/litre)
Sorbito	30	0
	20	800
	30	1200
Fructose	10	410
	20	820
	40	1640

Chapter III

ACID-BASE BALANCE:
BLOOD GAS LEVELS

IF THE body is to function normally the pH of the extracellular fluid must be kept within about 0·05 of 7·4. Acidity is determined by hydrogen ion concentration (or, more accurately, hydrogen ion activity; for an explanation of this see physical chemistry textbooks; in this chapter we will assume the two to be identical). Energy production from metabolism is linked to a series of stepwise reactions in which dehydrogenation is of great importance, the hydrogen being transferred to coenzymes such as NAD. Some of the resulting reduced coenzyme (for example $NADH_2$) supplies hydrogen for synthetic reactions. If oxygen is available most of the rest is dehydrogenated again, the hydrogen ultimately combining with the oxygen to form water during oxidative phosphorylation (water is neither an acid nor a base), and coenzyme being released for re-use. In the absence of oxygen an adequate supply of coenzyme can only be maintained if the hydrogen is passed on to some intermediate product of metabolism; for instance pyruvate is reduced by $NADH_2$ to form lactic acid, which cannot be metabolized further until oxygen is available.

Thus generation of hydrogen ions is linked with the energy production necessary for life, but, if the oxygen supply is adequate, any excess is converted to water, and pH changes are minimal. However, even during normal metabolism a sudden excess of hydrogen ions may be released following ingestion of food, or during a burst of energy requirement (for instance, muscular exercise), and a normal supply of oxygen may not be adequate to deal immediately with such a load. To prevent a change in pH this excess must either be eliminated from the body, or inactivated until it can be oxidized. Under normal circumstances homeostatic mechanisms are so effective that blood pH varies very little.

Since hydrogen, and not hydroxyl, ions are produced by metabolism the tendency to acidosis is greater than to alkalosis. Homeostatic mechanisms are more effective in dealing with hydrogen than with hydroxyl ions.

DEFINITIONS

Before he continues his study of acid-base balance the reader should be sure that he understands the relevant terminology.

An *acid* is a substance which can dissociate to produce hydrogen ions (protons: H^+): a *base* is one which can accept hydrogen ions. Table VIII includes examples of acids and bases of importance in the body.

TABLE VIII

1. Acid		2. Conjugate Base
Carbonic acid H_2CO_3 $\leftrightharpoons H^+$	$+ HCO_3^-$	Bicarbonate ion
Lactic acid $CH_3CHOHCOOH$ $\leftrightharpoons H^+$	$+ CH_3CHOHCOO^-$	Lactate ion
Ammonium ion NH_4^+ $\leftrightharpoons H^+$	$+ NH_3$	Ammonia
Dihydrogen phosphate		
$H_2PO_4^-$ $\leftrightharpoons H^+$	$+ HPO_4^-$	Monohydrogen phosphate ion
Acetoacetic acid		
CH_3COCH_2COOH $\leftrightharpoons H^+$	$+ CH_3COCH_2COO^-$	Acetoacetate ion
β-hydroxybutyric acid		
$CH_3CHOHCH_2COOH$ $\leftrightharpoons H^+$	$+ CH_3CHOHCH_2COO^-$	β-hydroxybutyrate ion.

An *alkali* is a substance which dissociates to produce hydroxyl ions (OH^-). Alkalis are of relatively little importance in the present discussion.

A *strong acid* is highly dissociated in aqueous solution: in other words it produces many hydrogen ions. Hydrochloric acid is a strong acid, and in solution is almost entirely in the form of H^+Cl^-. However, the examples given in the above list are, chemically speaking, *weak acids*, little dissociated in water and yielding relatively few hydrogen ions. Carbonic acid in solution is mainly in the form H_2CO_3, and little dissociated to H^+ and HCO_3^-; however, in the body even very small changes of pH are important and result in disturbances of physiology.

Buffering is the term used for the process by which a strong acid (or base) is replaced by a weak one, with a consequent reduction in the number of free hydrogen ions (H^+); the "shock" of the hydrogen ions is taken up by the buffer with a change of pH smaller than that which would occur in the absence of the buffer.

For example:

$$H^+Cl^- + NaHCO_3 \leftrightharpoons H_2CO_3 + NaCl$$

Strong acid   Buffer   Weak acid   Neutral salt

pH is a measure of hydrogen ion concentration. It is the $\log_{10}$ of the reciprocal of the hydrogen ion concentration ($[H^+]$). The $\log_{10}$ of a number is the power to which 10 must be raised to produce that number. Thus $\log 100 = \log 10^2 = 2$ and $\log 10^7 = 7$.

Let us suppose $[H^+]$ is 10^{-7} (0·000,000,1)

Then $\log [H^+] = -7$

But $pH = \log \dfrac{1}{[H^+]} = -\log [H^+] = 7$

For the non-mathematically minded only a few points need be remembered.

Since at pH 6 $[H^+] = 10^{-6}$ (0·000,001)
and at pH 7 $[H^+] = 10^{-7}$ (0·000,000,1)

Therefore a change of *one pH unit* represents a *tenfold change in* $[H^+]$.

This is a much larger change than is immediately obvious from the change in pH values. Although changes of this magnitude do not occur in the body during life, in pathological conditions changes of 0·3 of a pH unit can take place. 0·3 is the log of 2. Therefore a *decrease of pH by* 0·3 (e.g. 7·4 to 7·1) represents a *doubling of* $[H^+]$. Here again the use of pH makes a very significant change in $[H^+]$ appear deceptively small. (Compare the situation if the plasma sodium concentration had changed from 140 to 280 mEq/litre).

The Henderson–Hasselbalch equation.—We have already seen that a buffer absorbs the "shock" of the addition of H^+ to a system by replacing a strong acid by a weak one. It will be seen that when the bases in column 2 of Table VIII buffer H^+, the corresponding acid in column 1 is formed. This weak acid and its conjugate base form a *buffer pair*. In aqueous solution the pH is determined by the ratio of this acid to its conjugate base.

Let us take the bicarbonate pair as an example. Carbonic acid (H_2CO_3) dissociates into H^+ and HCO_3^- until equilibrium is reached (in this case very much in favour of H_2CO_3), and the ratio of the two forms will now remain constant (K). We can therefore write $K [H_2CO_3] = [H^+] \times [HCO_3^-]$ (that is, at equilibrium, the concentration of H_2CO_3 is K times that of the product of $[H^+]$ and $[HCO_3^-]$).

Transposing, $H^+ = K \dfrac{[H_2CO_3]}{[HCO_3^-]}$

But we are interested in $\log \dfrac{1}{[H^+]}$, or pH.

Taking logs (when multiplication becomes addition) and reciprocals throughout

$$\text{Log} \dfrac{1}{[H^+]} = \log \dfrac{1}{K} + \log \dfrac{[HCO_3^-]}{[H_2CO_3]}$$

$\text{Log} \dfrac{1}{K}$ is called pK

Therefore $\boxed{\text{pH} = \text{pK} + \log \dfrac{[\text{HCO}_3{}^-]}{[\text{H}_2\text{CO}_3]}}$

This equation (the Henderson–Hasselbalch equation) is valid for any buffer pair. It is important to notice that the pH depends on the *ratio* of the concentrations of base (in this case $[\text{HCO}_3{}^-]$) to acid (in this case $[\text{H}_2\text{CO}_3]$).

ACID-BASE HOMEOSTASIS

The following points should be noted:

1. *Hydrogen ions can be incorporated into water* maintaining normal pH.

(*a*) This is the normal mechanism of complete oxidation of H^+ during oxidative phosphorylation. Any H^+ not so oxidized has to be dealt with by homeostatic mechanisms.

(*b*) H^+ is converted to water during the conversion of H_2CO_3 to carbon dioxide (CO_2) and water. As this is a reversible reaction H^+ will only continue to be so inactivated if CO_2 is removed. This results in bicarbonate depletion.

2. *Hydrogen ions can be lost from the body only through the kidney and the intestine.*—This mechanism, unlike that of 1(*b*) is coupled, in the kidney, with regeneration and reabsorption of bicarbonate ion ($\text{HCO}_3{}^-$) and is therefore the ideal method of eliminating any excess H^+.

3. *Buffering of hydrogen ions is a temporary measure.*—The H^+ is still in the body, and the presence of the weak acid of the buffer pair causes a small change in pH (see the Henderson–Hasselbalch equation). If H^+ is not completely neutralized, or eliminated from the body, and if production continues, buffering power will eventually be used up and the pH will change abruptly.

The normal mechanisms of H^+ homeostasis are summarized in a simplified form in Fig. 2. We shall consider each mechanism in turn, following the small letters in the diagram.

(*a*) In the presence of equivalent amounts of oxygen the H^+ liberated by metabolism is converted to water and CO_2 is also produced (aerobic metabolism).

(*b*) Any unoxidized H^+ is liberated into the cell (conveniently referred to as "anaerobic" metabolism).

Tissue Cells

(*c*) Some of this H^+ is buffered by cell proteins, which can act as bases at body pH. The Henderson-Hasselbalch equation for this buffer pair could be written:

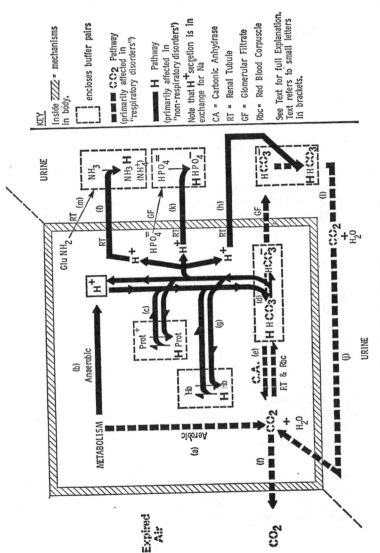

FIG. 2.—Cycle of acid-base control.

$$pH = pK + \log \frac{[Prot^-]}{[H\,Prot]}$$

As $Prot^-$ is converted to H Prot there will be a slight fall of cell pH.

Extracellular Fluid

(d) The rest of the H^+ diffuses into the extracellular fluid (ECF) where the *bicarbonate buffer pair* is of by far the greatest importance, and accounts for over 60 per cent of the blood buffering capacity (for acids other than carbonic acid). This H^+ is buffered by HCO_3^- and carbonic acid (H_2CO_3) is produced, with a slight fall in extracellular pH.

$$pH = pK + \log \frac{[HCO_3^-]}{[H_2CO_3]} \begin{array}{l} \leftarrow \text{used up in buffering} \\ \leftarrow \text{produced during buffering} \end{array}$$

Plasma proteins can, like cell proteins, act as buffers but are of little quantitative importance in this respect when compared with bicarbonate.

As H^+ is removed from the ECF a flow out of the cell is maintained, reconverting H Prot to $Prot^-$, and therefore returning cell pH to normal.

Erythrocytes and Lungs

(e) H_2CO_3 can dissociate spontaneously to CO_2 and water, but at pH 7·4, because of the low levels of H_2CO_3 found in the ECF, this is very slow. The dissociation is catalyzed by the action of the enzyme *carbonic anhydrase*, which is present in many cells, but is most important in renal tubular cells and erythrocytes (its function in the kidney will be discussed later). This is a reversible reaction, and would reach an equilibrium with a build up of H_2CO_3 and fall of pH if CO_2 were not removed (water is, of course, always freely available).

(f) CO_2 is eliminated in expired air as the blood passes through the lungs, thus keeping reaction (e) to the left: the concentration of H_2CO_3 therefore remains low and the ECF pH near normal.

It should be noted, however, that HCO_3^- has been used up and cannot be reformed in the absence of CO_2. This inactivation of H^+ is not linked to regeneration of buffering capacity, which would fall to very low levels if other mechanisms did not come into play.

(g) Any excess H_2CO_3 not eliminated in this way diffuses into the erythrocyte and is buffered by haemoglobin.

$$pH = pK + \log \frac{Hb^-}{HHb}$$

As H^+ is removed from H_2CO_3, HCO_3^- is formed: this diffuses out of the red cells in exchange for chloride (the "chloride shift") and, unlike reaction (f), repletes extracellular buffering. However, the H^+ is in a "dead end" and, unless it can be removed, haemoglobin buffering power will be used up.

As we will see later, haemoglobin accounts for only about a third of the buffering power of blood and is of relatively little importance, when compared with HCO_3^-, in buffering acids other than carbonic acid: however, it is of great importance in disturbances of acid-base balance due to respiratory causes.

The Kidneys

(h), (i), (j), (k), (l), (m). *The final restoration of acid-base balance to normal can only be effected by the kidneys.*—If we consider the position up to now we will see that some of the excess H^+ has been converted to water by the action of carbonic anhydrase, but that this has caused loss of HCO_3^-. Some of the latter is repleted during buffering by haemoglobin, but the H^+ so buffered is still in the body. Unless the kidney were functioning blood HCO_3^- levels would continue to be repleted only until the buffering power of haemoglobin was exceeded.

The whole length of the renal tubule can actively secrete H^+ into the urine. Although the mechanism is not known for certain, the net effect is exchange of one H^+ for one sodium ion (Na^+). Moreover, in the distal tubule the potassium ion (K^+) appears to compete with H^+ for secretion. The H^+ probably comes from H_2CO_3, either formed in the cell from CO_2 and water (e), or produced elsewhere by buffering (d). As H^+ is secreted, HCO_3^- is "left behind" and diffuses back into the ECF: the HCO_3^- of carbonic acid is thus reclaimed.

If the H^+ in the urine were unbuffered the urinary pH would fall to very low levels. In fact, urinary pH rarely falls below 4·5. There are three important buffer pairs in the urine.

Urinary Buffering

(h), (i), (j), *The bicarbonate buffer pair and bicarbonate reabsorption.*— Bicarbonate reabsorption from the urine is closely linked with and dependent on H^+ secretion by the renal tubule. HCO_3^- is filtered at the glomerulus in the same concentration as that in plasma.

1. *H^+ is secreted* by the tubule (h) and combines with this filtered HCO_3^- to form H_2CO_3. As the secreted H^+ comes from the cellular carbonic acid, *HCO_3^- is left behind* and diffuses into the ECF (compare HCO_3^- diffusing out of the erythrocyte after buffering of H^+ by haemoglobin).

2. As the concentration of urinary carbonic acid increases it dissociates to CO_2 and water (i).

3. The partial pressure of CO_2 (Pco_2) in the urine rises.

4. CO_2 diffuses back into the tubular cell (j).

5. In the tubular cell much of this CO_2, catalyzed by carbonic anhydrase, combines with water to form carbonic acid.

6. *H^+ is secreted* and *HCO_3^- is left behind* as in 1.

This mechanism reclaims HCO_3^- and repletes buffering power and much of the filtered HCO_3^- is reabsorbed in the proximal tubule. The lower the pH of the urine the more complete the reabsorption of HCO_3^-; thus in acidosis (if renal function is normal) bicarbonate reabsorption is high.

As the pH of the urine falls other buffers come into play, which, unlike bicarbonate, are not reabsorbed: thus H^+ is eliminated in a buffered form, and since secretion of H^+ leaves HCO_3^- behind (see 1 above) HCO_3^- is regenerated, even when all urinary HCO_3^- has been reabsorbed. These buffering mechanisms are of greatest importance in the distal tubule, because only here can the pH have fallen to levels at which they are active.

(*k*) *The phosphate buffer pair.*—At pH 7·4 most of the phosphate in the glomerular filtrate is in the form of monohydrogen phosphate ($HPO_4^=$), and this can accept H^+ to become dihydrogen phosphate ($H_2PO_4^-$).

$$pH = pK + \log \frac{[HPO_4^=]}{[H_2PO_4^-]}$$

As in even mild acidosis bone salts are ionized more than at normal pH (p. 176), requirement for increased urinary secretion of H^+ is linked with increased buffering capacity in the glomerular filtrate, due to an increase of phosphate liberated from bone.

(*l*) *Buffering by ammonia.*—The enzyme *glutaminase* is present in the renal tubular cells (*m*), and catalyzes the hydrolysis of the terminal amino group of glutamine to form glutamate and ammonia. Ammonia is a base and can accept H^+.

$$pH = pK + \log \frac{[NH_3]}{[NH_4^+]}$$

The activity of glutaminase increases as the pH of the urine falls. Thus, if renal function is normal, acidosis increases the availability of $HPO_4^=$ and NH_3 for buffering and leads to complete reabsorption and increased production of HCO_3^- in the tubular cell as H^+ is secreted.

Why Bicarbonate?

As we have seen, the bicarbonate buffer pair is the most important one in the extracellular fluid. Ideally the pK of the pair should be near to that of the required pH: the optimum extracellular pH is 7·4, and yet the pK of the bicarbonate pair is 6·1.

Bicarbonate does not behave exactly like any other buffer pair since H_2CO_3 dissociates readily to CO_2 and water: in the body this is catalyzed by carbonic anhydrase. CO_2 can then be lost in expired air keeping

[H_2CO_3] low and the pH above the pK. Respiratory rate (and CO_2 loss) is controlled by the pH (or P_{CO_2}) of blood flowing through the hypothalamic respiratory centre, so that elimination can be increased as required.

CO_2 is a product of aerobic metabolism and can combine with water to produce carbonic acid: thus the material for formation of HCO_3^- is abundantly available when required.

Role of Sodium, Potassium and Glomerular Filtration Rate in Acid-Base Balance

Sodium and the glomerular filtration rate.—Secretion of H^+ takes place in exchange for Na^+, and the latter is reabsorbed: H^+ secretion cannot occur if the amount of Na^+ in the tubular fluid is too low for quantitatively adequate exchange. Sodium is an abundant cation, and inadequate amounts of it are usually the result of a low glomerular filtration rate (GFR): however concentrated the sodium is in the glomerular filtrate (and it cannot differ from plasma sodium levels), a low flow may provide inadequate total amounts of cation. This is the situation in renal circulatory insufficiency (for example, water depletion) and in glomerular disease.

Since H^+ is a normal product of metabolism, acidosis is the usual accompaniment of a low GFR. However, in pyloric stenosis, water depletion is associated with abnormal loss of H^+ by an extrarenal route, and the low GFR is therefore accompanied by alkalosis. The H^+ deficit can be made up by the reaction between CO_2 and water (*e* in Fig. 2), but this can only continue if HCO_3^- is removed. HCO_3^- is present in the glomerular filtrate and will not be reabsorbed in the absence of H^+ secretion, thus tending to correct the alkalosis. However, if the GFR is low the total amount of HCO_3^- filtered is not quantitatively sufficient to keep reaction (*e*) to the right, even if none is reabsorbed by the tubules.

Thus *correction of either acidosis or alkalosis is impaired if the GFR is low.*

Potassium.—Potassium competes with H^+ for secretion in exchange for Na^+. If it is deficient *inside the distal tubular cell*, more H^+ will be secreted; if it is in excess at the same site H^+ secretion will be impaired.

Chloride in Acid-Base Balance

Bicarbonate and phosphate are *buffer anions*—that is, they can accept H^+ at physiological pH, and they play an important part in acid-base balance. Chloride, by contrast, cannot accept H^+ at physiological pH: it is therefore not directly concerned in H^+ homeostasis. However, plasma chloride and HCO_3^- levels sometimes vary inversely. To explain this combination of an acidosis and hyperchloraemia we must realize that sodium exchange for K^+ can occur under the influence of aldosterone (p. 34), independently of H^+ secretion. The K^+ lost in the urine during this process is mainly lost from cells, which maintain ECF concentrations of the ion (and therefore total ECF cation concentration) until late. Electrochemical neutrality is maintained in the ECF (that is, the sum of positively charged ions must be equal to that of negatively charged ones): in the absence of H^+ secretion (or of HCO_3^- formation) HCO_3^- is not available in normal amounts for this purpose, and extracellular Na^+ must be balanced by some other anion. In most conditions associated with low plasma bicarbonate levels (for instance, generalized renal failure and diabetic ketosis) other anions are retained, or are produced in abnormal amounts (for example phosphate, urate, etc., or acetoacetate, etc.), and can fulfil this function: in these conditions there is no constant change in plasma chloride concentration. However, if there is no such excess of other anions chloride is reabsorbed with sodium, and the result is the so-called "hyperchloraemic acidosis". This type of acidosis occurs in three conditions:

1. Isolated failure of H^+ secretion by the kidney without anion retention (renal tubular acidosis, p. 72).

2. Inhibition of carbonic anhydrase with loss of bicarbonate and reduced H^+ secretion (p. 73).

3. Transplantation of the ureters into the colon (p. 76).

Chloride depletion.—It has been suggested that if chloride depletion occurs without equivalent loss of sodium (for instance, when it is lost with H^+ or K^+), the chloride deficiency itself can adversely affect acid-base balance. Sodium is normally actively reabsorbed in the proximal tubule, and because electrochemical neutrality must be maintained, chloride, the predominant anion, follows passively. Deficiency of chloride limits this proximal sodium reabsorption, because the other anion present in significant amounts, HCO_3^-, cannot easily pass the tubular cell wall. More sodium will therefore be available for *exchange* with H^+ and the urine becomes acid. Bicarbonate reabsorption depends on H^+ secretion and more HCO_3^- will be reabsorbed. This mechanism is thought to aggravate the alkalosis in two conditions:

1. Pyloric stenosis (p. 77).

2. Some cases of potassium depletion (note that this is an extracellular alkalosis only) (p. 79).

Infusion of chloride helps to correct such alkalosis.

In most circumstances plasma chloride estimation is of little value in assessing the state of acid-base balance.

DISTURBANCES OF ACID-BASE BALANCE

We are now in a position to understand disturbances of acid-base balance.

Acidosis

The causes of acidosis can be summarized as follows:

1. Hydrogen Ion Excess with Normal Homeostatic Mechanisms

    (a) Ketosis   (i) Diabetic.

                           (ii) Starvation and tissue damage.

    (b) Absolute anoxia

    (c) Relative anoxia   (i) Muscular exercise (really physiological).

                           (ii) Starvation with increased catabolism.

    (d) Excessive intake of hydrogen ion. This is rare, but can occur for example, with ingestion of ammonium chloride.

2. Failure of Homeostatic Mechanisms

    (a) Failure of the kidney to excrete hydrogen ion.

        (i)   Generalized renal failure (p. 71).

        (ii) Renal tubular failure and renal tubular acidosis (p. 72).

        (iii) Low glomerular filtration rate (p. 72).

        (iv) Acetazolamide therapy.

    (b) Retention of carbon dioxide in pulmonary disease.

3. Relative Hydrogen Ion Excess in Bicarbonate Depletion

    (a) Loss of intestinal secretions containing bicarbonate.

    (b) Transplantation of the ureters into the colon.

1. Hydrogen Ion Excess with Normal Homeostatic Mechanisms

An excess of metabolic H^+ is produced in the conditions listed above.

(a) In ketosis acetyl CoA condenses to form acetoacetic acid which is reduced to form β-hydroxybutyric acid.

(b) and (c) More H^+ may be produced by metabolism than can be converted to water by the available oxygen. This may occur with the true oxygen deficiency of pulmonary disease, or as a temporary phenomenon when the supply of oxygen is normal, but the rate of catabolism is increased by muscular exercise: excess of H^+ may be also produced in starvation when catabolism exceeds anabolism, and this adds to the acidosis due to ketone production.

In true anoxia and in muscular exercise lactic acid is produced in excess.

(d) Excess ingestion of H^+ is rare, and usually iatrogenic in origin Ammonium chloride can produce acidosis because NH_4^+ is an acid.

The sequence of events is that which has been described as occurring during normal homeostasis. However, in these pathological conditions H^+ secretion and HCO_3^- reabsorption and regeneration by the kidney cannot keep pace with the rate of H^+ production. Stimulation of the respiratory centre speeds up CO_2 elimination (Fig. 2(f)), thus increasing

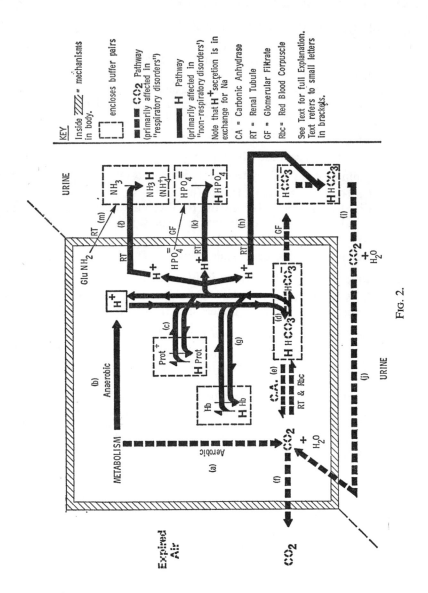

Fig. 2.

the rate of carbonic acid breakdown to CO_2 and water (e). The reduced H_2CO_3 balances the low HCO_3^- levels resulting from buffering of H^+ (d), but does nothing to restore them. The kidney secretes an acid urine containing very little HCO_3^-.

Only removal of the cause can allow the kidney to "catch up" with secretion of excess H^+ and restoration of depleted HCO_3^-.

Findings in arterial blood.—The findings at each stage of this disturbance are listed below, with abnormal values underlined. It should be noted that, in practice, it is assumed the H_2CO_3 is in equilibrium with CO_2, and the partial pressure of CO_2 (P_{CO_2}) is used as an estimate of carbonic acid levels.

The reader should consult Fig. 2 while studying this list.

Acute phase
1. H^+ is buffered by HCO_3^- (d)
   pH ↓ , [H_2CO_3] ↑ , [HCO_3^-] ↓ .

2. H_2CO_3 is converted to CO_2 and water (e). The CO_2 is lost through the lungs. pH returns towards normal but is still ↓ .

   [HCO_3^-] ↓ . (The immediate respiratory response usually maintains the P_{CO_2} in the normal range).

Since 1 and 2 take place almost simultaneously *the typical findings in the acute phase* are pH ↓ , [HCO_3^-] ↓ .

Compensatory
3. More CO_2 is lost in expired air (f).

   pH, P_{CO_2} (and [H_2CO_3]) return towards normal. P_{CO_2} may be ↓ if respiratory stimulation is effective. [HCO_3^-] still ↓ .

4. Carbonic acid is buffered by haemoglobin (g). $HCO_3^·$ diffuses into the ECF, but [HCO_3^-] is usually still ↓ .

The *typical findings in the compensatory phase* are a near normal pH, P_{CO_2} ↓ , [HCO_3^-] ↓ .

Correction phase
5. H^+ is secreted into the urine and HCO_3^- is retained. pH, [HCO_3^-], [H_2CO_3] and P_{CO_2} all become normal. (h, i, j).

2. Failure of Homeostatic Mechanisms

(*a*) **Failure of the kidney to eliminate hydrogen ions.**—Although the lungs can temporarily restore pH to normal by CO_2 elimination, final restoration of H^+ and HCO_3^- balance can only take place in the kidney.

(i) *Generalized renal failure.*

Commonly in renal failure both glomeruli and tubules are damaged and the disturbance of acid-base balance is a consequence of both these factors. More rarely, one of these lesions occurs in isolation.

(ii) *Renal tubular failure.*

If there is a reduction in the number of functioning renal tubular cells there is impairment of several factors concerned in renal tubular secretion of H^+.

1. H^+ secretion itself, in exchange for Na^+, is impaired (*h,*) (*k*) and (*l*).

2. The formation of ammonia from glutamine (*m*) is impaired.

3. HCO_3^- reabsorption (*i*), (*j*) and (*e*) and regeneration (which depends on H^+ secretion) is impaired.

As the remaining extracellular HCO_3^- buffers some of the retained H^+ (*d*) it is easy to see why its level falls: haemoglobin buffering (*g*) plays some part in buffering H^+ and in restoring $[HCO_3^-]$, but it has limited capacity. H^+ is inactivated by conversion to water in the erythrocytes (*e*), and CO_2 is lost through the lungs (*f*). This mechanism may help to maintain normal blood pH until late, but does not restore $[HCO_3^-]$.

Typically the findings are those of the compensatory phase described above. The pH is normal until late, when it falls, $[HCO_3^-] \downarrow$, $[PCO_2] \downarrow$.

Renal tubular acidosis.—This condition may be an inborn error of metabolism, but is more commonly an acquired tubular lesion. There is a failure to acidify the urine normally, even after ingestion of an acid load such as ammonium chloride (see Appendix, p. 88). It is probably either a deficit of the H^+ secreting mechanism itself, or an abnormal permeability of the distal tubular wall to the secreted H^+, allowing its diffusion back into the blood: unlike the situation in generalized tubular failure, the tubular cells retain the ability to form ammonia. Because there is no glomerular lesion the plasma urea and creatinine levels are often normal. However, prolonged acidosis increases ionization of calcium and its release from bone (p. 176): this calcium is often precipitated in the renal tubules and the subject may present with uraemia due to nephrocalcinosis. This increased breakdown of bone salts also explains the phosphaturia often accompanying renal tubular acidosis. This is one of the conditions in which hyperchloraemia may occur. Since normal H^+ secretion cannot take place, K^+ is lost in the urine: the resulting association of acidosis and hypokalaemia is rare (see also p. 73).

(iii) *Glomerular failure.*

As explained on p. 67, a low GFR whether due to water depletion or to glomerular disease impairs the ability of renal tubular cells to eliminate the H^+ produced in normal metabolism. Added to this the

H$^+$ load is often increased if the patient is not eating normally, when catabolism will exceed anabolism.

(iv) *Acetazolamide therapy.*

Acetazolamide is a drug, formerly used as a diuretic, and still used in the treatment of glaucoma, which inhibits the enzyme carbonic anhydrase. Since reaction (*e*) is inhibited in the renal tubular cell, bicarbonate reabsorption is impaired, and large amounts of bicarbonate are lost in the urine (the concomitant loss of sodium accounts for the diuretic action). As H$^+$ secretion depends on the formation of H$_2$CO$_3$, H$^+$ is retained. This condition is another example of acidosis which may be accompanied by hyperchloraemia. Because normal H$^+$ secretion cannot occur, potassium loss in the urine is increased and hypokalaemia may occur.

(*b*) **Retention of carbon dioxide in pulmonary disease.**—We have already seen that respiratory failure, by causing anoxia, can produce a lactic acidosis. However, this type of acidosis is usually included in the "non-respiratory" group of disturbances, and the "respiratory" group is usually defined as that in which the primary defect is in CO$_2$ (and carbonic acid) metabolism. To avoid confusion these groups should perhaps be classified as disturbances due to carbonic acid ("carbonic acidosis") and "non-carbonic acidosis". However, as the terminology "respiratory" and "non-respiratory" is generally accepted it will be used in this book.

In true respiratory acidosis the primary defect is carbon dioxide retention. As we shall see, this type of acidosis is accompanied by significantly different findings in the blood from those in non-respiratory disturbances.

Let us now follow the consequences of CO$_2$ retention by again studying Fig. 2. Because (*f*) cannot occur the Pco$_2$ in the blood rises.

The erythrocyte.—CO$_2$ diffuses into the erythrocyte, where reaction (*e*) is speeded up with formation of carbonic acid. Because HCO$_3$$^-$ cannot buffer the H$_2$CO$_3$, the buffering power of haemoglobin (*g*) is of great importance in respiratory failure. As the H$^+$ is buffered HCO$_3$$^-$ diffuses into the ECF and tends to bring the ratio of [HCO$_3$$^-$] to [H$_2CO_3$] (and therefore the pH) nearer normal. As the H$^+$ buffered by haemoglobin cannot be removed until it is lost by some other route, buffering power would eventually be used up.

The renal tubular cell.—Some of the excess of H$_2$CO$_3$ formed in the erythrocyte will diffuse out of the cell and reach the kidney; as Pco$_2$ is also high in the renal tubular cells, where carbonic anhydrase is also present, additional carbonic acid will be produced locally. The renal tubular cells secrete much of the excess H$^+$ into the urine (*h*), (*k*) and (*l*), with complete HCO$_3$$^-$ reabsorption and increased HCO$_3$$^-$ regeneration.

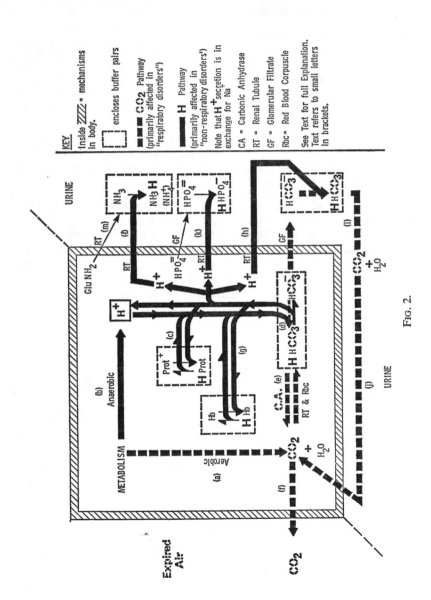

Fig. 2.

Plasma $[HCO_3^-]$ therefore rises and may compensate for the rise in H_2CO_3 bringing blood pH back to normal. However, as we have already seen, the kidney has a limited capacity to secrete H^+ and in long standing cases $[HCO_3^-]$ rises less than H_2CO_3 and the pH falls.

Findings in arterial blood.—The stages are as follows (abnormal values underlined):

Acute phase

   1. CO_2 is retained (failure of f)

      $P_{CO_2} \uparrow$, $[HCO_3^-]$ normal.

   2. CO_2 combines with water under the influence of carbonic anhydrase, in renal tubular cells and erythrocytes, to form carbonic acid (e).

      pH $\downarrow$, $[H_2CO_3] \uparrow$, $P_{CO_2} \uparrow$, $[HCO_3^-]$ normal.

1 and 2 take place almost simultaneously, and *typical findings in the acute phase* are pH___ , P_{CO_2}___ , $[HCO_3^-]$ normal.

Compensation (this takes some days to establish)

   3. H^+ is buffered by haemoglobin in the erythrocytes (g), releasing HCO_3^- which diffuses into the plasma.

   4. H^+ is secreted into the urine and HCO_3^- is reabsorbed (h, i, j).

The typical findings of the compensatory phase are, normal pH, $P_{CO_2} \uparrow$, $[HCO_3^-] \uparrow$.

Failure of compensation

   5. If pulmonary function fails to improve, bicarbonate reabsorption and haemoglobin cannot keep pace with increased H_2CO_3 formation.

The typical findings in failure of compensation are pH $\downarrow$, $P_{CO_2} \uparrow$, $[HCO_3^-] \uparrow$.

Mixed Disturbances

If anoxia is present as well as CO_2 retention some of the compensatory increase in blood $[HCO_3^-]$ is used to buffer lactic acid. The rise of $[HCO_3^-]$ is impaired, more H_2CO_3 is produced and pH falls at an earlier stage of the disease, and to lower levels than with CO_2 retention alone. (Mixed "respiratory" and "non-respiratory" acidosis). This commonly occurs in the "respiratory distress syndrome" of the newborn.

Mixed disturbances may also be due to coexistence of respiratory failure and, for example, ketosis or renal failure.

3. *Relative Hydrogen Ion Excess in Bicarbonate Depletion*

If HCO_3^- is lost, buffering capacity for H^+ is reduced. Reaction (d) goes to the right, increasing ionization of H^+. Compensatory mechanisms are secretion of H^+ in the urine and HCO_3^- reabsorption. If this is not possible, or is ineffective, the respiratory centre is stimulated, CO_2 is lost, and reaction (e) is shifted to the left; as usual, this mechanism does not replete HCO_3^-.

(a) **Loss of intestinal secretions.**—Many intestinal secretions are alkaline and have concentrations of HCO_3^- above that of plasma; for instance, the bicarbonate concentration of duodenal juice is about twice that of plasma. Excessive loss of these through fistulae, or in severe diarrhoea, may reduce plasma HCO_3^- concentrations and cause acidosis. If the kidney is able to excrete the relative excess of H^+ it may be able to restore plasma $[HCO_3^-]$ to normal.

Because electrolyte and water are also lost in the intestinal secretions such disturbances are accompanied by the changes described in Chapter II (p. 41).

(b) **Transplantation of the ureters into the colon.**—The cells of the colon, like those of the renal tubules, are capable of active transport of ions. Normally reabsorption of water and electrolytes in this part of the intestinal tract is almost complete: however, if fluid which contains chloride enters the lumen, the cells tend to reabsorb this chloride in exchange for HCO_3^-. Bicarbonate depletion may therefore occur if urine is delivered into the colon, as after transplantation of the ureters at this site. This operation may be performed, with total cystectomy, for carcinoma of the bladder. Unless large doses of oral bicarbonate are given, the result is a very low plasma $[HCO_3^-]$ and very high plasma chloride concentration—an example of "hyperchloraemic acidosis" (p. 68). Acidosis is aggravated by conversion of urea to ammonia (by the action of some intestinal bacteria). The ammonia accepts H^+ to form NH_4^+. The cells of the colon (unlike those of the renal tubule) are permeable to this ion which is absorbed and reconverted to urea in the liver. This may also, therefore, be a contributory cause for mild uraemia after this operation.

Secondary effects of acidosis on plasma potassium levels.—Because H^+ competes with K^+ for exchange with Na^+ across all cell walls, acidosis, by increasing $[H^+]$, leads to low cellular $[K^+]$ levels. In the renal tubular cell (also K^+ depleted), more H^+ than K^+ is secreted into the urine, and the excess extracellular potassium cannot be secreted. Acidosis therefore usually causes hyperkalaemia (compare effect of K^+ on H^+ secretion, p. 79). The exception to this rule occurs when the acidosis is due to failure of the mechanism for renal H^+ secretion as in renal tubular acidosis (p. 72), and acetazolamide therapy (p. 73): sodium reabsorption continues in exchange for relatively high amounts of potassium, and the high urinary loss causes depletion and eventually hypokalaemia.

Alkalosis

Because hydrogen, and not hydroxyl, ions are produced by metabolism, alkalosis is a relatively rare condition. The causes of alkalosis are:

1. Alkalosis with normally functioning homeostatic mechanisms.
   (*a*) Ingestion of large amounts of base (for instance HCO_3^- as sodium bicarbonate in the treatment of "indigestion").
   (*b*) Loss of hydrogen ion in an unbuffered form (pyloric stenosis).
   (*c*) Potassium depletion (this alkalosis is extracellular only).
2. Respiratory alkalosis due to overbreathing.

Alkalosis may present clinically as tetany in spite of normal total plasma calcium levels: this is due to a reduced ionization of calcium salts in an alkaline medium (p. 176).

Pyloric stenosis.—The vomiting of pyloric stenosis is probably the only condition in which an excess of unbuffered H^+ is lost. Gastric juice consists largely of hydrochloric acid—a strong acid—and if vomiting is due to an obstruction between the stomach and the duodenum this acid is lost in fairly pure form, accompanied by relatively little sodium and potassium. By contrast, vomiting with free communication between the stomach and duodenum results in additional loss of duodenal juice containing relatively high HCO_3^- concentrations and this loss tends to "correct" the potential alkalosis; such vomiting is accompanied by relatively less acid-base, and relatively more electrolyte disturbance than that of pyloric stenosis. Water, of course, is lost in either type, and the electrolyte disturbances of pyloric stenosis are secondary partly to this, and partly to the acid-base disturbance.

Loss of H^+ in pyloric stenosis causes reaction (*d*) (Fig. 2) to go to the right: HCO_3^- is liberated in a manner analogous to its regeneration in the kidney during H^+ secretion. Reaction (*e*) also goes to the right as H_2CO_3 is reduced, and more H_2CO_3 is formed, only to lose H^+ and become HCO_3^-. Plasma HCO_3^- levels rise, and this rise is accompanied by hypochloraemia due to loss of chloride in the vomitus: this chloride depletion may aggravate the alkalosis by preventing proximal sodium reabsorption (p. 68). The low GFR of the accompanying water depletion reduces urinary bicarbonate loss (p. 67), which would otherwise tend to correct the alkalosis.

Gastric juice contains relatively little potassium. Subjects with pyloric stenosis become potassium depleted because of urinary loss. This loss is secondary to:

1. H^+ deficiency with increased passage of K^+ into all cells and secretion of K^+ in the renal tubule, an effect common to all forms of cellular alkalosis (compare hyperkalaemia in acidosis, p. 76).
2. Water depletion, and stimulation of aldosterone production, with sodium retention and potassium loss in the urine (p. 35).

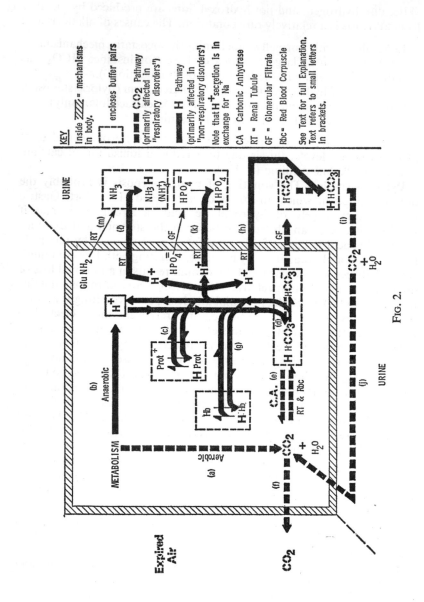

FIG. 2.

The hypokalaemia may be masked when the patient is dehydrated but should be anticipated as GFR is increased during treatment.

Thus, after vomiting due to pyloric stenosis the findings are as follows:

1. A low plasma chloride concentration.
2. A high plasma bicarbonate concentration.
3. Haemoconcentration (due to loss of water).
4. Hypokalaemia.

Late in the disease the urine may be relatively acid in reaction despite severe alkalosis because of the chloride depletion (p. 68). Two factors hinder renal correction of the alkalosis of pyloric stenosis: fluid depletion with a low GFR and chloride depletion.

Treatment of the biochemical disorder of pyloric stenosis.—Treatment consists (if renal function is normal) of replacing water and chloride by administering large amounts of saline. The kidney will then correct the alkalosis. The fluid (which, because of the pyloric obstruction must, of course, be given intravenously) should be at least isosmolar saline. If plasma chloride levels are very low hyperosmolar saline should be given. Potassium should be added to the saline if the plasma potassium concentration is low normal or low (see Appendix to Chapter II).

Extracellular alkalosis of potassium depletion.—The alkalosis of potassium depletion is an extracellular one; the cells are more acid than normal. Potassium is lost from the ECF and cells. Because of the action of the sodium pump, sodium cannot replace potassium in cells in equivalent proportions and the intracellular cation deficit is corrected by H^+ which moves from the ECF into the cells.

This shift of H^+ occurs in all cells of the body, including those of the renal tubules (also potassium deficient); more H^+ and less K^+ is available for secretion into the urine and the urine becomes acid (thus tending to correct the cellular acidosis rather than the extracellular alkalosis). Secretion of H^+ is, as usual, linked with HCO_3^- reabsorption, and an early sign of intracellular potassium depletion (which may be present without hypokalaemia) is a raised plasma bicarbonate level.

If chloride depletion accompanies that of K^+ the extracellular alkalosis may be aggravated (p. 68).

It should be noted that although extracellular acidosis (and intra-cellular alkalosis) could theoretically occur because of K^+ excess, such excess is extremely rare. The combination of acidosis and hyperkalaemia is therefore more likely to be due to a primary disturbance of acid-base balance, with a secondary shift of potassium from cells.

Alkalosis due to abnormal homeostatic mechanisms.—Overbreathing, whether due to hysteria or because of brain stem lesions, or due to excessive artificial ventilation, increases CO_2 loss from the body. Reaction (e) (Fig. 2) goes to the left in both renal tubular cells and erythrocytes, and H^+ is converted to water with a fall in its concentration and rise in pH. Reaction (d) also goes to the left and the concentration of plasma HCO_3^- falls. Because the Pco_2 of the renal tubular cell is also kept at low levels, HCO_3^- reabsorption is impaired.

The arterial blood findings in respiratory alkalosis are:

Acute phase
1. CO_2 is lost (f) and H_2CO_3 dissociates to CO_2 and water (e).
pH ↑, Pco_2 ↓, $[HCO_3^-]$ normal.

Compensatory phase
2. HCO_3^- is lost in urine because of failure of reabsorption. pH returns towards normal.
Pco_2 ↓, $[HCO_3^-]$ ↓.

Salicylates, by stimulating the respiratory centre directly, initially cause respiratory alkalosis. However, in overdosage, ketosis due to vomiting and starvation may superimpose a non-respiratory acidosis on this picture, and this may be the predominant factor especially in small children. Both respiratory alkalosis and non-respiratory acidosis result in low blood HCO_3^- levels, but the pH may be high if respiratory alkalosis is predominant, normal if the two "cancel each other out", or low if ketosis is predominant. Only by measurement of blood pH can the true state of acid-base balance be assessed.

The effect of alkalosis on potassium metabolism has been discussed in the section on pyloric stenosis.

ASSESSMENT OF ACID-BASE BALANCE

The measurement of the level of plasma bicarbonate *alone* tells us nothing about the state of acid-base balance. For instance, a low concentration may be associated with compensated or uncompensated non-respiratory acidosis, or respiratory alkalosis. The pH is determined by the *ratio* of $[HCO_3^-]$ to $[H_2CO_3]$ according to the Henderson-Hasselbalch equation.

Nevertheless, in many uncomplicated non-respiratory disturbances (in which the change in bicarbonate is the primary one) a careful clinical history and examination, together with a knowledge of plasma $[HCO_3^-]$, may yield adequate information for clinical purposes. For instance, the low bicarbonate levels of renal failure or diabetic ketosis are almost certainly associated with non-respiratory acidosis: that of renal failure is corrected temporarily by dialysis, but infusion of bicarbonate is usually contra-indicated because it involves administration of fluid and sodium with the risk of overloading the circulation: that of diabetic ketosis responds to insulin and rehydration, and a knowledge of its exact degree is usually unimportant.

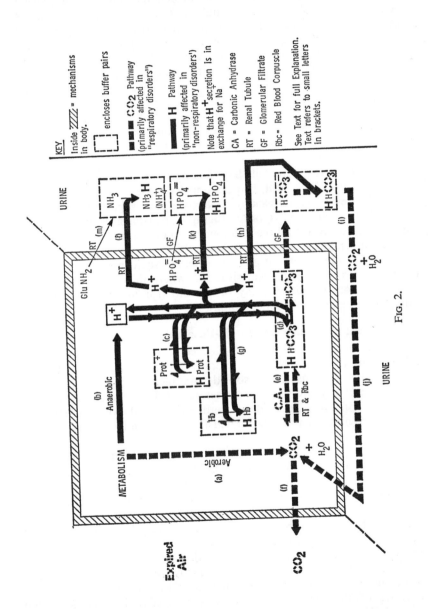

KEY

Inside ⟋⟋⟋ = mechanisms in body.

☐ encloses buffer pairs

▬▬▬ CO₂ Pathway (primarily affected in "respiratory disorders")

━━━ H⁺ Pathway (primarily affected in "non-respiratory disorders")

Note that H⁺ secretion is in exchange for Na

CA = Carbonic Anhydrase
RT = Renal Tubule
GF = Glomerular Filtrate
Rbc = Red Blood Corpuscle

See Text for full Explanation. Text refers to small letters in brackets.

Fig. 2.

Similarly, a subject with chronic bronchitis and a high plasma concentration of bicarbonate undoubtedly has a respiratory acidosis which may or may not be fully compensated. If there is no possibility of improving air entry into the lungs by use of physiotherapy, expectorants and antibiotics, treatment on a respirator is contra-indicated, because a reduction of P_{CO_2} will lead to a bicarbonate loss (by reversal of the changes described on p. 73): unless the patient continues to be respired artificially for life, removal from the respirator will result in return of the P_{CO_2} to its initial high levels, but with a delay of the compensatory increase in bicarbonate for some days. Nothing is to be gained, from the therapeutic point of view, by a knowledge of pH and P_{CO_2} in such a case.

The situation is different if there has been an acute exacerbation of the chronic bronchitis, or if the pulmonary disease is of acute onset and potentially reversible (especially as anoxia may superimpose a lactic acidosis). In such cases vigorous therapy or artificial respiration may tide the patient over until the pulmonary condition improves, and more precise information than the plasma bicarbonate concentration is required for adequate control of treatment. Such information is also desirable in any other clinical situation where mixed respiratory and non-respiratory conditions may be present (for instance, when renal failure is complicated by pneumonia).

Measurement of Parameters of Acid-Base Balance

It has been mentioned that P_{CO_2} is used as an index of carbonic acid concentration. Measurements of blood pH tells us whether the disturbance is fully compensated: if so little treatment is required. Note that knowledge of any two of the parameters pH, P_{CO_2} (converted into m. moles/litre of carbonic acid by multiplying by 0·03), and $[HCO_3^-]$ enables the third one to be calculated from the Henderson-Hasselbalch equation.

Although $[HCO_3^-]$ varies little whether measured on venous or arterial blood, or on plasma or whole blood, there is an arterio-venous difference in P_{CO_2}: moreover, the presence of erythrocytes is required for adequate measurement of P_{CO_2} using the Astrup method (see below). Full estimation of the state of acid-base balance should therefore be performed on *fresh arterial whole blood*, taken and kept under anaerobic conditions (it should not be expelled from the syringe) to prevent gas exchange before the estimation is made.

The usual method of estimating pH, P_{CO_2} and $[HCO_3^-]$ is to use the one devised by Astrup. Three readings of pH are made.

1. pH of the blood withdrawn anaerobically. This gives us the arterial pH.

The P_{CO_2} on this specimen is derived from this and two other readings.

TABLE IX
SUMMARY OF FINDINGS IN WHOLE ARTERIAL BLOOD IN ACID-BASE DISTURBANCES

			pH	Pco$_2$	Actual HCO$_3^-$	Std HCO$_3^-$	K Levels (plasma)
Acidosis							
Non-respiratory	Initial change		↓	N	↓ _(primary)_	↓ _(primary)_	Usually ↑ (↓ in renal tubular acidosis and acetazolamide therapy)
	Full compensation		N	(↓) _circled_	↓ _(primary)_	↓ _(primary)_	
Respiratory	Initial change		↓	↑ _(primary)_	N	N	↑
	Full compensation		N	↑ _(primary)_	(↑) _circled_	N	
Alkalosis							
Non-respiratory	Initial change		↑	N	↑ _(primary)_	↑ _(primary)_	
	Full compensation (usually slight)		N	(↑) _circled_	↑ _(primary)_	↑ _(primary)_	↓
Respiratory	Initial change		↑	↓ _(primary)_	N	N	
	Full compensation		N	↓ _(primary)_	(↓) _circled_	N	↓

Arrows underlined = Primary change.
     „   circled   = Compensatory change.

Note:
1. Generalized potassium depletion can cause extracellular alkalosis.
   Generalized alkalosis can cause hypokalaemia.
   Only the clinical history can differentiate the primary cause of the combination of alkalosis and hypokalaemia.
2. Overbreathing *causes* a low HCO$_3^-$ in respiratory alkalosis.
   Non-respiratory acidosis with a low HCO$_3^-$ *causes* overbreathing.
   Only measurement of blood pH and/or Pco$_2$ can differentiate these two.

2. The pH after equilibration of the blood with gas containing a known, high P_{CO_2} (usually about 60 mm Hg).

3. The pH after equilibration of the blood with gas containing a known, low P_{CO_2} (usually about 30 mm Hg).

As there is a relationship between pH of whole blood and its P_{CO_2}, from the knowledge of three pH and two P_{CO_2} values the third P_{CO_2} value (in the blood as withdrawn) can be calculated. (Note that normal equilibration with CO_2 can only take place in the presence of the carbonic anhydrase and haemoglobin in the erythrocytes). A nomogram, based on the Henderson-Hasselbalch equation, is used to calculate the HCO_3^- (this could, of course, be done arithmetically).

An alternative to this method is to measure only the actual pH, and to use an electrode which measures P_{CO_2} directly.

The bicarbonate level that we have been discussing is known as the *Actual Bicarbonate*—that is, it is the actual concentration which is circulating in the patient. Further information may be gained by measuring the *Standard Bicarbonate*. As we have seen, alterations in actual $[HCO_3^-]$ may be non-respiratory in origin (due to buffering of or loss of H^+), or due to respiratory changes: in the latter case the change in the actual $[HCO_3^-]$ is a compensatory one, in the early stages due to the red cell buffering, and if the P_{CO_2} were normal this component would be reversed, bringing the $[HCO_3^-]$ to normal levels. The standard bicarbonate concentration is that of the *whole* arterial blood equilibrated at a mean normal P_{CO_2} of 40 mm Hg, and this value can be read off the nomogram already described. An abnormal actual bicarbonate and normal standard bicarbonate suggests that the change is of purely respiratory origin. An abnormal standard bicarbonate usually suggests a non-respiratory component, but may be raised in chronic respiratory failure when part of the rise in $[HCO_3^-]$ is renal in origin and cannot be reversed by equilibrating erythrocytes with a normal P_{CO_2}. This reading is particularly useful in mixed respiratory and non-respiratory disturbances.

Typical findings in acid-base disturbances are summarized in Table IX.

BLOOD GAS LEVELS

In respiratory disturbances associated with acidosis a knowledge of the partial pressure of oxygen (the P_{O_2}) is as important as that of pH, P_{CO_2} and $[HCO_3^-]$.

Normal gaseous exchange across the pulmonary alveolus involves loss of CO_2 and gain of O_2. However, in pathological conditions a fall in P_{O_2} and rise in P_{CO_2} do not always coexist. The reasons for this are as follows:

1. *CO_2 is much more soluble than O_2 in water*, in which its rate of diffusion is 20 times as high as that of O_2. In *pulmonary oedema*, for example, arterial Po_2 falls because its diffusion across the alveolar wall is hindered by oedema fluid. Respiration is stimulated by the anoxia and by pulmonary distension, and CO_2 is "washed out". However, the rate of transport of O_2 through the fluid cannot be increased enough to restore normal Po_2. The result is a *low or normal arterial Pco_2 and a low Po_2.*

2. *The haemoglobin of arterial blood is normally 95 per cent saturated with oxygen*, and very little oxygen is carried in simple solution in the plasma: the dissolved O_2 is in equilibrium with the oxyhaemoglobin. Overbreathing air with a normal atmospheric Po_2 cannot significantly increase the amount of oxygen carried in the blood leaving normal alveoli: it can, however, reduce the Pco_2. (Breathing pure oxygen by increasing inspired Po_2 can increase arterial Po_2, but not the haemoglobin saturation.)

Let us consider the situation in many pulmonary conditions such as *pneumonia, collapse of the lung*, and *pulmonary fibrosis or infiltration*. In such conditions not all alveoli are affected by the disease to the same extent, or in the same way.

(*a*) Some alveoli will be unaffected. The composition of blood leaving these is initially that of normal arterial blood. Increased rate or depth of respiration can lower the Pco_2 to very low levels, but not alter either the Po_2 or the haemoglobin saturation in this blood.

(*b*) Some alveoli, while having a normal blood supply, may, perhaps because of obstruction of small airways, have little or no air entry. The composition of blood leaving these is near to that of venous blood (it is a right to left shunt). Unless increased ventilation can overcome the obstruction it will have no effect on this low Po_2 and high Pco_2.

(*c*) Some alveoli may have normal air entry, but little or no blood supply. These are effectively "dead space": increased ventilation will be "wasted", because however much air enters and leaves these alveoli, there is no gas exchange with blood.

Blood from (*a*) and (*b*) mixes in the pulmonary vein before entering the left atrium: the result is mixed venous and arterial blood. The high Pco_2 and low Po_2 stimulate respiration, and if enough unaffected alveoli (*a*) are present, the reduction of Pco_2 in blood leaving these to very low levels may "correct" the high Pco_2 from poorly aerated alveoli. For reasons discussed above, neither the Po_2 nor the haemoglobin saturation will be significantly altered. The final result is therefore *low or normal arterial Pco_2* with *a low Po_2*.

If the proportion of type (*b*) and (*c*) alveoli is very high Pco_2 cannot be adequately corrected by overventilation, and the result is a *high arterial Pco_2 and low Po_2*.

In conditions in which almost all the alveoli have a normal blood supply but poor air entry the result will be a *high arterial* P_{CO_2} and *low* P_{O_2}. This may be due to *mechanical or neurological defects in respiratory movement,* or to *obstruction of large or small airways.*

The two groups of findings in pulmonary disease are summarized in the list below. The conditions marked with * can fall into either group.

1. Low arterial P_{O_2} with low or normal P_{CO_2} can occur in such conditions as:

     Pulmonary oedema (diffusion defect)
     Pneumonia*
     Collapse of the lung*
     Pulmonary fibrosis or infiltration*

2. Low arterial P_{O_2} with high P_{CO_2} can occur in such conditions as:

     Chest injury, gross obesity, ankylosing spondylitis (impairment of movement of the respiratory cage)
     Poliomyelitis, lesions of the central nervous system affecting the respiratory centre (neurological impairment of respiratory drive)
     Laryngeal spasm, severe asthma, chronic bronchitis and emphysema (obstruction to airways)
     Pneumonia*
     Collapse of the lung*
     Pulmonary fibrosis or infiltration*

SUMMARY
ACID-BASE BALANCE

1. Any excess of hydrogen ions produced by metabolism can be:

     (a) Buffered as a temporary measure, with a small change in pH,
         (i)   By cellular proteins.
         (ii)   By bicarbonate in the extracellular fluid (this is quantitatively the most important in non-respiratory disturbances).
         (iii)   By haemoglobin in the erythrocytes (this is a very important buffer in respiratory acidosis).

     (b) Converted to water by the action of carbonic anhydrase in the erythrocytes; the CO_2 produced is eliminated by the lungs. While this mechanism at least partially corrects pH it does not replete bicarbonate buffering power.

     (c) Secreted by the kidneys, with reabsorption of bicarbonate from the glomerular filtrate, and regeneration of bicarbonate in the renal tubular cells.

2. Any hydrogen ion secreted into the urine which is not concerned with bicarbonate reabsorption is excreted in a buffered form, mainly as $H_2PO_4^-$ and the ammonium ion. Bicarbonate is regenerated by this process.

3. Renal correction of either acidosis or alkalosis is dependent on a normal glomerular filtration rate.

4. Potassium and hydrogen ions compete for exchange with sodium across all cell membranes and for secretion in the renal tubule. Disturbances of acid-base balance and potassium metabolism often coexist.

5. Acidosis may be due to excessive production of hydrogen ion, to failure of the lungs or kidneys, or to excessive loss of bicarbonate.

6. Alkalosis may be due to excessive ingestion of base, excessive loss of hydrogen ion (pyloric stenosis), or to overbreathing.

Blood Gas Levels

Low Po$_2$ and Normal or Low Pco$_2$

1. Carbon dioxide is very much more soluble than oxygen in water. Its level in the blood is therefore less affected than that of oxygen in pulmonary oedema, in which it may even be low due to respiratory stimulation.

2. Arterial blood is 95 per cent saturated with oxygen. Overbreathing therefore cannot increase oxygen carriage in blood from normal alveoli, but can reduce the Pco$_2$. In ventilation-perfusion defects, where some alveoli have a normal blood supply, but are ventilated poorly, mixture of the "shunted" blood with blood from normal alveoli results in a low Po$_2$ and normal or low Pco$_2$ in the peripheral arterial blood

Low Po$_2$ and High Pco$_2$

3. The Po$_2$ is low and Pco$_2$ is high in total alveolar hypoventilation when neither gas can be adequately exchanged.

FURTHER READING

CHRISTENSEN, H. N. (1964). *Body Fluids and the Acid-Base Balance*. Philadelphia: W. B. Saunders.

APPENDIX TO CHAPTER III

AMMONIUM CHLORIDE LOADING TEST OF URINARY ACIDIFICATION

The ammonium ion (NH_4^+) is acidic because it can dissociate to ammonia and H^+. If ammonium chloride is ingested the kidneys should normally secrete the excess of hydrogen ion.

Procedure

No food is taken after midnight.

8 a.m. Ammonium chloride 0·1 g/kg body weight is administered orally.

Hourly specimens of urine are collected between 10 a.m. and 4 p.m., and the pH of each specimen measured immediately with a pH meter (pH paper is not very accurate). If the pH of any specimen falls to 5·2 or below the test can be stopped.

Interpretation

In normal subjects the urinary pH falls to 5·2 or below between 2 and 8 hours after the dose. In *renal tubular acidosis* this degree of acidification fails to occur. In generalized renal failure the response of the functioning nephrons may give normal results (p. 8).

Chapter IV

ADRENAL CORTEX

THE adrenal glands are divided into cortex and medulla. This is an anatomical rather than a functional relationship as the medulla is part of the sympathetic nervous system: it is dealt with on p. 374. The cortex, however, is an important endocrine organ. Histologically the adult adrenal cortex has three layers. The outer thin layer (*zona glomerulosa*) is functionally distinct and secretes aldosterone. The inner two layers, the *zona fasciculata* and the *zona reticularis*, are apparently different forms of the same functional unit and secrete the bulk of the adrenocortical hormones. A wider fourth layer is present in the foetal adrenal gland but disappears after birth.

CHEMISTRY OF THE ADRENAL STEROIDS

All the adrenal cortical hormones are steroids with the same chemical skeleton, each carbon atom of which is numbered according to international agreement (Fig. 3). The usual chemical classification is based on the number of carbon atoms in the molecule. Most contain 21 of these (for example cortisol) and are therefore referred to as C_{21} steroids. They originate only in the adrenal cortex. The androgens (for example, androstenedione) contain only 19 carbon atoms (C_{19} steroids) and are derived both from the adrenal cortex and gonads. Oestrogens from the ovary are C_{18} steroids. Various groups are attached to the molecule: for example, cortisol has hydroxyl (—OH) groups at positions 11, 17 and 21 while androstenedione has an oxo (=O) group at position 17.

Such apparently small chemical differences produce a variety of biological actions. Intentional alterations can produce synthetic steroids more potent than the natural hormones (e.g. dexamethasone) or accentuate one particular activity, as in anabolic steroids.

PHYSIOLOGY OF THE ADRENAL STEROIDS

The adrenal cortex is essential for the maintenance of life but surprisingly little is known about its role in normal physiology. Most of the available knowledge is based on the effect of pharmacological doses of cortisone or its analogues and on the changes observed in adrenocortical disease.

On the basis of such observations, the adrenocortical hormones have been classified into three groups.

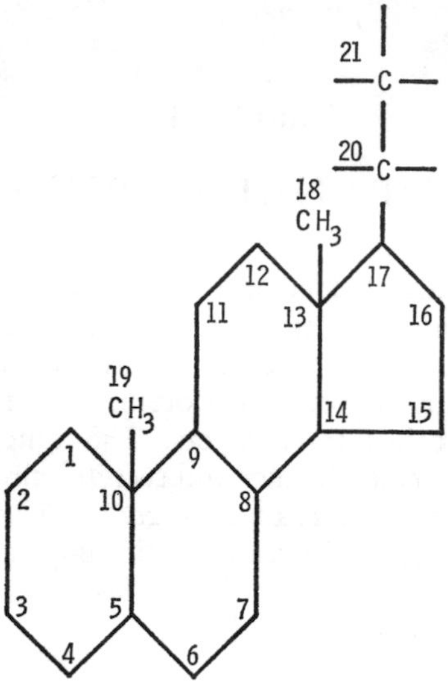

Numbering of the Steroid Ring

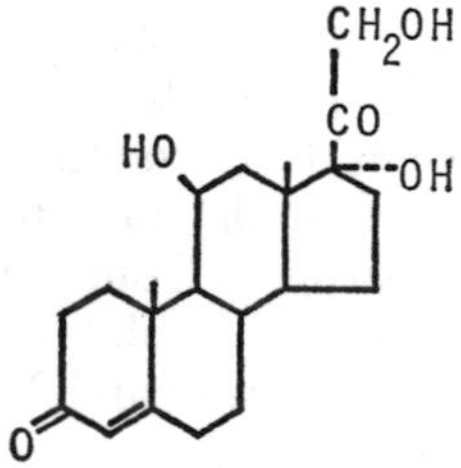

Cortisol

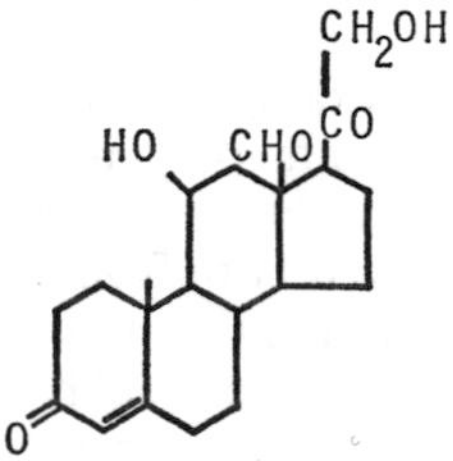

Aldosterone

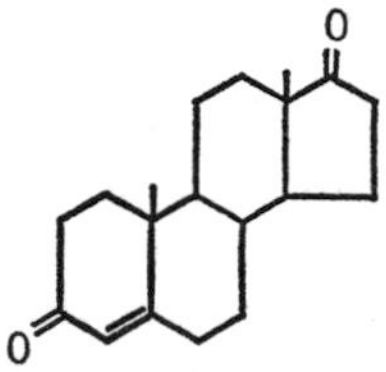

Δ^4 Androstenedione

FIG. 3—The more important adrenal steroids.

1. Glucocorticoids (C_{21} steroids)

Cortisol and *corticosterone* are the major glucocorticoids. Their action on carbohydrate metabolism is opposite to that of insulin and they tend to produce gluconeogenesis and impaired glucose tolerance (see later, p. 92). Protein breakdown is enhanced and fat metabolism altered. Cortisol also affects the ability of the kidney to excrete a water load and is important for the maintenance of normal blood pressure. The mechanism of these actions is unknown. Synthesis of these hormones is under the control of adrenocorticotrophic hormone (ACTH), secreted by the pituitary under feed-back control by circulating cortisol levels. There are also other controlling mechanisms (see p. 101).

Cortisol in the blood is mostly protein bound to a specific *cortisol-binding globulin* (CBG, transcortin) and to albumin. Only the unbound free fraction (about 6 per cent of the total) is the physiologically active part (compare with thyroxine, p. 159). Changes in the binding protein, such as the increase occurring in pregnancy, can produce high protein bound and therefore high total levels with a normal free cortisol level (again compare with thyroxine, p. 167). The glucocorticoids are metabolized in the liver, conjugated with glucuronic acid and excreted in the urine.

Cortisone is not a major secretion product of the adrenal cortex and is biologically inactive until it is converted *in vivo* to hydrocortisone (cortisol).

2. Mineralocorticoids (C_{21} steroids)

The most important hormone in this group is *aldosterone*. It is present in much smaller amounts than the glucocorticoids but has a powerful effect on the distribution of electrolytes (mostly sodium and potassium) across cell membranes. This action involves all cells but is clinically most evident in the renal tubule where it promotes sodium reabsorption and potassium excretion. Physiological levels of ACTH do not significantly influence aldosterone secretion, which is controlled by the renin-angiotensin system (p. 35). Aldosterone is also metabolized in the liver and excreted in the urine, mostly conjugated with glucuronic acid.

The actions of the C_{21} steroids may overlap. Cortisol in excess has a mineralocorticoid action. Aldosterone has a small but unimportant effect on carbohydrate metabolism.

3. Androgens (C_{19} steroids)

The main adrenal androgens are *dehydroepiandrosterone* and *androstenedione*. The control of their secretion is poorly understood. ACTH does increase their synthesis but its action is probably unimportant physiologically.

The adrenal androgens are only mildly androgenic at physiological levels and their role in normal metabolism is probably to promote growth by an anabolic nitrogen retaining action. The most powerful androgen, testosterone, comes from the testis, not the adrenal cortex.

There is extensive interconversion of the androgens from the adrenal cortex and the testis. The end products, *androsterone* and *aetiocholanolone*, together with *dehydroepiandrosterone*, are conjugated in the liver and excreted in the urine as glucuronides and sulphates.

DISORDERS OF THE ADRENAL CORTEX

The disease syndromes of the adrenal cortex can be correlated with the above classification.

1. Syndromes of Excess

(*a*) Excess of glucocorticoid (cortisol)—Cushing's syndrome.

(*b*) Excess of mineralocorticoid (aldosterone)—primary aldosteronism (Conn's syndrome) (p. 45).

(*c*) Excess of androgens, as seen in—adrenocortical carcinoma —congenital adrenal hyperplasia (p. 104).

2. Deficiency Syndromes

(*a*) Deficiency of glucocorticoids and mineralocorticoids— Addison's disease (primary adrenocortical hypofunction).

(*b*) Deficiency of glucocorticoids only—secondary to ACTH deficiency (p. 100) (secondary adrenocortical hypofunction).

CUSHING'S SYNDROME

The commonest presenting feature of Cushing's syndrome is obesity, limited usually to the trunk. Other clinical features are a round plethoric face (moon-face), hypertension, muscular weakness, osteoporosis and frequently hirsutism. Menstrual disturbances, especially amenorrhoea, are common.

The most prominent metabolic abnormalities in Cushing's syndrome reflect the *glucocorticoid* action of cortisol. About two-thirds of the patients have *impaired glucose tolerance* as shown by a diabetic glucose tolerance test and of these many have hyperglycaemia and consequent glycosuria. As cortisol has the opposite action to insulin the resultant picture resembles, in certain aspects, that of diabetes mellitus. There is true resistance to the action of insulin, and a diabetic on cortisone therapy will require an increased dose of insulin. Protein breakdown is accelerated and the liberated amino-acids are either converted to glucose (gluconeogenesis) or lost in the urine leading to a negative nitrogen balance. This is seen clinically in the muscle wasting and osteoporosis. The mechanism underlying the characteristic obesity is not known.

The *mineralocorticoid* effect of excess cortisol is seen in some, but not all, cases of Cushing's syndrome. *Sodium retention* by the renal tubules leads to an increase in total body sodium and therefore body water (p. 37). Plasma sodium concentrations are usually normal, however, because of this parallel water retention. *Potassium loss* through the renal tubule may lead to severe depletion, reflected usually as hypokalaemic alkalosis.

Androgen secretion may be increased and be a factor in the hirsutism, but marked virilization is uncommon.

ADDISON'S DISEASE

Addison's disease, or primary adrenocortical hypofunction, is caused by destruction of all zones of the adrenal cortex. Consequently there is a deficiency of glucocorticoids, mineralocorticoids and androgens.

Depending on the degree of adrenal destruction, the patient with Addison's disease may present in one of two ways. He may first be seen in a shocked dehydrated condition (Addisonian crisis); this is a medical emergency requiring immediate treatment. Alternatively the disease may be diagnosed only after a prolonged period of ill health. The clinical features of this form—tiredness, pigmentation of the skin and buccal mucosa, weight loss and hypotension—are common to many severe chronic diseases.

The most serious consequences are due to the *mineralocorticoid deficiency. Sodium deficiency* is the cardinal biochemical abnormality of the Addisonian state. Loss of sodium through the kidneys is accompanied by loss of water and while these parallel one another the plasma sodium concentration remains in the normal range (see Fig. 1). The dehydration and consequent haemoconcentration are nevertheless evident from the raised haematocrit and total protein concentration. During a crisis, however, there is almost invariably hyponatraemia, as sodium loss exceeds water loss. As the loss is mainly renal the urine may contain considerable amounts of sodium despite the dehydration and hyponatraemia. The Addisonian crisis is therefore the result of massive sodium depletion. Other abnormalities usually include a raised plasma potassium and metabolic acidosis (compare the reverse in mineralocorticoid excess). The fluid depletion leads to a reduced circulating blood volume and renal circulatory insufficiency with a reduced glomerular filtration rate and a moderately raised blood urea. In the more chronic form of Addison's disease only some of these features may be present.

The absence of *glucocorticoids* is shown by the marked insulin sensitivity of the hypoadrenal state. The glucose tolerance curve is flat and there may be fasting hypoglycaemia but this only occasionally gives rise to symptoms. Cortisol deficiency also results in impaired ability of the kidneys to excrete a water load (p. 91). This fact has been used as a test of adrenal insufficiency but is best avoided as it can be misleading and dangerous, especially in the presence of hyponatraemia. The extra-cellular osmotic pressure (determined mainly by sodium and associated anions, p. 32) is already low. An acute water load lowers it still further, so that the extra water cannot be retained in the extracellular space. As renal excretion is delayed because of cortisol deficiency, water moves into the cells. Cellular overhydration and water intoxication develop.

Androgen deficiency is not clinically evident because testosterone production by the testis is unimpaired.

The pigmentation that develops in Addison's disease is probably due to high circulating ACTH levels resulting from the lack of cortisol suppression of the feed-back mechanism. There are common amino-acid sequences in the ACTH and MSH (melanocyte-stimulating hormone) molecules and ACTH has some melanocyte-stimulating activity.

INVESTIGATION OF ADRENOCORTICAL FUNCTION

The changes discussed in the previous section all reflect, indirectly, the adrenocortical function. Direct evidence must be obtained by measuring the steroid output of the gland. Estimation of individual steroids is technically difficult and most of the routine tests measure "groups" of steroids. A brief outline of the synthesis of adrenal steroids (Fig. 4) will illustrate what these "group" estimations actually measure.

The adrenal steroids are synthesized via cholesterol: although cholesterol itself is colourless it is probably the associated high lipid content which accounts for the yellow colour of the adrenal cortex. At a later stage—pregnenolone—the pathway divides into two different lines of development. The first (C_{21} pathway) leads, via a series of hydroxylations (additions of OH groups) at positions 17, 21 and 11 to cortisol. Each step is controlled by a specific enzyme and absence of one of these enzymes gives rise to the condition of congenital adrenal hyper-plasia (p. 104). Corticosterone and aldosterone are also products of this pathway. The second (C_{19} pathway) finally produces the adrenal androgens which, by contrast with the steroids of the other pathway, lack the side chain at C-17. As outlined earlier (p. 91) the circulating hormones are further metabolized in the liver and excreted in the urine. Their synthesis is controlled by ACTH from the pituitary in response to circulating cortisol levels.

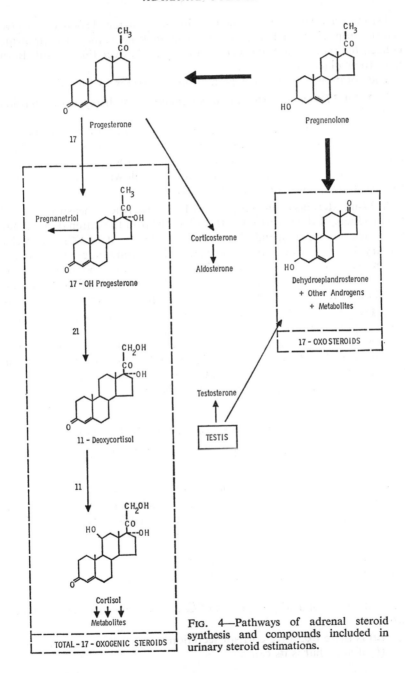

FIG. 4—Pathways of adrenal steroid synthesis and compounds included in urinary steroid estimations.

Estimations can be performed on blood or urine. Blood levels give information about a particular moment in time while 24-hour urine collections reflect the total secretion of steroids over this period. Both have their place in diagnosis.

The commonly performed estimations are (refer to Fig. 4):

1. **Total 17-oxogenic steroids** (also called 17-hydroxycorticosteroids or 17-OHCS).

The term oxogenic is used because during estimation the 17-OHCS are converted to the more stable and easily measured 17-oxo form. This group includes cortisol, its precursors and metabolites and is used as an index of cortisol output. This and the following estimations are usually done on a 24-hour urine collection.

2. **17-oxosteroids** (previously called 17-ketosteroids) measure most of the products of the androgen pathway, both from the adrenal and from the testes, and their metabolites. In the male about two-thirds of the urinary 17-oxosteroids are of adrenal and the remainder of testicular origin. As discussed earlier (p. 92), there is usually poor correlation with clinical androgenicity as the small amounts of testosterone metabolites included in the estimation are quantitatively insignificant.

3. **11-hydroxycorticosteroids (11-OHCS).**—This estimation has become popular recently and can be applied to blood or urine (plasma or urinary "cortisol"). The main steroids with an —OH group at position 11 are cortisol and corticosterone. These two form only 60 per cent of the measured plasma 11-OHCS but the estimation reflects the cortisol level with sufficient accuracy for clinical diagnosis.

Causes and Diagnosis of Cushing's Syndrome

The syndrome is produced by an excess of circulating cortisol. The causes of excess cortisol are:

1. Bilateral adrenal hyperplasia due to:

    (*a*) excessive ACTH secretion by the pituitary (commonest form);

    (*b*) ectopic ACTH production by a non-endocrine tumour. The most frequent cause of this is bronchogenic carcinoma (see Chapter XX).

2. Adenoma or carcinoma of the adrenal cortex.

3. Administration of cortisone or its analogues.

Investigation of a suspected case of Cushing's syndrome must answer two questions:

    (*a*) is there excessive cortisol secretion?

    (*b*) if so, what is its cause?

Certain clinical features may suggest the cause. The commonest form, due to excess ACTH secretion by the pituitary (see p. 98), occurs usually in women of reproductive age. Investigation is prompted by the physical appearance of the patient. Marked virilization is uncommon in this form and if present suggests carcinoma of the adrenal cortex. Non-endocrine tumours producing ACTH frequently present with severe hypokalaemic alkalosis with none of the physical stigmata of the common form: the explanation of this is not clear.

Measurement of the cortisol secretion rate provides a definite answer to the first question. This technique is beyond the scope of most routine laboratories but it has been valuable in evaluating the standard tests. It is now recognized that many of the earlier interpretations of these were misleading.

One of the main diagnostic difficulties is due to the fact that stress, from either mental or physical causes, can cause increased cortisol secretion and mimic the laboratory findings of Cushing's syndrome. There is no test of adrenal overactivity completely free from this drawback and clinical assessment is the only way of detecting stress. Another difficulty is that patients with simple obesity and hirsutism can have a raised urinary steroid excretion without an increased cortisol secretion rate, presumably due to altered cortisol metabolism. Means of overcoming this diagnostic problem will be discussed.

A suggested approach to the problem is outlined below.

1. Plasma 11-OHCS

There is normally considerable diurnal variation in plasma cortisol levels as measured by the 11-OHCS. Highest levels occur in the morning at 8–9 a.m. (normal 6–26 μg/100 ml) while the lowest levels are seen around midnight (below 9 μg/100 ml). In Cushing's syndrome the morning level may be raised or it may be normal. An elevated midnight level is more significant. This reduction or abolition of the diurnal variation is characteristic, but not diagnostic, of Cushing's syndrome, as it is also seen during stress.

2. Urinary 11-OHCS

This is abnormally high in most cases of Cushing's syndrome but again stress can cause raised levels. The level in simple obesity is usually normal.

These investigations are adequate as screening procedures and if both are normal the diagnosis is unlikely to be Cushing's syndrome. If levels are borderline or high one should proceed to the next test.

3. Dexamethasone Suppression Test

The normal feedback control responds to a raised plasma cortisol level by cutting off ACTH secretion. The basic abnormality in the common form of Cushing's syndrome seems to be that this mechanism is set at a higher level than normal so that higher levels of plasma cortisol are required to suppress ACTH secretion. Assessing the suppressibility of the feed-back centre offers a means of diagnosis. The potent synthetic steroid dexamethasone is used, as it has the same effect as cortisol only in much lower doses, which do not contribute significantly to the steroid estimations used to monitor the response. In addition, this test helps to establish the cause of the Cushing's syndrome.

When administered as a 2 mg/day dose, dexamethasone will suppress ACTH secretion in normal subjects and cases of simple obesity and hirsutism. The suppression is shown by a fall in urinary total 17-oxogenic steroid excretion. This will not happen in Cushing's syndrome but if the test is continued by giving 8 mg/day the levels achieved will suppress the abnormally high set control. If, however, the excess cortisol is due to ectopic ACTH production, or from an adenoma or carcinoma of the adrenal cortex, suppression of ACTH from the pituitary will have no effect on the production and urinary steroid excretion will not fall.

4. Other Tests

The tests discussed so far are sufficient to diagnose excess cortisol secretion and indicate the cause. Some additional information may be provided by the following estimations.

(*a*) **17-oxosteroids.**—Results of this estimation are usually within normal limits in hyperplasia and adenoma of the adrenal cortex when cortisol is the main secretion product. Adrenocortical carcinomata, however, are less specific in their action and frequently secrete a variety of steroids, including androgens, in large quantities. It is these patients who show virilization and the urinary 17-oxosteroid excretion (reflecting androgens) may be very high.

(*b*) **Total 17-oxogenic steroids.**—As an index of cortisol secretion in Cushing's syndrome this estimation can be misleading. Not only may raised levels occur in stress and simple obesity, but results within the normal range are found in about half the cases of proven Cushing's syndrome. Very high levels (over 50 mg/day) may occur in cases of adrenocortical carcinoma or hyperplasia due to ectopic ACTH secretion.

(*c*) **ACTH stimulation tests** have been used to distinguish normal subjects from those with adrenal hyperplasia (exaggerated response) or adrenocortical tumour (no response) but there is considerable overlap of results and interpretation is difficult.

TABLE X
SUMMARY OF TESTS USED IN CUSHING'S SYNDROME

Test	Normal	Cushing's syndrome due to		
		Hyperplasia	Adrenal carcinoma or adenoma	Ectopic ACTH-producing tumour
1. Urinary 11-OHCS	Normal	Usually raised	Raised May be very high	Raised
2. Diurnal variation of plasma cortisol	Normal	Reduced or absent	Reduced or absent	Reduced or absent
3. Dexamethasone (a) 2 mg/day (b) 8 mg/day	Suppression Suppression	No suppression Suppression	No suppression No suppression	No suppression No suppression
4. Total 17-oxogenic steroids	Normal	Often normal	May be very high	May be very high
5. 17-oxo-steroids	Normal	Usually normal	May be very high with carcinoma	Usually normal

CAUSES AND DIAGNOSIS OF ADDISON'S DISEASE

Primary adrenal hypofunction is due to destruction of the adrenal cortex. Tuberculosis was once the commonest cause but it has now been superseded in many countries by idiopathic atrophy of the gland, probably due to an autoimmune process. Rare causes of destruction include amyloidosis, mycotic infections and secondary malignancy.

If the patient presents in Addisonian crisis, immediate treatment is necessary and there is no time to perform diagnostic tests. Blood can be taken for plasma 11-OHCS estimation but further tests can await recovery from the crisis, as the underlying adrenal insufficiency will not be affected by the therapy.

Urinary steroid estimations are of little use in the diagnosis of Addison's disease for two important reasons.

(a) Low values occur non-specifically in many disorders and may be found in normal subjects.

(b) If the adrenal destruction is partial, *maximum* ACTH stimulation of the remnant via the feed-back mechanism may maintain steroid secretion within normal limits. There is, however, no reserve and in a stress situation the residual adrenal cortex is unable to respond to the increased need for cortisol and the patient may develop an adrenal crisis.

The *essential feature in the diagnosis of Addison's disease* is the demonstration that the adrenal cortex cannot respond to ACTH.

1. Synacthen Stimulation Test

Synacthen is a synthetic peptide comprising 24 of the 39 amino-acids of ACTH. It has the same biological action but as it lacks the antigenic part of the molecule there is much less danger of an allergic reaction to it. The simplest form of the test consists of measuring plasma 11-OHCS before and after an injection of Synacthen. A definite rise of plasma 11-OHCS excludes Addison's disease. Lack of response may be due to primary or secondary adrenal atrophy: to distinguish between these a more prolonged stimulus is needed.

2. Prolonged ACTH Stimulation Test

This consists of several injections of long-acting ACTH (see secondary adrenal atrophy, p. 103). Failure to respond to this prolonged stimulus confirms the diagnosis of Addison's disease (compare with the TSH stimulation test in primary and secondary hypothyroidism, p. 164). The chronic diseases often confused with chronic Addison's disease usually have high basal 11-OHCS levels (due to stress). If a patient is already on steroid therapy, substitution of dexamethasone (not contributing significantly to plasma 11-OHCS) for cortisone allows stimulation tests to be performed under the necessary steroid cover.

For details of these tests see the Appendix (p. 109).

SECONDARY ADRENAL HYPOFUNCTION

As already mentioned in the classification of adrenal disorders, adrenocortical hypofunction may be secondary to lack of ACTH. The secretion of the trophic hormones of the anterior pituitary is considered in the section on that gland (p. 114) and only the relevant points will be considered again here. In recent years the importance of the inter-relationships between the adrenal cortex, the anterior pituitary and the hypothalamus has been recognized.

The Hypothalamic-Pituitary-Adrenal Axis

(Fig. 5)

The immediate stimulus to secretion of the adrenocortical steroids is ACTH secreted by the anterior pituitary gland. This gland releases ACTH in response to corticotrophin releasing factor (CRF), a peptide which reaches it from the hypothalamus via the local portal vessels. The release of CRF is controlled by at least two centres in the hypothalamus.

(*a*) **The feedback centre** responds to the circulating cortisol level and varies CRF (and so ACTH) secretion to maintain it within the normal range.

(*b*) **The diurnal rhythm** of plasma cortisol follows on a similar one of CRF. The site and nature of the regulatory mechanism is unknown.

(*c*) **The stress centre** responds to stimuli from higher cerebral levels (triggered by stresses of various kinds). It can override both the feedback control and diurnal rhythm.

Disorders of the Hypothalamic-Pituitary-Adrenal Axis

ACTH release may be impaired by disease of the hypothalamus or anterior pituitary, most commonly due to tumour or infarction. Corticosteroid therapy suppresses ACTH release and after such therapy, especially if prolonged, the ACTH releasing mechanism may be slow to recover. This period of impaired response may last up to a year.

Complete anterior pituitary destruction results in the picture of hypopituitarism (p. 121) but if destruction is only partial there may be sufficient ACTH for basal requirements. As in partial adrenal cortical destruction (p. 100) the deficiency may only become evident under conditions of stress. In these patients, as in those on corticosteroid therapy, stress may precipitate acute adrenal insufficiency. The most usual sources of stress are infections and surgery.

The adrenal crisis due to ACTH deficiency is due to lack of glucocorticoids only. It differs from an Addisonian crisis in that aldosterone secretion (not under the influence of ACTH) is normal; consequently there is not the characteristic sodium depletion and dehydration. The condition is nevertheless potentially fatal and is ushered in by mental disturbance, nausea, abdominal pain and usually hypotension (cortisol deficiency). As in primary glucocorticoid deficiency there may be hypoglycaemia and marked insulin sensitivity. Plasma sodium levels may be low, not because of sodium loss as in Addisonian crisis, but because of dilution due to the delayed water excretion of cortisol deficiency.

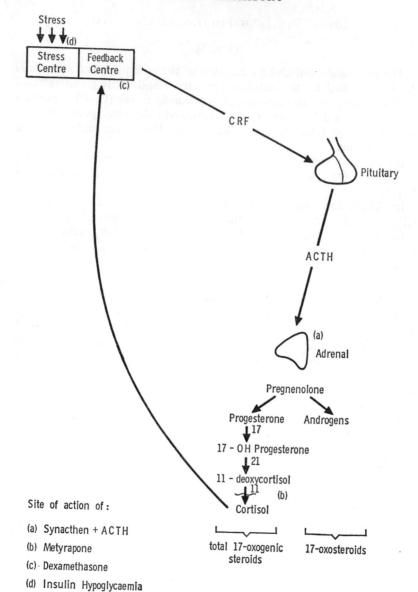

FIG. 5—The control of cortisol secretion.

If the patient presents in this state blood may be taken for plasma 11-OHCS but treatment should be instituted at once. This single estimation may distinguish acute adrenal insufficiency (low levels) from clinically similar conditions where normal adrenal response to stress produces raised 11-OHCS. It does not distinguish primary from secondary adrenal insufficiency.

Investigation of Secondary Adrenal Insufficiency

Each part of the hypothalamic-pituitary-adrenal axis may be assessed separately. In all the tests to be discussed adrenocortical steroid levels in blood or urine are measured to assess response. Therefore the first step must be to ensure that the adrenal cortex itself is functioning adequately.

1. **Assessment of the adrenal cortex.**—The limitations of urinary steroid estimations have been discussed (p. 99). A normal result of the Synacthen stimulation test makes the diagnosis of long standing secondary adrenal hypofunction unlikely.

The prolonged ACTH stimulation test usually results in a stepwise increase in response to a maximum on the third day. This is analogous to the response of the thyroid to TSH in secondary myxoedema. Having established the presence of a responsive adrenal cortex the ACTH releasing mechanisms can be investigated.

2. **Assessment of the feed-back mechanism.**—The dexamethasone suppression test (p. 110) will assess the ability of the feed-back centre to cut off in response to raised cortisol levels. In the present context, by contrast, we are investigating whether the centre can respond adequately to a low cortisol level. This can be done by the *metyrapone* test. The drug metyrapone blocks cortisol synthesis by inhibiting the final hydroxylation step. A normal feed-back centre responds to the consequent fall in circulating cortisol by increasing CRF and therefore ACTH secretion. This stimulates cortisol synthesis but, as the final stage is blocked, precursors accumulate and are excreted in the urine to be measured as an increase in the total 17-oxogenic steroids (Fig. 5). In congenital adrenal hyperplasia similar changes occur due to an inherited enzyme defect (p. 104). It should be noted that this test should preferably precede the ACTH stimulation test because ACTH invalidates it for a week.

3. **Assessment of the "stress" pathway.**—A normal response to metyrapone does not necessarily mean that the patient can respond adequately to stress. Ability to do this can only be established by measuring the response to a suitable stress stimulus. The most frequently used stimulus is hypoglycaemia.

Insulin hypoglycaemia test.—After an adequate dose of insulin by intravenous injection the blood sugar should fall to below 35 mg/

100 ml, and if the stress pathway is functional this leads to a rapid rise in plasma 11-OHCS. This test is potentially dangerous and the patient must be kept under continuous observation; if clinically indicated the test must be terminated by giving intravenous glucose.

4. **Lysine vasopressin.**—This peptide is related to arginine vasopressin |(antidiuretic hormone) and also to CRF. Administration by intramuscular injection or intravenous infusion evokes a prompt rise in plasma 11-OHCS. This is not due to a direct action on the adrenal cortex and the exact site of action is not known. A normal response to lysine vasopressin may be found in patients with impaired metyrapone or insulin responses.

THE HYPOTHALAMIC-PITUITARY-ADRENAL AXIS AND CORTICOSTEROID THERAPY

There is the risk of adrenocortical hypofunction when long term corticosteroid therapy is stopped. This may be due either to secondary adrenal atrophy or to impairment of ACTH releasing mechanisms. If the patient is taking dexamethasone (or any other synthetic steroid not measured by the plasma 11-OHCS), or if this is substituted for cortisone, the adrenal cortex can be tested during therapy by a prolonged ACTH stimulation test as already outlined (p. 100).

A simple means of testing the ACTH-releasing mechanisms is to estimate the morning plasma 11-OHCS levels two or three days after cessation of steroid therapy. A level within the normal range indicates a functioning pituitary and feed-back centre. It must be emphasized, however, that this does not test the all-important stress pathway (p. 101).

CONGENITAL ADRENAL HYPERPLASIA

This is a rare inherited condition in which there is a deficiency of one of the enzymes involved in the biosynthesis of cortisol (see Fig. 4). The enzyme most commonly affected is that controlling the hydroxylation step at C-21 (C-21 hydroxylase) which is the penultimate stage of the cortisol pathway. As a result, plasma cortisol levels tend to be low and the feed-back centre is stimulated to secrete greatly increased amounts of ACTH. This, in turn, increases steroid synthesis along both main pathways and may achieve normal cortisol levels if the block is not complete. There will, in any case, be increased production of androgens and of cortisol precursors behind the block. As in Addison's disease a "normal" cortisol level may merely represent a gland working at full capacity but with no reserve to meet stress. In addition, about one-third of the cases seen in infancy have associated impairment of aldosterone synthesis.

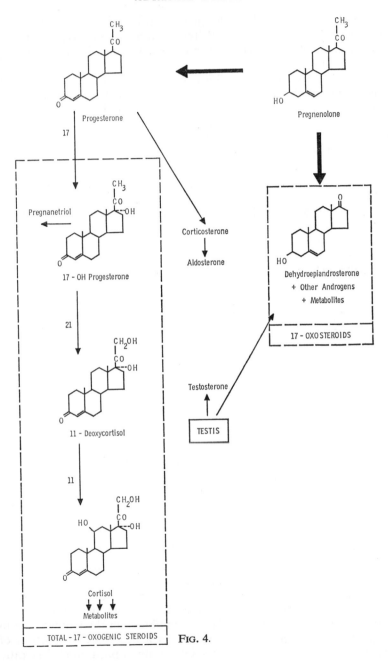

FIG. 4.

With this background of deficient cortisol production leading to excessive ACTH secretion and therefore to androgen overproduction, the clinical manifestations can be explained. The condition may present in several ways.

1. **Female pseudohermaphroditism.**—Because the foetal adrenals start functioning at about the third month of gestation, the abnormal steroid pattern is present *in utero* during the period of development of the external genitalia. In the female child the high levels of androgens can produce pseudohermaphroditism of varying degree.

2. **"Salt-losing" syndrome.**—The cases with impaired aldosterone production can present in the first few days of life with what is, in effect, an Addisonian crisis with the biochemical changes outlined on p. 93.

3. **Progressive virilization.**—This occurs in males at the age of 2–3 years with enlargement of the penis and rapid osseous development. As bone fusion occurs earlier than normal in these children, they are smaller than their fellows when they become adults.

4. **Milder virilization.**—This occurs at or after puberty in the female, often associated with amenorrhoea.

5. **Hypertensive form.**—A very much rarer form of congenital adrenal hyperplasia is that due to 11-hydroxylase deficiency. In these patients signs of virilization are accompanied by hypertension, due most probably to high levels of 11-deoxycorticosterone.

In any of the less acute forms of the syndrome there may be hyperpigmentation from the high ACTH levels (as in Addison's disease, p. 94).

STEROID EXCRETION AND DIAGNOSIS

The increased production of androgens and cortisol precursors results in raised urinary 17-oxosteroids and total 17-oxogenic steroids. One of the steroids included in this latter group—pregnanetriol—is greatly increased and its estimation is of value in diagnosis. All these abnormalities can be corrected by administration of cortisone or dexamethasone which cut off the excess ACTH secretion.

The major difficulty in diagnosis using the tests considered above is the necessity for a 24-hour urine collection. Not only is this difficult in infants, but in the patient presenting in a salt-losing crisis therapy should not be withheld for 24 hours.

A quicker method of diagnosis is to determine the *11-oxygenation index* using a *random* specimen of urine. Because the final stage of cortisol synthesis is 11-hydroxylation, any block in the pathway (as in congenital adrenal hyperplasia) results in a decreased proportion of total 17-oxogenic steroids with an —OH group at position 11. The ratio of the steroids without an 11-OH to those with 11-OH (the 11-oxygenation index) will be greater than normal.

SUMMARY

1. The steroids of the adrenal cortex can be classified into three groups.

(a) Glucocorticoids, e.g. cortisol.
(b) Mineralocorticoids, e.g. aldosterone. $\Big\}C_{21}$ steroids
(c) Androgens. $\quad C_{19}$ steroids

2. Steroids are usually estimated in "groups". The most commonly used tests are:

(a) Urinary total 17-oxogenic steroids which includes cortisol, its precursors and metabolites. This test is used as a measure of cortisol production.

(b) Urinary 17-oxosteroids which provide a measure of androgens, most of which are derived from the adrenal cortex.

(c) Plasma or urinary 11-hydroxycorticosteroids (11-OHCS) which measures mainly cortisol and corticosterone.

Urinary steroid estimation can be very misleading in the diagnosis of adrenocortical disease.

3. Cortisol secretion is increased by ACTH from the pituitary and this in turn is controlled by two hypothalamic centres:

(a) A feedback centre that responds to circulating cortisol levels.
(b) A stress centre responding to stresses of various kinds.

There is a diurnal variation in cortisol secretion. The lowest levels occur around midnight and the highest in the morning.

4. *Cushing's syndrome* is due to excess cortisol. The causes are adrenal hyperplasia due either to excess ACTH from the pituitary or a non-endocrine tumour, or to a tumour of the adrenal cortex. The biochemical features include impaired glucose tolerance and, in some cases, hypokalaemic alkalosis.

There are two stages in diagnosis.

(a) Demonstration of excess cortisol production.

(i) A raised midnight plasma 11-OHCS with loss of diurnal variation.
(ii) Dexamethasone suppression test.

(b) Determination of the cause:

(i) Dexamethasone suppression test.
(ii) Urinary 17-oxosteroids.

5. *Addison's disease* is due to destruction of the adrenal cortex with loss of all its hormones. Biochemically it is characterized by sodium depletion.

Diagnosis is made by demonstrating that the adrenal cortex cannot respond to ACTH by:

   (*a*) The Synacthen test.
   (*b*) Prolonged ACTH stimulation test.

6. *Secondary adrenal insufficiency* is caused by diminished ACTH secretion by the pituitary. This may be due to disease of the hypothalamus or pituitary or it may be a result of corticosteroid therapy.

After demonstrating a functional adrenal cortex the ACTH releasing mechanisms may be tested by:

   (*a*) Metyrapone test (feed-back mechanism).
   (*b*) Insulin hypoglycaemia (stress pathway).

7. *Congenital adrenal hyperplasia* is due to an inherited enzyme deficiency in the biosynthesis of cortisol. Symptoms are due to deficient cortisol and to excess androgen secretion. Diagnosis is made most rapidly by the 11-oxygenation index. Urinary 17-oxosteroids are raised.

FURTHER READING

MATTINGLY, D. (1968). Disorders of the Adrenal Cortex and Pituitary Gland In: *Recent Advances in Medicine*, Chap. 5, 15th edit. Eds. D. N. Baron N. Compston and A. M. Dawson. London: J. & A. Churchill.

APPENDIX TO CHAPTER IV

PLASMA 11-OHCS

10 ml of blood is collected into a heparin tube and sent to the laboratory as soon as possible. If there is any possibility of delay the specimen should be sent on ice. The method used for estimation depends on fluorimetry of plasma extracts and all these precautions aim to prevent an increase in non-specific plasma fluorescence.

Interpretation

This is discussed in the relevant sections but in addition it is worth remembering that *raised values not due to an increase in free cortisol* occur with:

1. Improperly collected specimens (non-specific fluorescence).
2. Raised levels of cortisol binding globulin (pregnancy, oestrogen therapy, contraceptive pill).

Prednisolone, fludrocortisone and dexamethasone are not measured. Aldactone interferes with the estimation.

SYNACTHEN (β^{1-24} CORTICOTROPHIN) STIMULATION TEST

The patient should preferably be resting quietly.

(*a*) 10 ml blood is taken for basal 11-OHCS.

(*b*) 250 μg of Synacthen, dissolved in about 1 ml of sterile water or isotonic saline, is given by intramuscular injection.

(*c*) 30 minutes after (*b*) a further 10 ml blood is taken for 11-OHCS.

A *normal response* is an increase in plasma 11-OHCS by at least 7 μg/100 ml with a final level of at least 18 μg/100 ml in the second specimen.

Although this test can be performed at any time of day, additional information about maximal basal levels can be obtained if it is started at about 9 a.m.

PROLONGED ACTH STIMULATION TEST

50 U. of ACTH gel is given by intramuscular injection twice daily for three days.

The response may be monitored by measurement of:

(*a*) Urinary total 17-oxogenic steroids.

Daily 24-hour collections are made, including two control collections before ACTH administration. A *normal response* is an increase in excretion of 20–60 mg a day above the control level.

(*b*) Levels of 11-OHCS in plasma taken before and five hours after the morning injection of ACTH. An increase of 20 μg/100 ml can be expected with a normally functioning adrenal cortex.

Both the ACTH and Synacthen stimulation tests may be performed under steroid cover if this is provided by a compound such as dexamethasone.

DEXAMETHASONE SUPPRESSION TEST

Daily 24-hour urine collections are made for five days.

(*a*) Day 1—control day;

(*b*) Day 2 and 3—dexamethasone 0·5 mg, 6-hourly (2 mg/day) is given by mouth;

(*c*) Day 4 and 5—dexamethasone 2 mg, 6-hourly (8 mg/day) is given by mouth.

Total 17-oxogenic steroids are estimated on the collections of days 1, 3 and 5.

Suppression by either of the two dose levels is shown by a fall to below 4 mg/day on day 3 (2 mg dose) or to below 50 per cent of the initial level on day 5 (8 mg dose).

For interpretation see p. 97.

METYRAPONE TEST

Twenty-four-hour urine collections are made for three days.

(*a*) Day 1—control urine collection;

(*b*) Day 2—metyrapone 750 mg is given at 4-hourly intervals for six doses (total 4·5 g);

(*c*) Day 3—urine collection.

Total 17-oxogenic steroids are measured in all three. A *normal response* is shown by a rise of more than 10 mg/24 hours above the control level. This may occur on day 2 or day 3.

INSULIN HYPOGLYCAEMIA TEST

After an overnight fast:

1. A suitable vein is cannulated at about 9 a.m. At least 30 minutes should pass after this, before starting the test, to minimize the effects of stress on the results. For the same reason an indwelling venous cannula is preferable to repeated venepuncture.

2. Insulin is injected intravenously (dose—see below).

3. Blood is taken for glucose and plasma 11-OHCS estimation at 0, 15, 30, 45, 60 and 90 minutes.

Interpretation

Provided the blood glucose falls below 35 mg/100 ml an intact stress pathway responds by causing a rise in plasma 11-OHCS by at least 9 μg/100 ml.

It is usually sufficient to estimate plasma 11-OHCS at 0 and 60 minutes, but the other samples should be available for estimation if necessary.

The *dose* required to achieve this degree of hypoglycaemia varies from patient to patient. 0·15 U./kg body weight is usually effective in normal subjects. Patients with Cushing's syndrome or acromegaly may require 0·2 or 0·3 U./kg body weight. In a patient suspected of having pituitary or adrenal insufficiency it is best to start with a dose of 0·1 U./kg body weight or less.

This test is potentially dangerous and glucose for intravenous injection, and hydrocortisone, should be readily available.

Chapter V

PITUITARY AND OVARIAN HORMONES

GENERAL

THE pituitary gland, like the adrenal, consists of two physiologically distinct parts, the adenohypophysis (anterior pituitary) and the neurohypophysis (posterior pituitary).

Adenohypophysis

The adenohypophysis has a special role in the normal functioning of the endocrine system in that many of its hormones control other endocrine glands. An intact pituitary gland is essential, not only for normal thyroid and adrenal function, but also for normal growth and sexual development and function. The hormones secreted by the adenohypophysis are:

Growth Hormone (GH).
Prolactin (Lactogenic Hormone).
Adrenocorticotrophic Hormone (ACTH).
Thyroid Stimulating Hormone (TSH).
Follicle Stimulating Hormone (FSH).
Luteinizing Hormone (LH)—also known as Interstitial Cell Stimulating Hormone (ICSH).
FSH and LH are also referred to as pituitary gonadotrophic hormones.

Each hormone is secreted by a single cell type as identified by special staining techniques, ultramicroscopy and immunological studies. Routine histological preparations show only three cell types: acidophil, basophil and chromophobe. On this classification, GH and prolactin are secreted by acidophil cells while ACTH, TSH and the gonado-trophin-secreting cells usually appear as basophils. The exact status of the chromophobe cell is uncertain: secretory granules can be demonstrated by ultramicroscopy and may represent a phase in the development of normal secreting cells. Most tumours of chromophobe cells are, however, apparently non-functioning.

Neurohypophysis

The neurohypophysis secretes two hormones:

(*a*) **Antidiuretic hormone (ADH),** which is concerned with maintaining osmolarity of the ECF. Deficiency leads to diabetes insipidus (see p. 39).

(*b*) **Oxytocin,** which acts on the lactating breast to promote milk secretion, and which has a role in producing uterine contractions during parturition.

PRINCIPLES OF CONTROL OF PITUITARY HORMONE SECRETION

The concept of the central role of the pituitary as the controller of the endocrine system has now been replaced by recognition of hypothalamic control of pituitary function. The adenohypophysis seems to be little

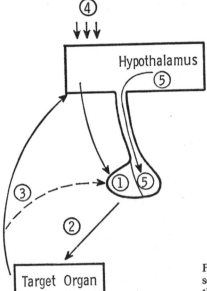

FIG. 6.—Control of pituitary hormone secretion. (The numerals correspond to those in the text p. 114)

more than a manufacturer of hormones controlled by hypothalamic nuclei and the neurohypophysis is merely a hormone store.

The general principles of control are outlined in Fig. 6. The neurohypophysis communicates directly with the hypothalamus via nerve fibres in the pituitary stalk. The adenohypophysis, on the other hand, has an intricate vascular connection. Branches of the superior hypophyseal artery divide into a network of capillary loops that enter the median eminence and are intimately applied to the hypothalamic nerve fibres. This network reforms into vessels that pass down the pituitary stalk into a second network of capillaries in the adenohypophysis. Hypothalamic regulatory factors are transported to the adenohypophysis by this *hypophyseal portal system*. Except in the case of prolactin (p. 117) these factors stimulate release of pituitary hormones and are referred to as releasing factors (RF).

The secretion of RF and therefore of pituitary hormones may be influenced in several ways (Fig. 6).

1. Humoral Feedback System

The RF causes release of a trophic hormone from the adenohypophysis (1) which stimulates the target organ (2) to secrete its hormone (3). The hypothalamic centre (or occasionally the adenohypophysis itself) is sensitive to the circulating level of target organ hormone—raised levels suppressing release of RF and low levels stimulating it. This *negative feed-back system* maintains levels of target hormone within the normal range.

2. Neural System

It may happen that greater than normal levels of target organ hormone, such as cortisol, are required during a time of stress. In such a case, stimuli of a different nature or from higher cerebral centres (4) can rapidly increase secretion of RF and so of the required target hormone. In this way emotional and physical stress can influence hormone secretion.

Diurnal and other biological rhythms of hormone secretion also originate in variations of RF secretion but the mechanism of such variation is poorly understood. The diagnostic importance of the diurnal variation in plasma cortisol levels is considered on p. 97.

The hormones of the neurohypophysis (ADH and oxytocin) are synthesized in the hypothalamus and travel down nerve trunks to accumulate in the neurohypophysis, from which they are released under hypothalamic control. Transection of the pituitary stalk or destruction of the pituitary, leading to adenohypophyseal insufficiency, does not, therefore, necessarily produce diabetes insipidus. The ADH-producing cells in the hypothalamus are not damaged and can still secrete the hormone into the bloodstream in response to the appropriate stimuli.

MEASUREMENT OF PITUITARY HORMONES

One of the main problems in the diagnosis of pituitary disease has been the difficulty of measuring the hormones directly. Conclusions have, in many cases, to be drawn from secondary effects on other endocrine glands. Direct measurement may be made in two ways:

(*a*) *Bioassay* involves measurement of the effects of blood or urine extracts on suitably prepared animals. These procedures are technically difficult and require considerable experience and rigid control. Such conditions are not generally available.

(*b*) *Radioimmunoassay* allows measurement of most of the pituitary hormones in the concentrations present in blood. This is the standard method of measuring growth hormone and methods are rapidly being perfected for other trophic hormones. Such estimations are available in special centres.

GROWTH HORMONE

Physiology

There are two facets of growth hormone activity.

1. **Growth.**—The central role of GH in regulating growth is well illustrated by the dwarfism or gigantism that occur with deficiency or excess of GH in childhood. The hormone stimulates growth of bone and other tissues, most probably by increasing protein synthesis. There is a complex interaction of GH with insulin and thyroxine, all being required for normal growth. Androgens are also involved as shown by the growth spurt at the onset of puberty.

2. **Intermediary metabolism.**—It was once thought that the pituitary secreted a diabetogenic hormone. The diabetogenic principle in pituitary extracts has been identified as GH, which antagonizes the effect of insulin on muscle. In excess, GH may produce carbohydrate intolerance, but this is usually counteracted by increased insulin secretion. GH also stimulates lipolysis and, as the resultant increase in FFA also antagonizes insulin release and its action, the effects are difficult to separate. GH secretion is stimulated by hypoglycaemia and suppressed by hyperglycaemia. The importance of GH in intermediary metabolism and in the maintenance of blood glucose levels is uncertain. Persons with isolated deficiency of growth hormone may have episodes of hypoglycaemia.

Control of Growth Hormone Secretion

Release of GH from the adenohypophysis is controlled by growth hormone releasing factor from the hypothalamus. This in turn is *stimulated* by stress, hypoglycaemia, fasting, and the infusion of a number of amino-acids. Hyperglycaemia and large doses of cortisone *suppress* hormone release and response to stimuli is impaired in some cases of Cushing's syndrome and hypothyroidism. Oestrogens potentiate GH response.

Measurement of Growth Hormone

Plasma GH levels may be measured by radioimmunoassay. The hormone is difficult to estimate in urine.

GH EXCESS: ACROMEGALY AND GIGANTISM

The usual cause of GH excess is a secreting acidophil tumour of the pituitary. The clinical manifestations depend on whether the condition develops before or after fusion of the bony epiphyses.

In childhood, GH excess leads to *gigantism.* In these patients epiphyseal fusion may be delayed by accompanying hypogonadism and extreme heights of over 8 feet may be reached. Mild acromegalic features may develop after bony fusion, but these giants frequently die in early adult life from infections or progressive tumour growth.

In adults *acromegaly* develops. Bone and soft tissues increase in bulk and lead to increasing size of the hands and other parts due to soft tissue thickening. There may be excessive hair growth and skin secretion. Changes in facial appearance are often marked due to increasing size of the jaw and sinuses.

The viscera also enlarge and cardiomegaly is common. The thyroid enlarges but, despite an increase in the basal metabolic rate (p. 169), these patients are usually euthyroid. Menstrual disturbances are common.

A different group of symptoms may occur due to the encroachment of the pituitary tumour on surrounding structures. With progressive destruction of the gland hypopituitarism develops.

Laboratory Findings

Several biochemical abnormalities may occur, but none is constant or specific enough for diagnosis.

1. **Impaired glucose tolerance** may be demonstrated in about 25 per cent of cases. Only about half of these develop symptomatic diabetes. In most cases, however, the insulin response during the GTT is greater than normal due to the antagonism of insulin by GH. It is probable that only those predisposed to diabetes will develop it under these conditions. In others, the pancreas can respond adequately to the antagonism.

2. **Plasma phosphate concentration** is *raised* above normal in most severe cases, but may be normal in the later stages despite activity of the disease.

3. **The BMR** may be raised, probably a direct effect of GH.

Diagnosis

The diagnosis of acromegaly is made essentially on the clinical features and x-ray findings, but may be confirmed by plasma GH estimations when these are available.

1. **Basal levels.**—Resting GH levels after an overnight fast may be raised, but may fall within normal limits. Samples from ambulant patients show an even greater degree of overlap between normals and acromegalics.

2. **Glucose Tolerance Test with GH levels.**—During the course of a GTT on a normal person, plasma GH falls to very low levels within 1–2 hours (p. 130). In acromegaly, where secretion is autonomous, this does not occur; levels remain constant or may even increase.

PROLACTIN

Prolactin has not been separated in the laboratory from growth hormone, but dissociation of action in pathological states indicates that the two are separate hormones. Unlike the other hormones of the adenohypophysis which are stimulated by hypothalamic factors, prolactin secretion is normally kept in abeyance by a hypothalamic prolactin-release inhibiting factor.

Several of the metabolic actions of prolactin are similar to those of GH. In addition, it acts directly on the breast, together with oestrogens and progesterone, to promote development, and it is required, with oxytocin for normal lactation. Hypersecretion of prolactin is suspected in states of abnormal lactation as seen in:

(*a*) Chiari-Frommel syndrome—amenorrhoea and lactorrhoea following pregnancy.

(*b*) Persistent lactation with some pituitary tumours.

(*c*) Persistent lactation seen occasionally in acromegaly.

The rapid breast involution and failure of lactation after post-partum pituitary infarction may be due, at least in part, to prolactin deficiency.

ADRENOCORTICOTROPHIC HORMONE

ACTH acts by stimulating cortisol secretion by the adrenal cortex. The only established extra-adrenal clinical effect of raised ACTH levels in man is an increase in pigmentation (p. 94).

ACTH may be measured by bioassay, but this is technically difficult. Radioimmunoassays are being developed.

The control of ACTH secretion is considered in detail on p. 101. In summary, it is controlled by hypothalamic corticotrophin releasing factor (CRF). Excessive ACTH secretion is seen in:

1. The common form of *Cushing's syndrome* (p. 96) where the negative feed-back control system is set at a higher level than normal, and feed-back control of CRF and ACTH does exist.

2. Very high ACTH levels may be found in patients who have had *total or partial adrenalectomy* for adrenal hyperplasia. Cortisol replacements are inadequate to suppress the abnormally set feed-back centre so there is presumably excessive CRF secretion. Some such patients develop pituitary tumours (usually chromophobe adenomata) after

operation, associated with excessive ACTH secretion and skin pigmentation. Whether or not the tumours develop from constant CRF stimulation is still to be proven, but it seems probable.

3. In *Addison's disease* raised levels of ACTH are found due to lack of feed-back suppression. The excessive pigmentation seen in this condition is probably due to this. Cortisol replacement in this condition is, however, sufficient to suppress the feed-back centre.

4. After metyrapone (p. 103) which blocks cortisol synthesis.

5. In a number of conditions of stress (p. 97).

THYROID STIMULATING HORMONE

TSH stimulates the secretion of thyroid hormones. TSH is regulated largely by a negative feed-back control that acts at the level of the pituitary itself. A hypothalamic thyrotrophin releasing factor (TRF) has been demonstrated and is secreted in response to certain stress situations such as exposure to cold. Until recently the only methods of measurement were bioassays. As in the case of the other pituitary hormones, however, radioimmunoassays are being developed.

Raised levels of TSH are found in primary hypothyroidism because of lack of feed-back control. Levels of up to 50 times normal have been found. In hyperthyroidism, the secretion of TSH is suppressed by the high levels of circulating thyroid hormones.

THE PITUITARY GONADOTROPHINS

The pituitary gonadotrophins are follicle-stimulating hormone (FSH) and luteinizing hormone (LH). LH is also called interstitial cell stimulating hormone (ICSH).

(*a*) FSH stimulates the development of ovarian follicles and, together with LH, stimulates oestrogen secretion by the follicle.

In males FSH stimulates spermatogenesis.

(*b*) LH acts with FSH in stimulating oestrogen secretion, and promotes ovulation in the prepared follicle with formation of a corpus luteum.

In males ICSH stimulates androgen production by the interstitial cells of the testis.

Both FSH and LH are controlled by releasing factors from the hypothalamus. Secretion is suppressed by oestrogen.

Measurement of Gonadotrophins

Pituitary gonadotrophins may be measured in urine collected for 24 to 72 hours depending on the method used. The hormones are labile and each 24-hour collection should be sent to the laboratory immediately for freezing and storage.

(a) *Bioassay.*—The commonly used test measures the increase in uterine size of immature mice and takes at least a week to complete. The effects of extracts of urine are compared with standard preparations. The test measures the combined effect of FSH and LH and the result is referred to as "pituitary gonadotrophin".

This is not a sensitive test and low or undetectable levels may be found in childhood, especially in boys. Even in apparently normal men the test may fail to detect gonadotrophin. High levels are found after the menopause when suppression by oestrogens is withdrawn.

More sensitive and specific bioassays exist for FSH and LH separately, but are not available in all laboratories.

(b) *Immunoassays* of both FSH and LH have been developed and are available in some centres.

OVARIAN HORMONES

Detailed consideration of the physiology and pathology of the ovary is beyond the scope of this book. Only the basis of the physiology will be considered in so far as it is relevant to the normal menstrual cycle.

(a) The developing follicle secretes oestrogens under the influence of FSH and LH. *Oestradiol* and *oestrone* are active oestrogens and are metabolized to the relatively inactive *oestriol*. Measurement of the individual fractions is difficult. The urinary excretion of oestriol in pregnancy is considered on p. 365.

(b) The corpus luteum secretes oestrogens and *progesterone*. Progesterone production can be assessed by measuring urinary *pregnanediol* excretion, but again the estimation is not available in most laboratories.

(c) The ovary probably also secretes small amounts of androgens.

The Normal Menstrual Cycle

Figure 7 outlines the hormone patterns.

1. In the first half of the cycle, FSH stimulates development of the follicle and, together with LH, oestrogen secretion. The rising level of oestrogens suppresses FSH secretion.

2. LH is present at low levels in the first half of the cycle and rises rapidly immediately before ovulation. This "ovulatory surge" induces ovulation and the formation of the corpus luteum.

3. In the second half of the cycle the corpus luteum produces progesterone and a second oestrogen peak. The corpus luteum probably has a limited life span unless pregnancy supervenes, and involution occurs. The falling oestrogen and progesterone levels produce menstruation and allow FSH levels to rise again.

The cyclic nature of this process means that the usual feed-back systems must be modified by the introduction of limiting factors. The

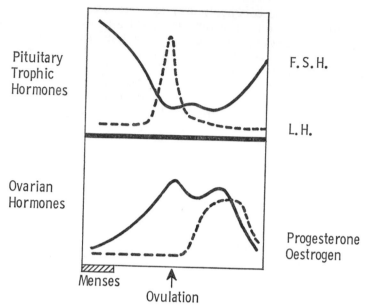

Fig. 7.—Changes in hormones during the menstrua cycle.
(Diagrammatic)

life span of the corpus luteum is one such factor. Another probable factor is that after the ovulatory surge of LH, reaccumulation of the hormone must take place.

Progesterone or allied substances can suppress the ovulatory surge of LH. The addition of small amounts of oestrogen further lowers basal levels of LH and FSH. This is the basis of the action of oral contraceptives.

The pathology of menstruation will not be considered other than to mention that the differentiation of amenorrhoea due to primary ovarian failure from that due to pituitary deficiency may be made by urinary gonadotrophin estimation. Urinary gonadotrophin excretion is high in primary ovarian failure (as it is after the menopause) and low or absent in pituitary insufficiency.

DEFICIENCY OF PITUITARY HORMONES

PANHYPOPITUITARISM

Panhypopituitarism has been considered as a chronic condition that does not threaten life except in stress situations. Total loss of the adenohypophysis is, however, incompatible with survival although total destruction as a result of disease is uncommon. The adenohypophysis has considerable functional reserve and clinical features are usually absent until destruction of about 75 per cent has occurred. Provocative tests may demonstrate lesser degrees of impairment.

Causes of Panhypopituitarism

1. Destruction by tumour, either non-functioning or as an end result of a functioning tumour, such as the acidophil adenoma of acromegaly.

2. Infarction, most commonly post-partum (Sheehan's syndrome), or rarely other vascular catastrophes.

3. Granulomatous lesions due to sarcoidosis, tuberculosis, rarely fungal infections.

4. Histiocytosis X in children.

5. Pituitary surgery or irradiation.

Clinical and Biochemical Features

In general, with progressively severe pituitary damage, gonadotrophin deficiency occurs followed by that of growth hormone, TSH and ACTH. Not all cases follow this pattern.

The following features may be seen in long-standing cases of hypopituitarism. Mild cases may present with any or all in varying degree.

1. Gonadotrophin deficiency leads to amenorrhoea, and atrophy of the genitalia. Libido is lost and impotence may develop. Characteristically axillary and pubic hair decrease progressively. Urinary gonadotrophins are absent.

2. GH deficiency in children causes dwarfism. In adults, and children, it may contribute to hypoglycaemia.

3. TSH deficiency produces secondary hypothyroidism which may be clinically indistinguishable from primary myxoedema (p. 160). Lethargy and cold sensitivity are common. The PBI (or total T_4) and BMR may be very low and radioactive iodine neck uptake is diminished.

4. ACTH deficiency leads to secondary adrenal cortical hypofunction (p. 100). The sodium depletion of Addison's disease is not seen as aldosterone secretion is not under pituitary control. Plasma sodium concentrations may be low, however, because of excessive water retention: cortisol deficiency impairs excretion of a water load. Hypotension may be present. Hypoglycaemia may manifest clinically and there is increased sensitivity to insulin. Urinary 17-oxosteroids and total 17-oxogenic steroid excretion is very low.

General apathy and fatigue are common and there may be mild anaemia. Decreased skin pigmentation leads to striking pallor (a differentiating feature from the hyperpigmentation of Addison's disease). In Sheehan's syndrome failure of lactation is often the first manifestation.

Fatal coma may develop in hypopituitarism especially after stress, such as infections. It resembles adrenocortical insufficiency except that the gross sodium depletion does not occur. Other potential hazards are hypoglycaemia, water intoxication and hypothermia.

Diagnosis of Panhypopituitarism

The most readily available means of diagnosis is the demonstration of secondary impairment of adrenal and/or thyroid action. The tests used are evaluated in the relevant chapters and are enumerated here.

1. *Secondary Adrenal Hypofunction* (p. 103).

(*a*) The feed-back system is evaluated by the metyrapone test.

(*b*) The stress system is evaluated by insulin hypoglycaemia and plasma cortisol levels.

(*c*) The integrity of the adrenal cortex is established by direct stimulation with Synacthen or ACTH.

2. *Secondary Thyroid Hypofunction* (p. 164). The integrity of the thyroid is established by TSH injections in conjunction with thyroid function tests.

In both these instances it must be remembered that *prolonged* hypopituitarism may lead to secondary atrophy of the target gland with consequent diminished response to stimulation.

3. Urinary *gonadotrophin* levels are usually low. The limitation of this test is discussed on p. 119.

4. Tests of *growth hormone* secretion are not usually required for the diagnosis of panhypopituitarism and are considered in the next section.

ISOLATED PITUITARY HORMONE DEFICIENCY

Isolated deficiency of one trophic hormone has been described, most commonly of gonadotrophins, but also of other pituitary hormones. It may represent a stage in the development of panhypopituitarism and detailed investigation may reveal associated deficiencies that are not obvious clinically.

Pituitary Dwarfism

About 10 per cent of cases of dwarfed children have growth hormone deficiency. In some there is deficiency of other hormones, but in others the deficiency is isolated. A familial, autosomal recessive form is described, but in many cases the cause is unknown. Growth failure is usually noted in the first two years of life. Growth hormone is the only means of treatment, and as supplies of this are limited it is essential that GH deficiency be demonstrated.

The finding of unequivocally normal levels of GH in the blood excludes serious deficiency. Basal levels in normal subjects may be very low, so that stimulation tests are required before ascribing low values to deficiency. The generally accepted stimulus is insulin-induced hypoglycaemia. Hypoglycaemia produces a rise in GH levels and a subnormal response indicates pituitary or hypothalamic deficiency. As mentioned earlier (p. 115) large doses of corticosteroids may suppress the response. This test is dangerous and constant supervision of the patient is essential.

Panhypopituitarism in children is diagnosed in the same way as in adults with the proviso that low or undetectable levels of gonadotrophin (as measured by bioassay) are not necessarily abnormal.

SUMMARY

1. The adenohypophysis (anterior pituitary) secretes growth hormone (GH), prolactin, adrenocorticotrophic hormone (ACTH), thyroid stimulating hormone (TSH), and the two pituitary gonadotrophins, follicle stimulating hormone (FSH) and luteinizing hormone (LH). The neurohypophysis secretes antidiuretic hormone (ADH) and oxytocin.

2. The secretion of adenohypophyseal hormones is controlled by releasing factors from the hypothalamus. These in turn are controlled by circulating hormone levels (humoral feed-back) or respond to stimuli from higher cerebral centres (neural) (p. 113). In the case of thyroxine, feed-back control is exerted on the adenohypophysis itself.

3. Pituitary hormones may be measured in blood or urine by bioassay or radioimmunoassay (p. 114).

4. GH controls growth and has a number of effects on intermediary metabolism (p. 115). Excessive growth hormone secretion causes gigantism or acromegaly (p. 116). Laboratory evidence of autonomous GH secretion is obtained by failure of suppression of plasma levels of GH during a glucose tolerance test (p. 117).

5. Excessive secretion of prolactin is incriminated in a number of conditions of abnormal lactation (p. 117).

6. Excessive ACTH secretion occurs in Cushing's syndrome, after adrenalectomy, in Addison's disease, during stress and after administration of metyrapone.

7. Raised TSH levels are found in primary hypothyroidism.

8. There is a complex interrelationship between pituitary gonadotrophins and ovarian hormones. The changing levels in the menstrual cycle are described (p. 119).

9. Destruction of the adenohypophysis leads to panhypopituitarism (p. 120). The clinical features are those of gonadotrophin and sex hormone deficiency and secondary hypofunction of adrenal cortex and thyroid. Diagnosis is based on the demonstration that such deficiencies are secondary to pituitary failure.

10. GH deficiency in childhood leads to dwarfism. Diagnosis of such deficiency is made by measurement of GH response to hypoglycaemia (p. 122).

Chapter VI

DISORDERS OF CARBOHYDRATE METABOLISM

GENERAL

In most parts of the world carbohydrate is the main source of calorie intake. Under normal circumstances starch is the main dietary carbohydrate, disaccharides contribute significantly and monosaccharides are a minor component of the diet.

CHEMISTRY

Monosaccharides

The basic units of carbohydrate are monosaccharides. These compounds are classified by the number of carbon atoms in the molecule. Physiologically the most important groups are the *hexoses* (six carbon atoms) and *pentoses* (five carbon atoms).

The main hexoses of physiological importance are *glucose, fructose* and *galactose*. These are all reducing sugars and therefore reduce Benedict's solution (p. 149). The important pentoses include *ribose* (in RNA) and *deoxyribose* (in DNA).

Disaccharides

The disaccharides are molecules composed (as the name suggests) of two monosaccharides. The commonly encountered disaccharides are *sucrose* (fructose + glucose), *lactose* (galactose + glucose) and *maltose* (glucose + glucose). Lactose and maltose are reducing sugars, sucrose is not.

Polysaccharides

Polysaccharides are long chain carbohydrates. *Starch* is found in plants and is a mixture of amylose (straight chains) and amylopectin (branched chains). *Glycogen* is found in animal tissue and has a highly branched structure. Both these polysaccharides are composed of glucose subunits.

DIGESTION AND ABSORPTION OF CARBOHYDRATES

This topic is considered more fully on p. 206 and will only be outlined here.

Amylase is present in saliva and pancreatic juice. Digestion in the mouth and stomach is limited by time and gastric acidity. In the small bowel the alkaline pH favours the action of amylase and poly-saccharides are split to smaller compounds such as maltose.

Further digestion by the disaccharidases of the intestinal cell wall pro-duces monosaccharides which are actively transported into the mucosal cell and thence to the blood stream.

OUTLINE OF GLUCOSE METABOLISM

A knowledge of the main pathways of glucose metabolism is essential to the understanding of disorders of carbohydrate metabolism.

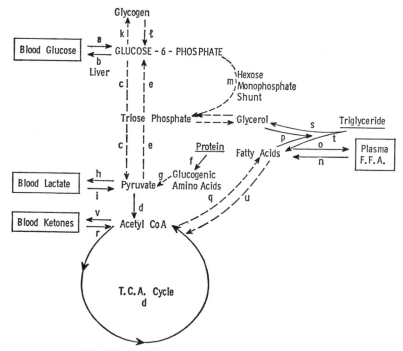

FIG. 8.—Pathways of carbohydrate metabolism.
See text for explanation of small letters.

The end products of breakdown of dietary carbohydrates are glucose (from polysaccharides, sucrose and lactose), fructose (from sucrose) and galactose (from lactose). Fructose and galactose are converted to glucose in the liver and will not be considered separately here.

Glucose enters cells and is converted to glucose-6-phosphate (G-6-P) (a in Fig. 8). This step is under the control of insulin. *G-6-P* is the central compound of glucose metabolism and can follow a number of pathways (refer to letters in Fig. 8).

Glucose Formation

G-6-P can be reconverted to glucose by the enzyme glucose-6-phosphatase found in liver and kidney (*b*).

Glycolysis and the Tricarboxylic Acid (TCA) Cycle (*c* and *d*)

Some G-6-P is used to provide energy. It is broken down through the glycolytic (Embden-Meyerhof) pathway (*c*) to pyruvate, which in the presence of oxygen is completely metabolized, via acetyl CoA, in the TCA (Krebs) cycle (*d*), the carbon forming carbon dioxide and the hydrogen water. Glycolysis can be reversed (not necessarily through the same reactions) so that glucose can be formed from substances on the pathway (gluconeogenesis (*e*)). The carbon chains resulting from deamination of some amino-acids can enter the pathway (*f* and *g*) and are therefore glucogenic. Gluconeogenesis can only occur in the liver. If oxygen is not available only glycolysis can proceed and the pathway stops at pyruvate. The unoxidized hydrogen ions convert this to lactate, with resultant acidosis (*h*). (Also see p. 69.) This step is reversible when oxygen becomes available (*i*).

Glycogenesis (*k*) and Glycogenolysis (*l*)

Some G-6-P is synthesized into glycogen, the storage form of glucose (*k*). This reaction can take place in most tissues of the body, but mainly occurs in liver and muscle. About 25 per cent of the daily carbohydrate intake is stored as liver glycogen. *Glycogenesis cannot occur in the brain*, which therefore cannot store glucose and is dependent on a regular supply from the blood.

Glycogen may be broken down again to G-6-P by *glycogenolysis* (*l*). The G-6-P formed by this process may enter the glycolytic pathway or may be converted to glucose.

Hexose-monophosphate Shunt (Pentose Shunt) (*m*)

This route of glucose metabolism by-passes part of the glycolytic pathway and has two important functions, the *generation of pentoses for nucleic acid synthesis* and the *generation of reduced nicotinamide adenine dinucleotide phosphate (NADPH)*. NADPH is required, among

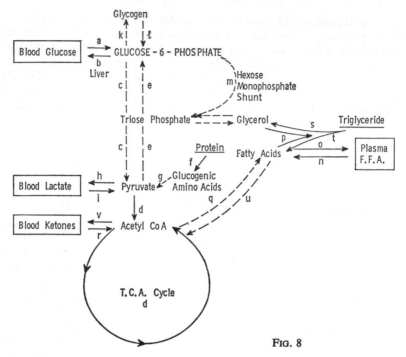

FIG. 8

other things, for anabolic processes, such as the *synthesis of fatty acids and steroids* and has a role in maintaining the *integrity of the erythrocyte*. A key enzyme in the hexose monophosphate pathway is *glucose-6-phosphate dehydrogenase* (*G-6-PD*), deficiency of which may be associated with *haemolytic anaemia*.

It is important to stress at this stage that brain cells can metabolize only glucose as an energy source: because they are unable to store it as glycogen they are dependent on the blood sugar level. Hypoglycaemia is dangerous.

<h2 style="text-align:center">MAINTENANCE OF BLOOD GLUCOSE CONCENTRATIONS</h2>

Hormonal Control

The importance of an adequately high blood glucose concentration for cerebral function and the relative unimportance of hyperglycaemia is reflected in the fact that only insulin reduces blood glucose, while several hormones can raise it.

The mechanism of action of these hormones and their interrelationships is complex. The following account is a simplification (refer to Fig. 8).

A fall in blood glucose levels is caused by:

Insulin which is secreted by the β cells of the pancreatic islets of Langerhans.

Action.—1. It increases entry of glucose into cells (*a*), glycolysis (*c*) and storage of glucose (glycogenesis) (*k*) and *reduces blood glucose levels.*

2. It inhibits fat breakdown (*s* and *t*) and speeds up its formation (*p*). It therefore causes *a fall in free fatty acid (FFA) levels* (*n*) and is *antiketogenic* (*q* and *r*) (p. 132).

3. It has an anabolic action on protein metabolism.

Control.—1. Probably the most important factor controlling insulin secretion is the *level of blood glucose.* As this rises insulin secretion increases.

2. During intestinal absorption of glucose a *glucagon-like hormone* is released from intestinal cells and may stimulate insulin secretion. This may be one of the reasons why the results of oral and intravenous glucose tolerance tests are not strictly comparable, even when allowance is made for the different rates of entry into the blood stream (p. 140).

3. Some amino-acids, notably *leucine and arginine*, stimulate insulin secretion. This is of importance in the relatively rare condition of leucine sensitivity (p. 145).

A rise in blood glucose levels is caused by:

Growth hormone. *Action.*—1. It opposes glycolysis (*c*) and glucose uptake by muscle cells (*a*), and causes a *rise in blood glucose.*

2. It stimulates triglyceride breakdown (*s* and *t*) and inhibits its formation (*p*). It therefore causes a *rise in plasma FFA* levels (*o*) and is *ketogenic* (*u* and *v*) (p. 132).

These two actions are opposite to those of insulin.

3. Like insulin it has an anabolic effect on protein metabolism.

Control.—GH secretion is *stimulated by hypoglycaemia.*

GH and insulin therefore tend to vary inversely.

Glucocorticoids (e.g. cortisol). *Action.*—1. Glucose uptake by muscle cells is impeded (*a*).

2. Protein breakdown is increased (*f* and *g*): formation of glucose from some of the released amino-acids (gluconeogenesis) is stimulated.

Control.—Hypoglycaemia stimulates cortisol secretion from the adrenal cortex by the *stress* pathway (p. 114).

Adrenaline (epinephrine).—Adrenaline stimulates release of glucose by breakdown of glycogen (glycogenolysis) (*l*). Its secretion by the adrenal medulla is stimulated by *stress.*

Glucagon.—Glucagon is secreted by the α cells of the pancreas, and a glucagon-like substance is secreted from the bowel wall during intestinal absorption. Glucagon raises blood glucose levels by actions opposite to those of insulin, but its importance in glucose homeostasis is not clear. Paradoxically glucagon stimulates insulin secretion by the pancreas, this action tending to lower blood glucose levels.

The fact that the diabetes of complete pancreatic destruction is often controlled by a lower dose of insulin than is primary diabetes may be due partly to the loss of the insulin-opposing action of glucagon in the former condition.

Physiological Interaction of Hormones Affecting Glucose Metabolism

A decrease of blood glucose concentration may adversely affect brain metabolism. Under normal circumstances the hormones mentioned above act together and blood glucose rarely falls below critical levels.

Ingestion of glucose.—After a meal containing carbohydrate, or after an oral dose of glucose such as is given in a glucose tolerance test, the sequence of events is as follows:

1–2 hours—As glucose is absorbed from the gastro-intestinal tract blood glucose levels rise. Feed-back control results in

(*a*) A 10- to 15-fold *rise in insulin levels*;
(*b*) Almost complete *disappearance of GH* from the plasma.

Insulin is acting almost unopposed. This ensures storage of glycogen while glucose is available: without insulin glucose would be lost in the urine. As a result of this *blood glucose levels reach a peak at about an hour* and then fall as rate of utilization exceeds that of absorption. The level falls *below about 120 mg./100 ml. at two hours after ingestion.*

Under the following circumstances this fall of blood glucose will fail to occur to the normal extent:

Insulin deficiency (diabetes mellitus)
Growth hormone excess (acromegaly)
Excess of other hormones antagonizing insulin
    Corticosteroids (Cushing's syndrome and stress)
    Adrenaline (phaeochromocytoma and stress).

The level of blood glucose will fail to rise to the normal extent in the opposite set of circumstances.

This is the sequence of events during a glucose tolerance test.

It should be noted in passing that as glucose utilization is increased phosphate and potassium enter cells and blood levels fall. FFA levels also fall.

2–4 hours—GH gradually *rises* to almost basal levels and those of *insulin fall*, although remaining at several times the initial concentration. These changes minimize "overswing" of blood glucose levels which would occur if insulin alone were acting and ensures a continuing supply to brain cells.

In any condition in which there is a relative excess of insulin at this time *reactive hypoglycaemia* (p. 144) may occur.

Fasting.—If fasting continues *insulin almost disappears* from the blood stream and *GH rises to very high levels.* The latter stimulates oxidation of fat and release of FFA, while metabolism of glucose and glycogen falls to a minimum: moreover, both FFA and ketone bodies can be utilized as an energy source by most tissues other than brain, and under fasting conditions supply up to half the energy requirement

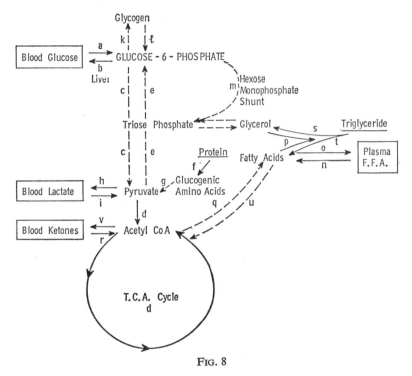

Fig. 8

of the body. Thus blood glucose is spared at a time when the supply is poor, and glycogen is reserved for stress situations.

FFA ultimately form acetyl CoA (*u*, Fig. 8). Under fasting conditions this may be produced more quickly than it can be utilized in the TCA cycle, and under these circumstances ketosis occurs (*v*, Fig. 8).

Deficiency of insulin results in increased protein breakdown. Some of the released amino-acids can enter the glycolytic pathway (*f* and *g*, Fig. 8) and can be used to supply energy or form glucose (gluconeogenesis (*e*)): these also help to maintain blood glucose levels and glycogen stores at the expense of protein.

Thus in fasting *blood glucose levels remain normal until late* but *ketosis* occurs. Utilization of fat causes loss of weight, and breakdown of protein causes muscle wasting.

Stress.—Under conditions of stress adrenaline is released from the adrenal medulla and cortisol secretion from the adrenal cortex is stimulated through the stress pathway (p. 114). These hormones both tend to increase blood glucose levels at a time when it is needed by the brain. *Hyperglycaemia* and *glycosuria* may occur under severe stress (for instance, in "shock"). This may also happen

(*a*) with excess of adrenaline due to phaeochromocytoma;
(*b*) with excess of cortisol due to Cushing's syndrome.

KETOSIS

The exact mechanism of ketosis is obscure. It occurs whenever glucose cannot be metabolized and when energy is therefore supplied largely from fat breakdown. This occurs in:

Fasting;

When there is inability to metabolize glucose due to insulin deficiency.

In the latter case blood glucose levels are high because glucose is not being used. In the former blood glucose levels are normal or, in advanced cases, low.

As we have seen, fatty acids are broken down to acetyl CoA (*u*, Fig. 8). Excess acetyl CoA condenses, two moles forming one of *aceto-acetate*. This is reduced to *β-hydroxybutyrate* and decarboxylated to *acetone*. These three substances are *ketone bodies* and are normally present in the blood in very small amounts (*v*, Fig. 8). During ketosis they accumulate in the circulation (*ketonaemia*) and are excreted in the urine (*ketonuria*). Ketone bodies are acidic and cause metabolic acidosis (*ketoacidosis*) (p. 69).

GLYCOSURIA

Unless there is renal glycosuria (p. 150), the presence of glucose in the urine indicates hyperglycaemia. Glycosuria usually occurs only when the blood glucose level exceeds about 180 mg/100 ml, and this figure is referred to as the "renal threshold" for glucose. However, the tubules can actually absorb a maximum amount of glucose per unit time and this amount corresponds to blood levels of 180 mg/100 ml only when the glomerular filtration rate (volume per minute) is normal. With a reduced GFR (due to glomerular damage or circulatory insufficiency) and reduced volume of fluid delivered to the tubules, far higher *concentrations* of glucose (but the same amount/minute) may be completely reabsorbed and glycosuria may not occur even with severe hyperglycaemia. The clinical significance of this is discussed on p. 141.

DISTURBANCES OF CARBOHYDRATE METABOLISM

The blood sugar concentration was one of the first biochemical estimations to be applied clinically and stress has been laid on abnormalities of blood glucose levels in disturbances of carbohydrate metabolism. Low blood glucose levels are indeed dangerous in themselves, since brain cells cannot form glucose from other substances and cannot metabolize other foodstuffs. However, moderate hyperglycaemia *per se* is almost harmless and it is the metabolic consequences of the inability of cells to utilize glucose which are dangerous. Despite this we will discuss the pathological disturbances of carbohydrate metabolism under the headings of hyper- and hypoglycaemia.

MEASUREMENT OF BLOOD GLUCOSE

Interpretation of blood glucose levels requires a knowledge of the method of estimation used. There are two main groups of methods.

(*a*) Glucose oxidase methods which depend on enzymatic breakdown of glucose by glucose oxidase. The result is considered to represent "true glucose".

(*b*) Methods which depend on the reducing property of glucose which (because of the presence of non-glucose reducing substances) may overestimate glucose by 5–20 mg/100 ml or more. The percentage error is greatest at low levels of glucose.

Either method can be adapted for use on the Autoanalyser (Technicon). The most commonly used is a reduction method, but, when automated, this method gives values closely approaching those using glucose oxidase.

Values quoted in this chapter are those of "true glucose".

HYPERGLYCAEMIA AND DIABETES MELLITUS

The Nature and Causes of Diabetes Mellitus

Diabetes mellitus is a syndrome due to absolute or relative insulin deficiency. Relative deficiency occurs if there is an excess of hormones which tend to raise the blood sugar (that is, oppose the action of insulin on glucose).

A simple working classification of the causes of the syndrome of diabetes mellitus is given below. This and the clinical classification od p. 135 are roughly based on the recommendations of the Medical ann Scientific Section of the British Diabetic Association.

Absolute insulin deficiency.—1. Primary diabetes (essential or idiopathic diabetes).

2. Secondary diabetes due to pancreatic destruction with chronic pancreatitis, pancreatic carcinoma and haemochromatosis, or after total pancreatectomy.

Relative insulin deficiency.—1. *Excess of glucocorticoids.* Cushing's syndrome or steroid administration.

2. *Excess of growth hormone.* Acromegaly.

3. *Excess of adrenaline.* Phaeochromocytoma (rare).

4. Severe thyrotoxicosis (rare).

It is possible that the latter group consists of latent essential diabetics (see p. 135).

Primary Diabetes

A commonly used clinical classification of primary diabetes is based on the severity and behaviour of the disease. In young persons diabetes tends to be severe and patients are liable to develop ketosis and coma. Management may be difficult. This group is sometimes referred to as *juvenile-onset diabetes.* In older persons (*maturity-onset diabetes*) the disease may have a milder course and is frequently associated with obesity. Severe ketosis is uncommon and weight reduction may ameliorate the process.

Primary or essential diabetes has a familial incidence, but the exact mode of inheritance, like that of hyperuricaemia (p. 303) is uncertain. Insulin levels may be above normal in early juvenile and in maturity-onset diabetes. In severe juvenile and long-standing maturity diabetes insulin levels may be low or undetectable. This finding has led to suspicion that initially the islet cells are responding maximally (but apparently ineffectively) to some stimulus and that long continued stimulation leads to eventual exhaustion. A number of theories has been proposed.

1. It is suggested that an excess of FFA from fat stores impairs the stimulatory effect of insulin on uptake of glucose by muscle and results in hyperglycaemia. This may stimulate further insulin secretion, leading to raised insulin levels but eventual pancreatic exhaustion. The primary abnormality in this case would be in fat, not carbohydrate metabolism, and it is a possible aetiological factor in obese maturity-onset diabetics.

2. Circulating insulin may be inactivated by binding or other means but still be detectable by immunological methods. This could result in hyperglycaemia, stimulation and exhaustion as above.

3. The primary abnormality may be a circulating antagonist to insulin, hormonal or non-hormonal, with similar results.

Evidence has been presented for and against these theories.

Chronic diabetes mellitus is associated with a number of complications, many with a vascular basis. Vascular, retinal and renal disease as well as neuromuscular disorders may occur. The relationship of these changes to the disorder of carbohydrate metabolism is uncertain, but some of them may be related to the hypercholesterolaemia that is frequently found.

Diabetic women tend to give birth to large babies.

Pathophysiology and Clinical Features of Diabetes Mellitus

Several stages of diabetes have been defined. Those given below are based on the classification recommended by the Medical and Scientific Section of the British Diabetic Association.

1. **Potential diabetic.**—A person who has a normal glucose tolerance test, but a strong family history of the disease, or a history of bearing a child of 4·5 kg (10 lb.) or over.

2. **Latent diabetic.**—A person who has a normal glucose tolerance test but who has had a diabetic glucose tolerance test at some time of stress such as pregnancy, after cortisone administration, when obese, or during severe infection.

3. **Asymptomatic diabetic.**—A person with a diabetic type of glucose tolerance test but without symptoms of diabetes.

4. **Symptomatic diabetic.**—*Mild diabetes.* The diagnosis of maturity-onset diabetes is not infrequently made after an unexpected finding of glycosuria or a raised blood glucose found in the investigation of ill-health. Symptoms are often due to the vascular changes. The carbohydrate abnormalities may be very mild and revealed only by carbohydrate loading. *Fasting blood glucose levels are frequently normal.*

Severe diabetes. In severe, uncontrolled diabetes, fasting blood glucose levels are above normal. Osmotic diuresis with loss of glucose, fluids and electrolytes may be severe and lead to dehydration and thirst. Much of the glucose is derived from muscle by increased gluconeogenesis and there is muscle wasting and weight loss, described by Areatus as "melting into urine". Hyperlipidaemia occurs. Levels of triglyceride, cholesterol and phospholipid are raised and the lipoprotein electrophoretic pattern shows increased pre-β lipoprotein (see p. 256).

Diagnosis of Diabetes Mellitus

The diagnosis of diabetes mellitus depends on the demonstration of carbohydrate intolerance either as frank hyperglycaemia or as an impaired response to a load.

1. **Glycosuria.**—Testing of the urine is the oldest method of diagnosing diabetes and certainly the simplest. It can, however, lead to false conclusions. The renal threshold for glucose is about 180 mg/100 ml and glycosuria is an indirect indicator of hyperglycaemia. While a positive result requires further investigation a negative test by no means excludes diabetes. There are two main reasons for *false negative* results:

(*a*) The *timing of the urine specimen* tested is important. Early morning specimens of urine are used for many tests because the urine is usually most concentrated at that time of day. However, as it is collected after a period of fasting the test will be positive for sugar only if the blood glucose level has exceeded 180 mg/100 ml during this period—that is, in severe diabetes. A specimen of urine passed about one hour after a meal is the most valuable one for a screening test.

(*b*) In the presence of renal disease with a *reduced glomerular filtration rate* (p. 132), tubular reabsorption may remove glucose at concentrations well above the usual "renal threshold" of 180 mg/100 ml. This is seen particularly in elderly people and in cases of undiagnosed diabetes with renal damage.

False positive tests may be found in *renal glycosuria* (p. 149).

2. **Random blood glucose level.**—This test is only of value if glucose levels are very high, when they are almost certainly due to diabetes. A normal result does not exclude the diagnosis. In either case a fasting blood glucose estimation should also be performed.

3. **Fasting blood glucose level.**—The blood glucose level after an overnight fast is commonly used to diagnose diabetes. While a glucose level of greater than 120 mg/100 ml (glucose oxidase method) is strongly suggestive, and one over 130 mg/100 ml almost diagnostic, many diabetics have fasting glucose levels in the normal range. A high fasting blood sugar indicates inadequate insulin output for even basal requirements and no further test is required. A normal fasting level may be present in mild diabetes (Fig. 9) and under these circumstances further tests should be performed.

4. **Two-hour post-glucose blood glucose level.**—This is probably the simplest screening test for diabetes mellitus and is in fact a "modified" glucose tolerance test. By two hours after a meal the blood sugar has normally returned to below 120 mg/100 ml. Although a meal is often recommended as the load a more standardized stimulus is that given by 50 g of glucose orally, as in the GTT. A normal result almost certainly excludes clinical diabetes.

5. **Glucose Tolerance Test (GTT).**—There are only two indications for performing a GTT in the diagnosis of diabetes:

(*a*) Detection of mild diabetes when there are normal fasting and random glucose levels. In this respect it is probably no more successful than a single estimation two hours after a glucose load.

(*b*) To ascertain the renal threshold for glucose. Knowledge of this is of value if the patient is to control insulin dosage by testing for urinary sugar.

There is little point in performing a GTT on a subject with markedly raised fasting or random glucose values and similarly, in a patient with fasting hyperglycaemia and glycosuria, no further information on the renal threshold will reward the investigator or the patient for the discomfort of a GTT.

It is convenient to consider the glucose tolerance test in more detail here.

Factors influencing the result of the GTT.—1. *Dose of glucose.* The use of a dose of 50 g is adequate. The use of 100 g does not improve diagnostic accuracy and the larger volume may cause nausea and variable gastric emptying (compare xylose absorption test, p. 224).

2. *Capillary or venous blood.* Although there is very little difference in glucose levels between these two types of sample during fasting, at the high levels found during the GTT capillary tends to give higher results than venous blood and to return to fasting levels more slowly. These differences should be allowed for in the interpretation of the test.

3. *Age.* In older persons peak levels tend to be higher than "normal" but the 2-hour value is usually below 120 mg/100 ml.

4. *Previous diet.* No special restrictions are necessary if the patient has been on a normal diet for 3–4 days. If, however, the test is performed after a period of carbohydrate restriction, such as found in reducing diets, abnormal glucose tolerance may be shown. The probable reason for this is that metabolism is set in the "fasted" state favouring gluconeogenesis.

Types of glucose tolerance curve.—The GTT is performed to assess the response to glucose. This depends not only on insulin and other hormone secretion, but also the rate of absorption of glucose and on the integrity of other compensatory mechanisms such as hepatic glycogenesis.

(*a*) *The "normal" GTT* (Fig. 9*a*).—The criteria outlined are those recommended by the Medical and Scientific Section of the British Diabetic Association. The values quoted are those obtained with a glucose oxidase method or on the Autoanalyser (Technicon), using capillary blood samples.

1. The concentration at 2 hours is below 120 mg/100 ml (p. 130). It is *not* necessary that it should return to the fasting level at this stage.

2. At no stage of the test does the level exceed 180 mg/100 ml (capillary) or 160 mg/100 ml (venous).

3. The urine is glucose free at all times.

In many cases, if the test is prolonged for 3–4 hours, the level of glucose will be found to fall below the fasting level and return to normal in half to one hour later. This is considered further on p. 144.

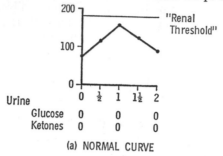

(a) NORMAL CURVE

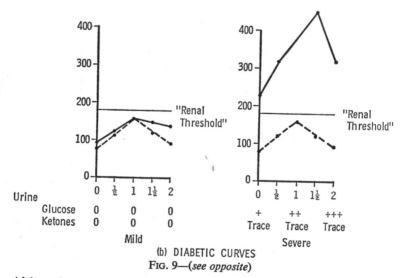

(b) DIABETIC CURVES

FIG. 9—(*see opposite*)

Although usually only the changes in glucose levels are followed, these are accompanied by alterations in insulin and growth hormone levels as well as in plasma potassium and phosphorus concentrations. These latter changes probably reflect the uptake of glucose by cells under the influence of insulin.

(*b*) *Diabetic glucose tolerance curve* (Fig. 9b).—The most significant finding in the diagnosis of diabetes is the failure of glucose levels to fall below 120 mg/100 ml (capillary) or 110 mg/100 ml (venous) by two hours. The peak level is frequently above normal and fasting levels may or may not be raised (see p. 137). If the peak concentration exceeds the renal threshold for glucose glycosuria will be present. Note that, because of the delay in urine reaching the bladder, maximum glycosuria is found in the next specimen *after* the highest blood glucose concentration is reached.

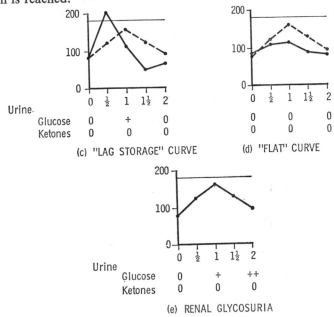

Dotted Lines = Normal. Curve
Fig. 9.— Glucose tolerance curves.

(c) *Lag storage curve* (Fig. 9c).—The peak blood glucose level may be higher than normal but the 2-hour value is within normal limits or often low. This implies a delay in early compensatory mechanisms ("lag") without necessarily impairment of insulin response. The hypoglycaemia may be due to outpouring of insulin in response to the initial high glucose levels. Such a curve may be seen in:

(i)   Apparently normal individuals (reactive hypoglycaemia).

(ii) After gastrectomy or gastro-jejunostomy where rapid entry of glucose into the intestine leads to rapid absorption and sudden outpouring of insulin with "overswing".

(iii) In very severe liver disease, probably due to a decreased glycogenesis. This is rarely of diagnostic value.

(iv) Rarely in thyrotoxicosis, probably due to rapid absorption of glucose.

If the glucose concentration at the peak of the curve is above the renal threshold level, glycosuria will occur in the next urine specimen.

(*d*) *Flat glucose tolerance curve* (Fig. 9*d*).—Blood glucose levels fail to rise normally following a glucose load. This type of curve is usually considered to indicate malabsorption. It may, however, be found in completely healthy individuals and interpretation is difficult. It can also occur due to lack of glucocorticoid in Addison's disease or due to lack of GH in hypopituitarism. It should never be used as the sole evidence for malabsorption.

(*e*) *Renal glycosuria* (Fig. 9*e*).—The blood glucose levels follow the normal pattern, but glucose is found in some or all of the urine specimens.

Other Types of Glucose Tolerance Test

Cortisone-glucose tolerance test.—In some patients with a normal glucose tolerance curve the administration of 100 mg of cortisone in the eight hours preceding the test will produce a "diabetic" curve. These patients are considered to have latent diabetes mellitus. This category of latent diabetics also includes persons who develop abnormal glucose tolerance during acute infections, pregnancy and after trauma, that is, during periods of stress when endogenous steroid levels are high.

Intravenous glucose tolerance tests.—Several tests have been devised to overcome variable absorption of glucose from the bowel. Such tests suffer from two major disadvantages:

(*a*) The normal response is even less well-defined than that of the oral test and interpretation is correspondingly more difficult.

(*b*) Intravenous administration by-passes the intestinal phase of homeostasis (p. 129).

Diabetic Ketosis

The severe diabetic is at continual risk of developing ketosis and passing into diabetic coma. This state of events may be precipitated by infection or gastro-intestinal upsets with vomiting. Insulin may mistakenly be withheld by the patient, who reasons "no food, therefore no insulin". The changes which occur are due to two main factors—*glycosuria and ketosis.*

In diabetic ketosis the blood glucose levels, derived mostly from gluconeogenesis, are usually in the range of 400–600 mg/100 ml. The resultant severe glycosuria, as mentioned above, produces an osmotic diuresis with fluid loss and depletion of body electrolytes. Vomiting is frequently present in ketosis and adds to the fluid and electrolyte depletion. The fluid loss involves both intra- and extracellular fluid with reduction of circulating blood volume, reduced renal blood flow and glomerular filtration rate, and severe cellular dehydration. As tubular reabsorption of glucose (Tm$_G$, p. 2) depends on volume of glomerular filtrate as well as concentration of glucose therein, reduced GFR allows greater proportional reabsorption of glucose. In some cases this may be complete and glucose is no longer present in the urine despite hyperglycaemia. In such cases the blood urea is usually raised and there is evidence of haemoconcentration such as elevated haematocrit and total protein levels. Both these findings are the result of *dehydration.*

Ketosis develops as a result of reduced glucose metabolism. Lipolysis exceeds resynthesis of depot fat, and released FFA form ketone bodies. Ketone bodies are acidic and are buffered by plasma bicarbonate. They are also excreted in the urine and urinary pH drops. The influx of ketone bodies usually exceeds the ability of the kidney to secrete hydrogen ions and plasma bicarbonate levels fall. The developing metabolic acidosis stimulates the respiratory centre and breathing becomes deeper with a lowering of Pco_2. This compensatory respiratory alkalosis may maintain blood pH within the normal range for a while, but at the cost of further lowering of the plasma bicarbonate and very low levels are found. The deep sighing respiration (*Kussmaul respiration*) with the odour of acetone on the breath is a classical feature of diabetic ketosis.

A further important biochemical consideration is the plasma potassium level. Although urinary losses are high and there is a total body deficiency of potassium, plasma levels are usually raised before treatment is started. This is most probably associated with deficient entry of glucose into cells (p. 29). The importance lies in the rapid fall which may occur as potassium enters the cells during therapy and reveals the deficiency.

In the treatment of diabetic ketosis it is important to realize that there is a tremendous body deficiency of water (4–7 litres or more) and of electrolytes.

The findings in diabetic ketosis are therefore:

Clinical —overbreathing (acidosis)
        dehydration (osmotic diuresis)

In blood —hyperglycaemia
        ketonaemia
        low bicarbonate with acidosis
        hyperkalaemia (occasionally normokalaemia)
        haemoconcentration (p. 27) and mild uraemia.

In urine —glycosuria ⎫ while the urinary flow is adequate
        ketonuria ⎬
        low pH (unless there is renal failure).

Hyperosmolar Coma in Diabetics

In addition to diabetic ketosis and hypoglycaemia due to insulin overdosage, there is some evidence that gross hyperglycaemia can by itself be a cause of coma. Several cases have been described with blood glucose levels of over 1000 mg/100 ml and minimal acidosis. All show severe dehydration and it is postulated that the hyperosmolarity of the ECF causes dehydration of cerebral cells and coma. (Compare hypernatraemia, p. 33.)

Secondary Diabetes

Secondary diabetes, whether pancreatic or due to high circulating levels of insulin-opposing hormones, is rarely severe enough to cause diabetic ketosis.

In *damage to the pancreas* by pancreatitis, tumour or haemochromatosis, or after surgical removal, there is non-specific destruction of pancreatic cells. Steatorrhoea is common due to loss of exocrine secretion (p. 211). Insulin requirements, even after total pancreatectomy, are often less than those of a severe primary diabetic, possibly partly due to loss of glucagon-secreting α cells as well as insulin-secreting β cells.

The diagnosis of diabetes due to *relative insulin deficiency* is usually made secondarily to that of the primary disease. In phaeochromocytoma (p. 375) hyperglycaemia is often intermittent.

Principles of Treatment of Diabetes

Young severe diabetics usually require *insulin* because the pancreatic islet cells contain none.

In *maturity-onset diabetes* the subject is often obese and in many cases *weight reduction alone* controls the diabetes. If this is not adequate the islet cells can often be stimulated to produce insulin by the *sulphonyl urea* drugs such as tolbutamide, which are ineffective in juvenile-onset diabetes. Only rarely do maturity-onset diabetics require insulin.

Diabetic ketosis is a medical emergency. The patient may die of acidosis and dehydration. Large doses of insulin are required, some intravenously: once glucose metabolism starts acidosis will soon be corrected. Fluid replacement must be vigorous and preferably should consist of sodium bicarbonate or lactate to help restore buffering capacity. Initially plasma potassium levels are high, but because of the danger of hypokalaemia as potassium moves into cells during treatment, they should be monitored and potassium given (preferably orally) as soon as they start to fall.

HYPOGLYCAEMIA

Hypoglycaemia is defined as a true blood glucose level of below 40 mg/100 ml. Symptoms may develop at levels greater than this when there has been a rapid fall from a previously elevated, or even normal, value; by contrast, some people may show no symptoms at levels below 40 or even 30 mg/100 ml, especially if these have fallen gradually. As discussed earlier, cerebral metabolism is dependent on an adequate supply of glucose from the blood and the symptoms of hypoglycaemia resemble those of cerebral anoxia. Faintness, dizziness or lethargy may progress rapidly into coma and, if untreated, death or permanent cerebral damage may result. If the fall of blood glucose is rapid there may be a phase of sweating, tachycardia and agitation due to adrenaline secretion, but this phase may be absent with a gradual fall. Existing cerebral or cerebrovascular disease may aggravate the condition. Rapid restoration of blood glucose concentration is essential.

Causes of Hypoglycaemia

There is no completely satisfactory classification of the causes of hypoglycaemia as overlap between different groups occurs. An approach that the authors have found useful is to consider three main groups:

(*a*) Insulin or drug induced hypoglycaemia;
(*b*) Fasting hypoglycaemia;
(*c*) Reactive hypoglycaemia.

Insulin or drug induced hypoglycaemia.—This is probably the commonest cause. Hypoglycaemia in a diabetic may follow accidental overdosage, be due to changing *insulin* requirements, or to failure to take food after insulin has been given. Self-administration for suicidal purposes is not unknown and homicidal use is a remote possibility. *Sulphonylureas* may also induce hypoglycaemia, especially in the elderly. Other drugs such as antihistamines have been suspected in some cases and a drug history is an important part of investigation.

Fasting hypoglycaemia.—As discussed on p. 128, the maintenance of normal blood glucose in the fasting subject depends on several factors.

(*a*) Levels are lowered by insulin which stimulates glucose metabolism.

(*b*) Levels are maintained or raised by:

(i) Glycogenolysis, which depends on *adequate stores of hepatic glycogen. Adrenaline* promotes this.

(ii) Gluconeogenesis, which occurs mainly by conversion of amino-acids to glucose in the liver. This process is again dependent on *hepatic integrity* and is promoted by *glucocorticoids.*

(iii) Uptake of glucose by muscle is hindered by *glucocorticoids* and *growth hormone.*

Alterations in this delicate balance can cause hypoglycaemia.

1. *Hyperinsulinism*—(a) islet cell tumour (insulinoma).
                     (b) islet cell hyperplasia.

These conditions are discussed on p. 146.

2. *Hepatic disease.* Despite the central role of the liver in intermediary metabolism, hypoglycaemia is seen only when liver damage is very extensive. This rarely presents diagnostic problems.

3. *Glycogen storage disease.* This condition is seen primarily in childhood and is considered on p. 148.

4. *Endocrine causes.* Hypoglycaemia may occur in adrenal or pituitary insufficiency. Rarely it is the sole manifestation and these conditions are considered in Chapter IV.

5. *Non-pancreatic tumours.* Although many types of malignant tumours, carcinoma as well as sarcoma, have been incriminated in the production of hypoglycaemia, it occurs most commonly in association with mesodermal tumours, resembling fibrosarcomata, that occur mainly retroperitoneally. They are slow-growing and may become very large. Hypoglycaemia may be the presenting feature. The mechanism is uncertain and may be secretion of an insulin-like substance or excessive utilization of glucose (p. 381).

6. *Idiopathic hypoglycaemia of infancy* is considered on p. 148.

Reactive hypoglycaemia.—Hypoglycaemia may occur as a reaction to an ingested substance. In such cases there is frequently a recognizable pattern of attacks related to meals or to particular foodstuffs.

1. *Functional hypoglycaemia* (sensitivity to glucose).—Certain persons develop symptoms of hypoglycaemia 2–4 hours after a meal or after a glucose load. Unconsciousness usually does not occur. The diagnosis is made by performing a glucose tolerance test and collecting blood at intervals for 5–6 hours. There is exaggeration of the normal dip below fasting level at $2\frac{1}{2}$–3 hours (p. 139). Interpretation is not easy as patients suspected of having functional hypoglycaemia may not develop symptoms coinciding with this low level and levels as low as 30 mg/100 ml may be seen, without symptoms, in glucose tolerance tests on normal patients. A similar "reactive" hypoglycaemia may be seen after *gastrectomy.* These patients show a "lag storage" glucose tolerance curve. In both these conditions the underlying abnormality is probably excessive insulin secretion.

A further cause of hypoglycaemia 3-5 hours after a carbohydrate meal is early diabetes. It may be the presenting symptom and is due to the delayed but exaggerated plasma insulin response seen in early diabetes.

2. *Leucine sensitivity.*—In the first six months of life *casein* may precipitate severe hypoglycaemia. This is due to its content of the amino-acid, leucine. Leucine sensitivity is probably due to excessive stimulation of insulin secretion and there is often a familial incidence. Diagnosis is confirmed by the demonstration of hypoglycaemia within half-an-hour after an oral dose of leucine or casein. Treatment is a low leucine diet.

Normal individuals do not show a significant drop in blood glucose after leucine, but a number of patients with insulinoma do demonstrate leucine sensitivity.

3. *Galactosaemia.*—Reactive hypoglycaemia seen only after milk (lactose) is included in the infant diet, may be due to galactosaemia (p. 343).

4. *Hereditary fructose intolerance.*—This is a rare cause of hypo-glycaemia. Symptoms start after the introduction of sucrose or fruit juice to the diet. Fructose administration leads to symptoms of hypo-glycaemia in half to one hour, accompanied by nausea or vomiting and abdominal pain. There is failure to thrive and progressive liver damage with hepatomegaly, jaundice and ascites. Cirrhosis may develop. Diagnosis is based on the demonstration of fructosuria and hypo-glycaemia after oral or intravenous administration of fructose. The basic defect is a deficiency of the enzyme fructose-1-phosphate aldolase and accumulation of fructose-1-phosphate. The hypoglycaemia is probably due to inhibition of glycogenolysis and gluconeogenesis by fructose-1-phosphate.

5. *Alcohol-induced hypoglycaemia.*—Hypoglycaemia may develop 2-10 hours after ingestion of alcohol, usually in considerable amounts. The incidence of this complication is unknown. It is described most frequently in chronic alcoholics when starvation or malnutrition is present, but may occur in young persons after first exposure. The mechanism is uncertain, but probably there is reduced hepatic output of glucose due to suppression of gluconeogenesis during metabolism of the alcohol. This is potentiated in the fasting or starved state when gluconeogenesis is the main source of blood glucose. Clinical differ-entiation from alcoholic stupor may be impossible and requires blood glucose estimation. Frequent infusions of glucose may be required in treatment. It is difficult to reproduce the hypoglycaemia after infusion of alcohol unless the patient fasts for 12-72 hours.

Insulinoma

An uncommon, but usually curable cause of spontaneous hypo-glycaemia, is a functioning β-cell tumour of the pancreas. Such tumours are usually benign and single, but may rarely be multiple.

Symptoms may be vague at first. Hypoglycaemic attacks occur typically at night and before breakfast. Personality or behavioural changes may be the first feature and many of these patients present to psychiatrists.

The diagnosis of insulinoma depends in the first place on demon-strating fasting hypoglycaemia. If insulin assay is available the low fasting glucose level may be shown to be associated with raised insulin levels. Demonstration of such hypoglycaemia may require a fast of up to 72 hours, but without such evidence the diagnosis of insulinoma is untenable.

Two provocative tests can be used to aid diagnosis of insulinoma in doubtful cases:

Intravenous tolbutamide test.—The neoplastic β cell is more sensitive to tolbutamide than is the normal. Following administration of tol-butamide insulin secretion is stimulated and the blood glucose in a patient with insulinoma falls to lower levels and recovers more slowly than normal (see Appendix, p. 154). Properly performed, this test is positive in about 90 per cent of cases. The procedure is not without risk.

Glucagon test.—The response of blood glucose to glucagon administration has also been used. In both normal subjects and patients with insulinoma glucagon administration causes a rise in blood glucose, followed in the case of insulinoma by hypoglycaemia. This test is safer than the tolbutamide test, but has been less extensively evaluated.

Measurement of insulin levels can enhance the accuracy of both tests.

The *treatment* of insulinoma is surgical removal.

Diagnosis of Hypoglycaemia in Adults

Symptoms can only be attributed to hypoglycaemia if such hypo-glycaemia is demonstrated. This statement may seem superfluous, but it is not unknown for patients to be submitted to multiple tests for differential diagnosis of a hypoglycaemia that does not exist.

As always, any investigations are preceded by careful clinical appraisal. Points of special note in the history are times of symptoms in relation to meals or any particular food, drug history and whether or not true unconsciousness has ever occurred. This should help to classify the condition as spontaneous or reactive hypoglycaemia, and to suggest any underlying endocrine deficiency.

A 72-hour fast is of value in proving the existence of spontaneous hypoglycaemia. Normal subjects or persons with reactive hypoglycaemia will not develop a low blood glucose level under these conditions. Failure of the blood glucose to fall to hypoglycaemic levels is a strong point against insulinoma, or indeed, against spontaneous hypoglycaemia. This test should only be carried out in hospital with constant observation of the patient.

Further tests depend on the suspected diagnosis and may include:

1. Prolonged glucose tolerance test. This is of value *only* in the diagnosis of "reactive" functional hypoglycaemia (p. 144).

2. I.V. tolbutamide test ⎫
3. Glucagon test ⎭ for suspected insulinoma (p. 146).

4. Specific provocative tests for reaction to fructose (p. 145), galactose (p. 343), leucine (p. 145) or alcohol (p. 145).

5. Tests for suspected endocrine deficiencies (see relevant chapters).

Hypoglycaemia in Children

Hypoglycaemia in infancy is not uncommon and is important because permanent brain damage can result, especially in the first few months of life. Detailed consideration of neonatal and infancy hypoglycaemia is beyond the scope of this book and only the main causes will be outlined.

(*a*) **Neonatal period.**—Blood glucose levels in the neonatal period as low as 40 |mg/100 ml or, in the first 72 hours, 30 mg/100 ml may be considered "normal". Signs of hypoglycaemia at this age are convulsions, tremors and attacks of apnoea with cyanosis. Neonatal hypoglycaemia occurs particularly in two groups:

1. *Babies of diabetic mothers.* If the foetus is exposed to hyperglycaemia during pregnancy, islet cell hyperplasia occurs and the consequent hyperinsulinism may produce hypoglycaemia when the supply of excess glucose from the mother is removed after parturition.

2. *Babies suffering from intra-uterine malnutrition.* These are usually small for dates and may show a tendency to hypoglycaemia for the first week, possibly due to poor liver glycogen stores. Prematurity is an aggravating factor as most of the liver glycogen is laid down after 36 weeks.

(*b*) **Early infancy.**—Soon after birth, or after the introduction of milk or sucrose, hypoglycaemia may be due to:

1. Glycogen storage disease (p. 148).
2. Galactosaemia (p. 343).
3. Hereditary fructose intolerance (p. 145).

(c) **Infancy.**—1. Idiopathic hypoglycaemia of infancy consists of a group of cases, probably of multiple aetiology. Symptoms usually develop after fasting or after a febrile illness. The diagnosis is made by excluding other causes. There is a high incidence of brain damage.

2. Leucine sensitivity is seen mainly in the first six months of life and is considered on p. 145.

3. Ketotic hypoglycaemia is seen in the second year of life and manifests after fasting or a febrile illness. Ketonuria precedes the hypoglycaemia (as it does in starvation) and the diagnosis can be established by feeding a ketogenic diet for 48 hours. The underlying mechanism is not well understood.

(d) **"Adult"** causes, including insulinoma, must be considered at all times.

Treatment of Hypoglycaemia

Prolonged hypoglycaemia produces irreversible cerebral changes and treatment is a matter of urgency. Early cases respond dramatically to intravenous 50 per cent glucose solution. Blood for glucose estimation *must* be withdrawn before glucose is given if dangerous diagnostic errors are to be avoided.

GLYCOGEN STORAGE DISEASE

Glycogen is synthesized from G-6-P (p. 127) by several specific enzymes and broken down to G-6-P by a different pathway also involving several enzymes. Deficiencies of any of these enzymes may result in the formation of abnormal glycogen, or the accumulation of normal glycogen. At least six types of glycogen storage disease have been recognized. Only the commonest form will be discussed here.

Von Gierke's Disease (Type 1)

This is the classical form of glycogen storage disease and is due to deficiency of the enzyme glucose-6-phosphatase. As discussed on p. 127, this enzyme is essential for conversion of glucose-6-phosphate to glucose and patients with a deficiency of the enzyme are liable to profound hypoglycaemia. Small amounts of free glucose may be liberated during breakdown of glycogen to glucose-6-phosphate and contribute to blood glucose. Glycogen accumulates in the liver and kidneys and hepatomegaly is present. The metabolic consequences include:

1. Hypoglycaemia.

2. Raised levels of FFA leading to ketosis and endogenous hyperlipoproteinaemia (secondary to deficient intracellular glucose).

3. Lactic acidosis.

4. Hyperuricaemia.

The diagnosis is confirmed by demonstrating the absence of the enzyme on liver biopsy. If this test is not available, two indirect clinical tests are of value:

(i) Administration of glucagon produces a rise in blood sugar in normal subjects by accelerating glycogenolysis. This will not occur in glucose-6-phosphatase deficiency.

(ii) Infusion of galactose or fructose in normal subjects is followed by a rise in blood glucose after conversion in the liver. When the last enzyme, that which converts G-6-P to glucose, is absent, this does not occur.

In both tests there is an excessive rise of blood lactate. Treatment is to take frequent meals to maintain blood glucose levels and prevent cerebral damage.

REDUCING SUBSTANCES IN THE URINE

Although Benedict's test for urinary reducing substances is still used in many laboratories, it has been replaced in most ward side-rooms by Clinitest tablets (Ames) or Clinistix (Ames). Clinistix contains the enzyme glucose oxidase, and is specific for glucose; it is used for detection of glycosuria. Clinitest, like Benedict's test, on which it is based, gives a positive result with any reducing substance. It is semiquantitative and is valuable in control of diabetic therapy, whereas Clinistix is unsatisfactory for this purpose. Urine screening in neonates and infants should be done by Benedict's test or Clinitest because of the diagnostic importance of non-glucose reducing substances, such as galactose, in this age group.

A positive Benedict's test or Clinitest may be due to:

1. Glucose
2. Glucuronate
3. Galactose
4. Fructose
5. Lactose
6. Pentoses
7. Homogentisic acid.

Clinistix will confirm the presence or absence of glucose. Non-glucose reducing substances are further identified by chromatography and specific tests.

The significance varies with the substance.

Glucose

(a) Diabetes mellitus (p. 133).
(b) Renal glycosuria.

Glucose may be present in the urine when blood levels are normal. This is due to a low renal threshold and may be seen in *pregnancy* or as an *inherited* (autosomal dominant) characteristic. The condition is usually benign. Differentiation from diabetes mellitus is made by simultaneous blood and urine glucose estimation or, if necessary, by a glucose tolerance test.

Glucuronates

A large number of drugs and their metabolites are excreted in the urine after conjugation with glucuronic acid in the liver (p. 263). These glucuronates are a relatively common cause of reducing substances in the urine.

Galactose

Galactose is found in the urine in galactosaemia (p. 343).

Fructose

Fructose may appear in the urine after very large oral doses or excessive fruit ingestion, but in general fructosuria occurs in two rare inborn errors of metabolism, both transmitted by autosomal recessive genes.

(*a*) *Essential fructosuria* is seen almost exclusively in persons of Jewish origin and is a harmless condition.

(*b*) *Hereditary fructose intolerance* (p. 145) is a serious disease characterized by hypoglycaemia that may lead to death in infancy.

Lactose

Lactosuria may occur in:

(*a*) Pregnancy—in late pregnancy and during lactation.
(*b*) Congenital lactase deficiency (p. 218).

Pentoses

Pentosuria is very rare. It may occur in:

(*a*) *Alimentary pentosuria* after excessive ingestion of fruits such as cherries and grapes. The pentoses excreted are arabinose and xylose.

(*b*) *Essential pentosuria* is a rare recessive disorder characterized by the excretion of xylulose due to a block in the metabolism of glucuronic acid. It is seen usually in Jewish persons and is harmless.

Homogentisic Acid

Homogentisic acid appears in the urine in the rare inborn error alkaptonuria (p. 343). It is usually recognizable by the blackish precipitate formed.

Reducing substances found in the urine during late pregnancy may be:

(*a*) Glucose—due to previously unrecognized diabetes mellitus or to lowered renal threshold.

(*b*) Lactose.

SUMMARY

1. Carbohydrates after digestion and absorption are mostly metabolized as glucose.

2. Glucose, after conversion to glucose-6-phosphate, may be stored as glycogen (glycogenesis) or utilized for energy production (glycolysis) (p. 127). During the fasted state blood glucose levels are maintained (p. 131) by breakdown of glycogen (glycogenolysis) or formation of "new" glucose largely from protein (gluconeogenesis). The liver plays a central role in this process which is regulated by insulin, glucocorticoids, adrenaline and growth hormone (p. 128).

3. Ketosis develops when there is deficient intracellular metabolism of glucose. The ketone bodies aceto-acetic acid, acetone and β-hydroxybutyric acid are acidic and produce keto-acidosis.

4. Glycosuria develops if blood glucose levels exceed the renal threshold, usually about 180 mg/100 ml. This threshold level is higher with reduced glomerular filtration rates (p. 132) and lower in renal glycosuria (p. 150).

5. Diabetes mellitus is a disorder probably of multiple aetiology (p. 133). The clinical and chemical effects can be explained on a basis of impaired or absent insulin activity, relative or absolute. In young persons insulin levels may be low or absent and the disease is severe, carrying with it the risk of ketosis and coma (p. 134). In older persons the disease may be milder and is usually associated with obesity. Insulin is present and ketosis rare (p. 134). In both groups, vascular and other complications may occur.

6. The diagnosis of diabetes mellitus is made by blood glucose estimation. If fasting or random levels are not unequivocally raised a 2-hour post-prandial glucose level or full glucose tolerance test is required (p. 137). The glucose tolerance test is affected by a number of variables (p. 138).

7. Hypoglycaemia, particularly in infants, is a dangerous manifestation of a number of conditions. The commonest cause is insulin administration. Other causes may be grouped into those occurring during fasting and those occurring as a reaction to ingestion of a particular substance (p. 143).

8. Reducing substances in the urine are not necessarily glucose. The significance of the finding depends on the particular substance. Many causes are harmless, others not.

FURTHER READING

Beckett, A. G. and Samols, E. (1964). Carbohydrate Metabolism. In: *Recent Advances in Medicine*, Chap. 5, 14th edit. Ed. by D. N. Baron *et al.* London: J. & A. Churchill.

APPENDIX TO CHAPTER VI

Blood for glucose estimation must be taken into special containers containing fluoride. This inhibits glycolysis by erythrocytes which may produce falsely low levels. In theory, rapid separation of plasma from cells would obviate the need for a preservative, but this is rarely possible in practice.

Glycosuria

Glycosuria is best detected by enzyme reagent strips such as Clinistix (Ames). Directions for use are supplied with the strips. Clinistix detects about 100 mg/100 ml of glucose in urine, but is not suitable for the relatively accurate quantitation required for control of diabetic therapy. The concentration of glucose in normal urine varies from 1–15 mg/100 ml.

False negative results may occur if the urine contains large amounts of ascorbic acid, as may occur from therapeutic doses or after injection of tetracyclines which contain ascorbic acid as preservative.

False positive results may occur if the urine container is contaminated with detergent.

Reducing Substances

Reducing substances in the urine may be detected by:

(*a*) Benedict's qualitative solution. 0·5 ml (about 8 drops) of urine is boiled with 5 ml of reagent for a few minutes. A positive result is the formation of a yellow–red precipitate that discolours the urine from a greenish solution (+) to orange–red with heavy precipitate (+ + + +).

(*b*) Clinitest tablets (Ames)—used as directed. These tablets are more convenient than Benedict's solution for patients controlling their own insulin dosage, but are caustic and require careful handling.

These two tests are less sensitive than Clinistix but are more accurate for quantitation. Results correspond fairly well between the two.

$$+ \text{ represents } \pm 0·2–0·5 \text{ g/100 ml}$$
$$++ \text{ represents } \pm 0·5–1 \text{ g/100 ml}$$
$$+++ \text{ represents } \pm 1–2 \text{ g/100 ml}$$
$$++++ \text{ represents over } 2 \text{ g/100 ml}$$

expressed as glucose.

The significance of positive results of these tests is discussed on p. 149.

Detection of Ketones

Most simple urine tests for ketones detect aceto-acetate, because of the greater sensitivity of reagents to this than to acetone, and because aceto-acetic acid is present in greater concentration. β hydroxybutyrate is not measured.

Rothera's test.—5 ml of urine is saturated with a mixture of ammonium sulphate and sodium nitroprusside (as a powder). 1–2 ml concentrated ammonium sulphate is added and mixed. A purple–red colour indicates the presence of aceto-acetate (or acetone).

Ketostix and Acetest (Ames) are strips and tablets respectively impregnated with the reagents of Rothera's test. Instructions are supplied with the reagents and they are more convenient to use.

Rothera's test detects about 5 mg/100 ml aceto-acetate while the tablet tests are slightly less sensitive (10–20 mg/100 ml). After a fast of several hours ketonuria may be detected by these methods. Occasional colour reactions resembling, but not identical to that of acetate, may be given by phthalein compounds such as phenolphthalein, bromsulphthalein (BSP) or phenol-sulphthalein (PSP).

Acetest tablets may be adapted for a rough index of plasma ketone levels.

Gerhardt's test.—3 per cent ferric chloride is added drop by drop to 5 ml of urine. A red–purple colour develops if aceto-acetate is present in quantities of 25–50 mg/100 ml or greater.

This test is less sensitive than those described above and, if the latter are negative, need not be done. If however, ketone bodies are found, Gerhardt's test gives additional information about the severity of the ketosis.

A large number of compounds that may be found in urine give a colour with ferric chloride. The commonest are salicylates which give an identical colour. Boiling the urine for several minutes will destroy ketone bodies and subsequent testing will give a negative result. Salicylates are unchanged by this treatment.

Glucose Tolerance Test

Procedure: After an overnight fast, blood is withdrawn for a fasting level and 50 g glucose dissolved in water given orally. Further specimens of blood are taken at half-hourly intervals for 2 or 2½ hours. Urine is collected at hourly intervals and tested for glucose. The patient should be at physical and emotional ease and smoking during the test should be avoided.

See p. 139 for interpretation.

Intravenous Tolbutamide Test

Procedure: After an overnight fast, blood is taken for fasting glucose estimation. 1 g of sodium tolbutamide is injected intravenously and blood taken for glucose estimation at 15-minute intervals for the first hour and every 30 minutes for a further 2 hours.

Interpretation: In a normal person the blood glucose level falls to 25–50 per cent of the fasting value within 30–45 minutes. Thereafter levels rise and by 2–3 hours are at least 70 per cent of the fasting value. In persons with an insulinoma the fall may be greater, but the diagnostic point is the failure to respond and glucose levels at 3 hours are less than 70 per cent of the initial value.

Cases of functional "reactive" hypoglycaemia may show a greater than normal fall, but return to at least 70 per cent of the fasting value at 2–3 hours.

The fall in diabetes is less than normal. In patients with "lag storage" due to liver disease the I.V. tolbutamide test gives a normal result.

The dose for *children* is 20 mg/kg.

Note: 1. The patient should have been on a normal diet for at least three days before the test.

2. This test is potentially dangerous and should not be attempted if there is fasting hypoglycaemia of less than 40 mg/100 ml. Glucose should be immediately available for intravenous administration should serious hypoglycaemia develop.

Chapter VII

THYROID FUNCTION

INTRODUCTION

THE three hormones known to be produced by the thyroid are thyroxine, tri-iodothyronine and calcitonin. Thyroxine and tri-iodothyronine are products of the thyroid follicular cell and influence metabolism throughout the body. Calcitonin is produced by a specialized cell (the C cell) and influences calcium metabolism. As in the case of the adrenal cortex and medulla, this is an anatomical rather than a functional relationship. In lower animals the calcitonin-secreting cells may be completely separated from the thyroid. Calcitonin is considered briefly on p. 177.

CHEMISTRY, METABOLISM AND FUNCTION

The thyroid hormones are synthesized in the thyroid gland by iodination and coupling of two moles of the amino-acid tyrosine. Thyroxine has four iodine atoms and is referred to as T_4; tri-iodothyronine has three and is therefore often known as T_3. The chemical structures are shown in Fig. 10.

Iodine is essential for thyroid hormone synthesis and will be considered in more detail.

METABOLISM OF IODINE AND THYROID HORMONES

Iodide in the diet is absorbed rapidly in the small bowel. Most natural foods contain adequate amounts of iodine except in regions where the iodine content of the soil is very low. In these areas there used to be a high incidence of goitre, but general use of artificially iodized salt has made this a less common occurrence. Sea foods have a high iodine content and fish and iodized salt are the main dietary sources of the element.

Normally about one-third of the absorbed iodide is taken up by the thyroid and the other two-thirds is excreted via the kidneys.

Biosynthesis of Thyroid Hormones

The steps in the biosynthesis of the thyroid hormones are outlined below and in Fig. 11. An understanding of the sequence of events is helpful in appreciating both the mechanism of action of the drugs used

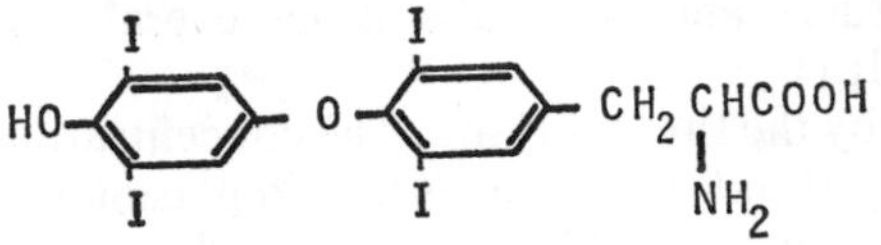

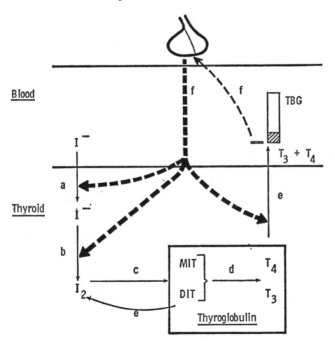

Thyroxine (T$_4$)

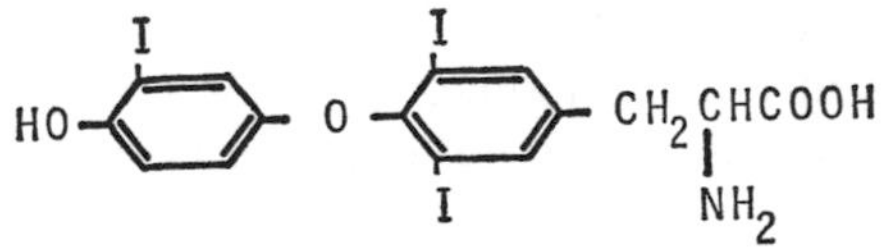

Triiodothyronine (T$_3$)

FIG. 10.—Chemical structure of the thyroid hormones.

MIT = Monoiodotyrosine

DIT = Diiodotyrosine

TBG = Thyroxine - Binding Globulin

FIG. 11.—Synthesis and regulation of thyroid hormones
(See text for explanation of small letters.)

in the treatment of thyroid disorders, and the results of the several congenital enzyme deficiencies (p. 161).

(*a*) Iodide is actively taken up by the thyroid gland. The concentration of iodine in the gland is normally about twenty times that in plasma but may exceed it by a hundred times or more. The salivary glands, gastric mucosa and mammary glands are also capable of concentrating iodine but as this fraction is returned to the gastro-intestinal tract it does not represent a source of loss.

Uptake is blocked by thiocyanate or perchlorate.

(*b*) Trapped iodide is rapidly converted to iodine.

(*c*) It is then incorporated into mono- and di-iodotyrosine (MIT and DIT).

(*d*) MIT and DIT are coupled to form thyroxine (T_4) (2 moles of DIT) and tri-iodothyronine (T_3) (1 mole of DIT and 1 mole of MIT). The organic binding of iodine is inhibited by thiouracil.

The iodotyrosines and T_3 and T_4 do not exist in a free state in the thyroid gland, but are incorporated in the large protein molecule thyroglobulin. This iodoprotein is the main component of the colloid of the thyroid follicle.

(*e*) Release of T_3 and T_4 occurs by breakdown of thyroglobulin by proteolytic enzymes. The hormones pass into the blood. Mono- and di-iodotyrosine released at the same time are de-iodinated by another enzyme and the iodine re-utilized.

Each step is controlled by specific enzymes and congenital deficiency of any of these enzymes can lead to hypothyroidism.

Control of Thyroid Hormone Synthesis (Fig. 11)

The uptake of iodide (*a*), conversion to iodine (*b*) and release of thyroid hormones (*e*) are promoted by the action of thyroid stimulating hormone (TSH) from the anterior pituitary gland. TSH is, in turn, controlled mainly by the level of circulating thyroid hormone, raised levels inhibiting release. This feed-back mechanism acts at the level of the pituitary (unlike the action of cortisol on ACTH release, p. 101). In certain situations, such as exposure to cold, TSH may also be released in response to thyrotrophin releasing factor from the hypothalamus (compare corticotrophin releasing factor, p. 101).

CIRCULATING THYROID HORMONES

Ninety per cent of the circulating thyroid hormone is thyroxine and tri-iodothyronine forms only 10 per cent, although the latter is physiologically more potent. For the sake of brevity in this and following discussions only thyroxine will be referred to. Probably release of tri-iodothyronine obeys the same laws and its action is similar.

Thyroxine in plasma occurs in free and protein-bound forms. Several plasma proteins, including albumin, are capable of binding thyroxine but the main one is an α-globulin called thyroxine-binding globulin (TBG). Almost all the plasma thyroxine is so bound. The free 0·1 per cent or less, is, however, the physiologically active fraction and it is this that controls the pituitary secretion of TSH (compare calcium, p. 177). The relationship between the two fractions is important in interpreting results of tests (p. 167).

Small amounts of inorganic iodide are also present in plasma.

ACTIONS OF THYROID HORMONES

Thyroxine influences and speeds up many metabolic processes in the body. The mechanism is poorly understood but the hormone may control the production and storage of energy in the form of ATP derived from oxidative processes. This action is reflected in oxygen consumption: measurement of this may be used to assess thyroid function (BMR, p. 168). If thyroxine is present in excess energy production is increased, but it cannot be efficiently stored and is lost as heat. There is an increased rate of metabolism and oxygen consumption.

DISORDERS OF THE THYROID GLAND

Excess or deficiency of circulating thyroid hormone produce characteristic clinical changes. Thyroid disease may exist without hyper- or hypo-function. These changes, and the causes of the abnormal thyroid activity, will be considered only in so far as they influence the results of thyroid function tests.

HYPERTHYROIDISM (THYROTOXICOSIS)

The syndrome produced by sustained excess of thyroid hormone may be easily recognized or may remain unsuspected for a long time. The key feature is a speeding up of metabolism. Clinical features include tremor, tachycardia (and sometimes arrhythmias), weight loss, tiredness, sweating and diarrhoea. Anxiety and emotional symptoms may be prominent. In some cases a single feature predominates, such as weight loss, diarrhoea, tachycardia or atrial fibrillation.

There are two common causes of hyperthyroidism:

(a) Graves' disease.
(b) A functioning thyroid adenoma.

Rarely a thyrotrophin-like substance is secreted by non-thyroid neoplasms and gives rise to hyperthyroidism (p. 381).

Ingestion of thyroid hormones, either as a slimming aid or as a form of malingering, is a further cause of hyperthyroidism.

(a) Graves' Disease

This occurs at any age, is commoner in females and presents with any or all of the above features. The thyroid is usually diffusely enlarged and there may be exophthalmos (exophthalmic goitre). Rarely this may be the only feature. In recent years much work has been done on the aetiology of Graves' disease. The stimulus to thyroid secretion in this disease is probably a substance known as long-acting thyroid stimulator (LATS). TSH levels are not raised and in fact are usually low because of the feed-back from raised thyroxine levels. LATS is a gamma-globulin (an IgG). The exact site of origin is not known but is probably the reticulo-endothelial system: it is also not known what stimulates its production in Graves' disease. Exophthalmos is probably produced by some factor other than TSH or LATS, and possibly of pituitary origin. Much remains to be learnt about the causation of Graves' disease.

(b) Functioning Thyroid Adenoma

This occurs classically in the older age groups and may present only as cardiac disease. The adenoma is the source of the circulating thyroxine and production of the hormone is not subject to feed-back control (compare parathyroid adenoma, p. 180). Once this is present in excess, TSH secretion is cut off and the remainder of the thyroid ceases to function.

The common feature in all cases of hyperthyroidism is that the stimulus to excess secretion is *not* TSH. In Graves' disease it is probably LATS, and the functioning thyroid adenoma is autonomous.

HYPOTHYROIDISM (MYXOEDEMA)

Many of the features of hypothyroidism are, not unexpectedly, the opposite of those seen in hyperthyroidism. There is a generalized slowing down of metabolism, with mental dullness, physical slowness and weight gain. The skin is dry, hair falls out and the voice becomes hoarse. In the most severe form, myxoedema coma with profound hypothermia may develop. In children, growth may be impaired and intra-uterine thyroid hormone deficiency leads to cretinism. The fully developed case of myxoedema is easily recognized but lesser degrees with slow onset may be commoner than previously thought.

The causes of hypothyroidism are:

1. Primary:
   (a) Disease of the gland (auto-immune thyroiditis):
      (i) "Primary" myxoedema
      (ii) Hashimoto's disease
   (b) The result of treatment:
      (i) post-thyroidectomy
      (ii) post-^{131}I therapy for hyperthyroidism
   (c) Uncommon causes:
      (i) dyshormonogenesis
      (ii) exogenous goitrogens and drugs
   (d) Long-standing secondary hypothyroidism.

2. Secondary to TSH lack in hypopituitarism (p. 121).

The essential difference between primary and secondary hypothyroidism is that TSH levels are raised in the former (except cause 1 (d)), and low in the latter. As TSH is not routinely measured this evidence must be obtained indirectly.

Hashimoto's disease and "primary" myxoedema are now considered to be different manifestations of the same basic disorder. There is progressive destruction of thyroid tissue and circulating thyroid antibodies are present. The term "dyshormonogenesis" includes the congenital deficiencies of the enzymes involved in thyroxine synthesis. Deficiencies have been described at each of the stages shown in Fig. 11, with differing biochemical features. The end result in each case is reduced thyroxine synthesis and hypothyroidism. Goitre is almost invariable in dyshormonogenesis due to continuous TSH stimulation. The commonest form is failure to incorporate iodine into tyrosine (stage (c) of Fig. 10).

If secondary hypothyroidism is long-standing, irreversible atrophic changes occur in the thyroid gland and thyroid function tests give the results seen in primary hypothyroidism.

Euthyroid Goitre

Thyroxine synthesis may be impaired by iodine deficiency, by drugs such as para-aminosalicylic acid, or possibly by minor degrees of enzyme deficiency. The consequent slight reduction of circulating thyroxine level results, by the feed-back mechanism, in increased TSH secretion. This stimulates thyroxine synthesis and levels are therefore maintained in the normal range. As a result the thyroid enlarges (goitre) but hypothyroidism is avoided. In areas with low iodine content of the soil, iodine deficiency used to be common (endemic goitre).

Inflammation of the thyroid (thyroiditis), whether acute or subacute, may produce marked but temporary aberrations of thyroid function tests. These conditions are relatively uncommon.

THYROID FUNCTION TESTS

It is desirable to confirm a clinical diagnosis of thyroid disease by laboratory tests. Treatment may be prolonged and, in the case of primary hypothyroidism, life-long. During treatment the original clinical picture disappears and it is not an uncommon problem to be faced with a patient who has taken thyroxine for many years for probable "thyroid trouble". Without an adequately established diagnosis it may be difficult to assess the past history.

Thyroid function tests may conveniently be divided into three groups, reflecting three stages in thyroid metabolism.

(a) Measurement of Uptake of Iodine
    Radioactive iodine uptake tests.
(b) Assessment of Circulating Hormone
    Protein-bound iodine (PBI)
    Resin uptake tests
    Total thyroxine levels and free thyroxine index
(c) Assessment of the Peripheral Effect of Thyroxine
    Basal metabolic rate (BMR)
    Plasma cholesterol levels.

RADIO-IODINE UPTAKE TESTS

Ingested radioactive iodine enters the body iodine pool and is metabolized in the same way as the natural element. For example, after 24 hours about 40 per cent of the dose has accumulated in the thyroid gland, about 60 per cent has been excreted in the urine and about 0·05 per cent has appeared in the blood as labelled PBI.

Its appearance at any or all of these sites can be measured to estimate thyroid function. The most commonly used method is direct counting over the thyroid gland. Measurements of urinary loss require a 24-hour collection and assume normal renal function. Measurement of radioactive PBI is technically more difficult than that of neck uptake.

Neck Uptake Tests

The technique is simple. The patient drinks a suitable tracer dose of radioactive iodine and an equivalent dose is set aside as a standard. After the required period of time the radioactivity over the thyroid gland is counted and compared with that of the standard. As physical decay affects both equally, the uptake may be directly expressed as a percentage of the dose.

In hyperthyroidism the uptake is usually above normal and in hypothyroidism it is usually low. Any time period between administration of the dose and counting may be allowed but 4 or 24 hours are commonly chosen. In hyperthyroidism 4 hours is preferable as a significant percentage of the dose may have been discharged from the thyroid as thyroxine within 24 hours. In hypothyroidism, on the other hand, the longer period gives a better separation from the normal.

Two isotopes are in common use. ^{131}I has a half-life of 8 days and can be used for prolonged tests such as the 24-hour uptake, and measurement of PB ^{131}I. Measurable radioactivity from this isotope persists for several weeks. ^{132}I has a half-life of 2·3 hours and can only be used for 4-hour uptake tests. It has the advantage that there is a much lower radiation dosage to the patient and that tests can be repeated on the next day if necessary: this is of great advantage when borderline answers are obtained.

Extrathyroidal Factors Affecting Neck Uptake

1. A dose of radioactive iodine enters the body pool of iodine and is diluted by it. The thyroid gland takes up iodine constantly from the body pool and of this a certain proportion will be radioactive. If the body iodine pool is greatly increased, the radioactive iodine is diluted more than normal and a smaller amount will be taken up by the thyroid although the total iodine uptake (radioactive plus non-radioactive) is normal. This will be interpreted as a low uptake. Moreover, large amounts of iodine directly inhibit uptake of iodine by the gland.

Causes of increased body iodine are:—

(a) Excess oral iodine intake as, for example, Lugol's iodine and iodides in cough mixture.

(b) Iodine containing radio-opaque contrast media, as used in, for example, IVP, cholecystogram, myelogram.

The latter group particularly may invalidate the results of neck uptake for months, especially if injected into a site from which excretion is slow (myelogram). The recommended periods after administration of such substances which should be allowed before performing the test are given in the Appendix (p. 174).

2. Drugs used in the treatment of thyroid disease alter the uptake so that it no longer accurately reflects thyroxine output. Thiouracil and its derivatives block thyroxine synthesis. They do not directly affect iodine uptake, but the drop in circulating T_4 may stimulate TSH secretion and *increase* neck uptake. Administered thyroxine may depress TSH secretion and cause a low neck uptake despite normal or raised levels of circulating thyroxine.

Interpretation of Neck Uptake Tests

(a) **High neck uptakes.**—Very high uptakes (approaching 100 per cent) may be seen in hyperthyroidism, but frequently levels are only moderately raised. The level of neck uptake is not necessarily an index of the severity of the disease, this being essentially a clinical assessment. When there is iodine deficiency there is an increased uptake because of a small iodine pool, with less dilution than normal of the activity (p. 161), and because TSH levels are often raised (p. 161). Iodine also has a direct inhibitory effect on uptake and deficiency may contribute to the raised uptake. If the result is borderline, further tests are used to differentiate "high normal" from pathological results.

In differentiating these conditions it is useful to review the basic cause of the raised uptake.

Cause of Raised or "High Normal" Uptake	Stimulus
(i) Hyperthyroidism { Graves' disease	LATS
Adenoma	Autonomous secretion
(ii) Iodine deficiency	TSH
(iii) Antithyroid drugs	TSH
(iv) Dyshormonogenesis	TSH
(v) "High normal" uptake	TSH

The T_3 suppression test is useful here. The neck uptake is repeated after a short course of tri-iodothyronine in doses about twice that of normal thyroid hormone output (that is, about 120 μg/day for six days). This depresses TSH secretion and the uptake will be markedly reduced in (ii), (iii), (iv) and (v) above. High uptakes due to hyperthyroidism remain unchanged.

Alternatively, if iodine deficiency is suspected, the test may be repeated one month after repletion with iodine.

(b) **Low neck uptakes.**—If falsely low uptakes due to iodine excess have been excluded, results far below normal are diagnostic of hypothyroidism. Borderline results may be due to:

(i) Primary hypothyroidism
(ii) Secondary hypothyroidism
(iii) "Low normal" uptake.

To resolve these causes a TSH stimulation test is performed. TSH is given and the uptake repeated on the following day; the uptake may, if necessary, be measured at daily intervals after successive injections of TSH. The test in this form is only possible if ^{132}I has been given. There are several possible responses to TSH.

1. *A rapid rise of uptake to high normal or high levels* after one dose of TSH indicates a *normally functioning gland.*

2. *No response* indicates that the gland cannot increase its uptake in response to TSH, indicating *primary hypothyroidism.*

3. *A subnormal response with no further increase after a second dose of TSH* indicates that the gland is already almost maximally stimulated by endogenous TSH (*mild hypothyroidism*).

4. *A stepwise increase with successive injections* indicates a functional gland with the sluggish response seen in *secondary hypothyroidism* (compare with adrenal, p. 100).

MEASUREMENT OF CIRCULATING THYROID HORMONE

The use of a single blood sample to diagnose thyroid disease has two major advantages for the patient. He is spared a visit to the laboratory and is not exposed to any radioactive substance (although the dosage

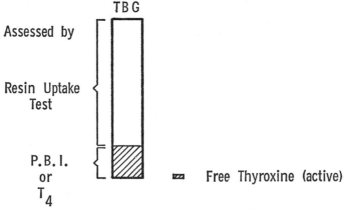

FIG. 12.—Assessment of circulating thyroid hormone.

of this is much lower than that from a chest x-ray). Methods are rapidly being developed for estimation of plasma thyroxine but at the present time the most commonly used tests are the PBI and resin uptake tests.

Thyroxine in plasma occurs in two forms (p. 158). The small (less than 1 per cent) active fraction that determines the thyroid status of the patient cannot easily be measured. The larger (99 per cent) protein bound fraction can be measured in one of two ways. Figure 12 shows that thyroxine binding globulin is normally about 20 per cent saturated with thyroxine.

(*a*) Protein Bound Iodine

After separation and digestion of the serum proteins the iodine content of the extract is a measure of the bound thyroxine. Normal levels of PBI are 4–8 μg/100 ml and include small amounts of other iodo-proteins. The main disadvantage of the PBI estimation is the ease with which contamination can occur. Rigid laboratory precautions are taken against this but the main source of trouble is non-hormonal iodide circulating in the patient's blood stream. The causes of this are the same as those invalidating the radioactive iodine uptake tests (p. 163) and again x-ray contrast media are the main culprits. A recently described cause of contamination is the withdrawal of blood through certain plastic cannulae. These often contain iodine to render them radio-opaque. PBI levels of greater than 25 μg/100 ml are almost certainly due to contamination.

Another test used is the measurement of serum butanol extractable iodine (BEI): non-thyroxine iodoproteins are not extracted by this method. As these are normally present in low concentrations only, and because the BEI does not exclude iodine from contrast media, the test does not offer much advantage over PBI in routine use.

(b) Resin Uptake Tests

A completely different approach is to measure the unoccupied binding sites on TBG (Fig. 13). This allows an indirect assessment of thyroxine levels but also depends on TBG levels. A sample of serum is treated with radioactive T_3 or T_4 under conditions that ensure saturation of all unbound binding sites (that is, an excess of the radio-active hormone) (a and b, Fig. 13). A resin is then added to the mixture to extract all unbound hormone which is then estimated by counting the radioactivity (c, Fig. 13). It follows that the greater the number of binding sites available on TBG, the less T_3 or T_4 will be taken up by the resin and vice versa. Note that the result is expressed as the *resin* uptake, not TBG uptake.

The great advantage of this test is that it completely avoids the problem of iodine contamination.

Interpretation of PBI and resin uptake (Fig. 14).—In hyperthyroidism the circulating thyroxine is increased. This includes both bound and free fractions and the PBI is raised because of the high protein bound fraction. Levels up to 20 μg/100 ml may be found. Because more binding sites on TBG are occupied by the excess thyroxine the resin uptake is also raised (a).

In hypothyroidism circulating thyroxine is decreased. The PBI is low and, because fewer binding sites on TBG are occupied, the resin uptake is also low (b).

So far we have assumed that measurement of the bound thyroxine is a valid reflection of the important free fraction and therefore a measure of the patient's thyroid status. In three sets of circumstances this is not

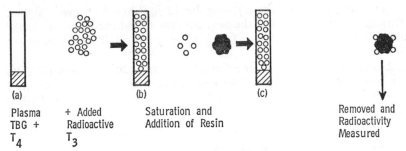

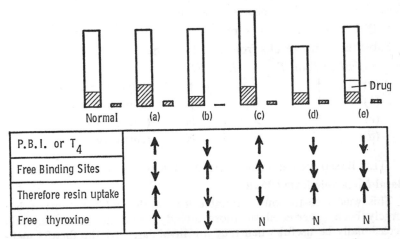

FIG. 13.—Principle of T_3 resin uptake test.

true and abnormal results may be found with normal free thyroxine in a euthyroid patient.

1. *Increased TBG concentration* (*c*).—If increased levels of TBG are present more thyroxine than normal is taken up by it from the plasma. This tendency to reduced free thyroxine results in increased thyroxine synthesis (via the feed-back mechanism) until TBG is again 20 per cent saturated and the free thyroxine is normal. The PBI is therefore raised and, because of the increased number of unsaturated TBG binding sites, resin uptake is low. This combination of *raised PBI and low resin uptake* occurs with:

    (i) Pregnancy
   (ii) Oestrogen therapy
  (iii) Oral contraceptives.

	Normal	(a)	(b)	(c)	(d)	(e)
P.B.I. or T_4		↑	↓	↑	↓	↓
Free Binding Sites		↓	↑	↑	↓	↓
Therefore resin uptake		↑	↓	↓	↑	↑
Free thyroxine		↑	↓	N	N	N

FIG. 14.—Interpretation of tests of circulating hormone (see text).

The PBI in late pregnancy may be 12 μg/100 ml or even higher. This same level is found in the *newborn infant,* and may increase in the first few weeks of life: it then falls gradually to "adult" levels at about one year of age.

2. *Decreased TBG concentration (d).*—With reduced levels of TBG the reverse process occurs. The PBI is low and, because of reduced binding sites, resin uptake is high. This combination, *low PBI and raised resin uptake,* is seen with:

    i. Protein loss, such as in the nephrotic syndrome.

    ii. Congenital TBG deficiency (rare).

3. *TBG binding sites occupied by drugs (e).*—Certain drugs, notably salicylates and diphenyl hydantoin (Epanutin), occupy binding sites on TBG and displace thyroxine. The resultant low PBI and raised resin uptake can only be distinguished from the previous category on clinical grounds.

(c) Total Plasma Thyroxine Levels

In recent years several methods have been devised for estimation of plasma thyroxine (T_4) other than by its iodine content. The major advantage of this approach is the independence of iodine contamination. The problem of changes in bound, and therefore total, thyroxine with normal free thyroxine still exists.

(d) Free Thyroxine Index

Many formulae have been devised using PBI or total plasma T_4 levels and resin uptake to calculate the free thyroxine. The aim of these formulae is to eliminate changes due only to altered TBG. In principle:

PBI or total T_4 level $\times$ resin uptake = free thyroxine index.

Substituting the results from Fig. 14 we have:

	PBI or Total T_4		RU	FTI	
(a)	↑	$\times$	↑ =	↑↑	(hyperthyroid)
(b)	↓	$\times$	↓ =	↓↓	(hypothyroid)
(c)	↑	$\times$	↓ =	N	(euthyroid)
(d)	↓	$\times$	↑ =	N	(euthyroid)

Test Based on the Peripheral Action of Thyroid Hormones

Basal Metabolic Rate (BMR)

This was once the only available test of thyroid function; it has largely been superseded by those already mentioned, but may still occasionally be useful when they are invalidated by the factors mentioned in the Appendix. Reliable results are obtained only by an experienced operator under quiet conditions and without these the test is useless. With them the results are reproducible and reliable.

The basal metabolic rate is defined as the calorie production of the body at complete mental and physical rest. Measurement of oxygen consumption is used to determine calorie production. Peripheral oxygen consumption is increased by physical and mental stress (partly as the result of adrenaline secretion) as well as by circulating thyroxine levels, and the conditions of the test are designed to keep stress reactions to a minimum.

The result is expressed as calories produced per square metre of body surface per hour and is compared with the mean normal value for a subject of the same age, sex and surface area. It is therefore usually expressed as a percentage of normal. The accepted normal range is 85–120 per cent (−15 to +20 per cent) of mean normal, but with an experienced operator anything over 110 per cent of mean normal suggests thyrotoxicosis.

The *advantage* of the test is that it measures the peripheral action of thyroid hormone and is not affected by the factors interfering with neck uptake and PBI estimations.

The *disadvantages* are:

(*a*) The basal state may be difficult to attain in an anxious subject. The test must be performed on two consecutive days with two measurements on the second day. On the first day the subject becomes accustomed to the apparatus: on the second the two results should agree to within 10 per cent.

(*b*) The calculation of surface area depends on a formula which includes height and weight of the patient and an increase in either increases the surface area. Any increase of weight due to non-metabolizing tissue will cause an apparently low result, because the "mean normal" assumes that all the tissue contributing to body weight is metabolizing at a normal rate. The most important of such conditions is *oedema*, but *gross obesity* can affect the result similarly, as adipose tissue is relatively inactive metabolically.

(*c*) Any abnormally high rate of metabolism in infection or malignancy will give falsely high results. In infection a rise of body temperature by 1°F raises the BMR by approximately 10 per cent.

Causes of a Raised BMR
1. Due to Excess of Thyroid Hormone
    Hyperthyroidism
2. Due to Excess of Adrenaline
    Non-basal state (stress)
    Phaeochromocytoma

3. Due to Excess of Other Hormones
Some cases of Cushing's syndrome and acromegaly
4. Due to Abnormally Metabolizing Tissue
Malignancy
Pyrexia
5. Pregnancy (No normals available for various stages of pregnancy).

Causes of a Lowered BMR

1. Deficiency of Thyroid Hormone
Primary myxoedema
Hypopituitarism
2. Presence of Tissue with Abnormally Low Rate of Metabolism
Oedema
Gross obesity
3. Deficiency of Metabolites (malnutrition)

The main indication for a BMR estimation is when other tests are not valid or available.

They are not valid:

(a) Soon after radio-opaque media.

(b) For following up a patient on treatment for thyroid disease, as drugs for treatment of both hypo- and hyperthyroidism affect neck uptake of iodine anomalously (p. 163).

Cholesterol Level

In *hypothyroidism* the synthesis of cholesterol is impaired but its catabolism is even more impaired and plasma cholesterol levels are high. This may help both in diagnosis and in following the effect of treatment but many other factors cause raised cholesterol levels. Although, statistically, low cholesterol levels occur with *hyperthyroidism*, plasma cholesterol estimation is of little value in the individual case because of overlap with the normal range.

Several clinical tests of thyroid function, such as Achilles tendon reflex duration and ECG, depend on the peripheral action of thyroxine (on muscle contraction and on cardiac muscle).

Other Biochemical Findings in Thyroid Disease

1. **Hypercalcaemia** is very rarely seen with severe thyrotoxicosis. There is an increased turnover of bone, probably due to a direct action of thyroid hormone (p. 178).

2. **Glucose tolerance tests** may show a "lag" curve in thyrotoxicosis probably due to rapid absorption. In hypothyroidism by contrast the glucose tolerance curve may be flat. This test is of little use in diagnosis.

TABLE XI

RESULTS OF TESTS IN VARIOUS THYROID CONDITIONS

	Hyper-thyroidism	Hypo-thyroidism	Iodine deficiency	Iodine excess (contrast media)	Ingestion of thyroxine	Raised TBG levels (pregnancy, oral contraceptives)	Low TBG levels (nephrotic)	Dys-hormono-genesis (common form)
Radioactive iodine neck uptake	←	→	←	→	→	Not done in pregnancy	N	←
(a) suppressed by T_3 (b) stimulated by TSH	No —	— primary—no secondary—yes	Yes —	— Yes	— Yes	N with oral contraceptives		Yes —
PBI or T_4 levels	←	→	N	← PBI N—T_4	←	←	→	→
T_3 resin uptake test	←	→	N	N	←	→	←	→
Free thyroxine index	←	→	N	N (using T_4 not PBI)	←	N	N	→
BMR	←	→	N	N	←	← in pregnancy compared to non-pregnant	N	→

3. **Urinary total 17-oxogenic steroid** and **17-oxosteroid** values are low in untreated hypothyroidism, and this finding does not necessarily indicate a pituitary origin of the disease.

Thyroid Antibodies

Although not tests of thyroid function, circulating thyroid antibodies should be sought in the diagnosis of thyroid disease. The two antibodies most useful clinically are:

    (*a*) Complement fixing microsomal antibody.
    (*b*) Antibody to thyroglobulin.

Antibodies may be detected in high titre in most cases of Hashimoto's thyroiditis and many cases of "primary" myxoedema. Their role, if any, in the aetiology of these conditions is uncertain. A high incidence of antibodies in thyrotoxicosis reflects the focal thyroiditis often seen in the gland and correlates with development of post-operative hypothyroidism in these cases.

Further consideration of thyroid antibodies is beyond the scope of this book.

SUMMARY

1. There are two circulating thyroid hormones (apart from calcitonin)—thyroxine and tri-iodothyronine (p. 156). Their synthesis depends on an adequate supply of iodine (p. 158), and is controlled by circulating thyroid hormone levels via TSH from the anterior pituitary gland (p. 158).

2. An excess of circulating thyroxine produces the syndrome of hyperthyroidism (p. 159). This may occur in Graves' disease where the whole thyroid is stimulated by LATS (p. 160), or may be due to a functioning adenoma of the thyroid.

3. A decreased circulating thyroxine level produces the syndrome of hypothyroidism (p. 160). This may be primary, due to disease of the thyroid gland, or be secondary to pituitary disease. TSH levels, though not usually measured, are raised in the first group and absent in the second.

4. Euthyroid goitre represents compensated thyroid disease. Thyroid function tests may be abnormal (p. 161).

5. Thyroid function tests may be considered under three headings (p. 162).

    (*a*) Measurement of iodine uptake by the thyroid.
    (*b*) Assessment of circulating thyroid hormones.
    (*c*) Measurement of peripheral action of thyroid hormones.

6. Iodine uptake may be measured by radio-iodine neck uptake. Borderline results may be clarified by the T_3 suppression test (high) (p. 164) or the TSH stimulation test (low) (p. 164).

7. Circulating thyroid hormone levels may be assessed by the PBI or T_4 estimation (p. 165) and resin uptake test (p. 166). Changes in TBG may give abnormal results (p. 167). The free thyroxine index is an expression of thyroid status regardless of TBG changes (p. 168).

8. The peripheral action of thyroxine may be assessed by the BMR (p. 168) or by measurement of plasma cholesterol levels (p. 170).

9. Many thyroid tests are invalidated by extra-thyroidal factors:

(*a*) Iodine-containing drugs or radio-opaque media invalidate the radioactive neck uptake and the PBI.

(*b*) TBG changes during pregnancy, oestrogen therapy or on oral contraceptives require special interpretation of results of PBI and plasma T_4 estimations. They do *not* affect neck uptake.

(*c*) During and shortly after the treatment of thyroid disease the radio-iodine neck uptake results may not reflect circulating hormone levels.

APPENDIX TO CHAPTER VII

Many factors alter thyroid function tests so that the results no longer reflect the thyroid status of the patient. The commoner (and avoidable) ones are listed below with the time periods that should elapse before measuring the PBI or radioactive iodine uptake. In the case of drugs used in the treatment of thyroid disease the PBI reflects the resultant thyroid status of the patient whereas the neck uptake does not. The times given are approximate—for greater detail on individual drugs or radio-opaque media see:

1. DAVIS, P. J. (1966). *Amer. J. Med.*, **40**, 918 (for PBI).
2. MAGALOTTI, M. F., HUMMON, I. F., and HIERSCHBIEL, E. (1959). *Amer. J. Roentgenol.*, **81**, 47 (for radio-iodine uptake).

TABLE XII

SUBSTANCES INTERFERING WITH THYROID FUNCTION TESTS

	PBI	Neck uptake
Iodine Interference		
Dietary iodide (fish, iodized salt, etc.)	—	3 days
Drug iodide such as KI (suspect in cough mixtures and amoebicides such as "Enterovioform")	2 weeks	8 weeks
Iodine-containing contrast media		
(a) Rapidly cleared (for example, IVP, angiogram, cholecystogram, salpingogram, bronchogram)	8 weeks	8 weeks
(b) Slowly cleared (for example, myelogram)	1 year + (may be indefinite)	1 year +
Interference with Thyroxine Metabolism		
(a) Blocking uptake (for example, perchlorate, thiocyanate, nitrate)	—	2 weeks
(b) Inhibiting organic binding—thioureas, thiouracils	—	6 months
(c) Thyroid hormones, PAS	—	8 weeks

Chapter VIII

DISEASES OF CALCIUM, PHOSPHATE AND MAGNESIUM METABOLISM

MOST of the body calcium is in bone, and a significant deficiency of it causes bone disease. However, the extraosseous fraction, although amounting to only 1 per cent of the whole, is of great importance because of its effect on neuromuscular excitability and on cardiac muscle. Most calcium salts in the body contain phosphate. This radical is very important in its own right (for instance in the formation of "high energy" phosphate bonds), but clinically, apart from its buffering power, it is only of interest because of its association with calcium.

More than half the body magnesium is in bone: most of the remainder is intracellular, but, as in the case of calcium, the small extracellular fraction (about 1 per cent) is important because of its neuromuscular action. Because of this similarity in distribution and physiological action, calcium and magnesium metabolism will be discussed in one chapter.

CALCIUM METABOLISM

TOTAL BODY CALCIUM

The total amount of calcium in the body depends on the balance between intake and loss.

Factors Affecting Intake

The amount of calcium entering the body depends on the amount in the *diet*. Calcium in the intestine may be rendered insoluble by large quantities of *phosphate, fatty acids* and phytate (in cereals) and in this form will not be absorbed. In practice phytate is rarely of clinical importance, but oral phosphate can be used therapeutically to control calcium absorption (p. 193), and an excess of fatty acids in the gut lumen in steatorrhoea contributes to calcium malabsorption.

Vitamin D is required for adequate absorption of calcium.

Factors Affecting Loss

Calcium is lost in urine and faeces. *Faecal calcium* consists of that which has not been absorbed, together with that which has been secreted into the intestine: this fraction is increased by the presence of phosphate in the gut.

Urinary calcium.—This depends on the *amount of calcium circulating* through the glomerulus, on *renal function,* and to a lesser extent on *urinary phosphate excretion.* The amount of calcium circulating through the glomerulus is increased after a calcium load or during decalcification of bone not due to calcium deficiency (e.g. osteoporosis or acidosis). Such decalcification rarely causes hypercalcaemia because of the rapid renal clearance of calcium. Conversely, hypercalcaemia, whatever the aetiology, causes hypercalcuria if renal function is normal. Glomerular insufficiency reduces calcium loss in the urine, even in the presence of hypercalcaemia.

PLASMA CALCIUM

Estimation of plasma calcium should be accurate to about 0·2 mg/100 ml, and changes of less than this are probably insignificant. Calcium circulates in the plasma in two main states. The albumin bound fraction accounts for a little less than half the total calcium as measured by routine analytical methods: it is physiologically inactive and is probably purely a transport form comparable to iron bound to transferrin (p. 309). Most of the remaining plasma calcium is ionized (Ca^{++}), and this is the physiologically important fraction (compare with thyroxine, p. 159, and cortisol, p. 91). Ideally, ionized rather than total calcium should be measured, but techniques for this are unsuitable for most routine laboratories. Whenever a plasma calcium value is assessed an effort should be made to decide whether the ionized fraction is normal by comparing the value for total calcium with that for protein on the same specimen.

The ionization of calcium salts is greater in acid than in alkaline solution. In alkalosis tetany may occur in the presence of normal levels of total calcium because of the reduction in the ionized fraction. In clinical states associated with prolonged acidosis (for instance after transplantation of the ureters into the colon or in the inborn error, renal tubular acidosis, p. 72), the increased solubility of bone salts removes calcium from bone and leads to osteomalacia, even in the presence of an adequate supply of the ion to bone and of normal parathyroid function.

Control of Plasma Calcium

The level of circulating ionized calcium is controlled within narrow limits by parathyroid hormone (PTH), secreted by the parathyroid glands. Calcitonin produced in the thyroid has an opposite action to that of PTH on calcium levels: its importance in calcium homeostasis is less certain than that of parathormone. Both these hormones control ionized calcium by using bone as a reservoir from which plasma levels can be controlled. Vitamin D increases calcium absorption from the intestine, and in physiological amounts appears to be necessary for the action of PTH.

Action and control of parathyroid hormone.—Parathyroid hormone raises the plasma ionized calcium concentration. Its mechanism of action is twofold:

1. By acting directly on osteoclasts it releases bone salts into the extracellular fluid. This action tends to increase both calcium *and* phosphate in the plasma.

2. By acting on the renal tubular cells it decreases the reabsorption of phosphate from the glomerular filtrate, causing phosphaturia. This action tends to *decrease* the plasma phosphate: this in turn, by a mass action effect, increases release of phosphate salts (and therefore calcium) from bone.

A less clinically important effect is the decreased calcium loss from the intestinal tract.

The secretion of PTH, like that of insulin from the pancreas, is not controlled by any other endocrine gland. It is influenced only by the concentration of calcium ions circulating through it (again compare the effect of blood sugar on insulin secretion). Reduction of this concentration increases the rate of release of hormone, and this increase is maintained until the ionized calcium level returns to normal, when hormone production stops.

Bearing in mind the two actions of PTH, and the fact that its secretion is controlled by the level of ionized calcium, the consequences of most disturbances in calcium metabolism on plasma calcium and phosphate levels can be predicted. A low ionized calcium from any cause (other than hypoparathyroidism) by stimulating the parathyroid, causes phosphaturia: this loss of phosphate over-rides the tendency to hyperphosphataemia due to the direct action of PTH on bone, and serum phosphate levels are normal, or even low. Conversely, a high calcium concentration due to any cause (except excess of PTH) cuts off production of the hormone and causes a high phosphate level. As a general rule, therefore, calcium and phosphate levels tend to vary in the same direction unless there is an inappropriate excess of PTH (as in primary hyperparathyroidism), or in the presence of renal failure when the phosphaturic effect is absent (see, however, "Action of vitamin D", below).

Action and control of calcitonin.—Calcitonin reduces plasma calcium by decreasing osteoclastic activity, and therefore bone resorption. It also has a phosphaturic effect. It is produced in the C cells of the thyroid (and has been called thyrocalcitonin) and its secretion is stimulated by high ionized calcium levels. Its clinical importance is doubtful.

Action of vitamin D.—As has been mentioned, vitamin D increases intestinal absorption of calcium, and appears to be necessary for the action of PTH. It also has a phosphaturic effect of its own. Usually in the hypercalcaemia of vitamin D excess this effect is over-ridden by the reduction in phosphate excretion following reduction of parathormone secretion. Occasionally, however, phosphate levels are low or low normal when hypercalcaemia is due to this cause.

Action of thyroid hormone on bone.—Thyroid hormone excess may be associated with the histological lesion of osteoporosis, and with increased faecal and urinary excretion of calcium, probably due to release from bone. Unless there is very gross excess of thyroid hormones, effects on plasma calcium levels are over-ridden by the homeostatic reduction of PTH secretion and hypercalcaemia rarely occurs. Some cases of post-thyroidectomy hypocalcaemia may be due, not to parathyroid damage, but to re-entry of calcium into depleted bone when the circulating thyroid hormone levels fall (p. 184).

Calcium homeostasis follows the general rule that body content is regulated by control of plasma levels. In the presence of normal parathyroid, kidney and intestinal function, and of sufficient supply of calcium and vitamin D, this is usually adequate. In the absence of one or more of these, control of plasma levels may be effected at the expense of the total amount of calcium in the body (compare sodium and water, p. 34).

CLINICAL EFFECTS OF DISORDERS OF CALCIUM METABOLISM

Clinical Effects of Excess Ionized Calcium

1. *On the kidney.*—The most dangerous consequence of prolonged, mild hypercalcaemia is *renal failure*. The high ionized calcium causes the solubility product of calcium phosphate in the plasma to be exceeded, and this salt is precipitated in extraosseous sites. The most important of these sites is the kidney, where it may cause renal damage. At an earlier stage calcification of the renal tubules may reduce their ability to reabsorb water, so that the presenting symptom of hypercalcaemia may be *polyuria*. It is because of this danger of renal damage that every attempt should be made to diagnose the cause of even mild hypercalcaemia and treat it at an early stage.

The high ionized calcium concentration in the glomerular filtrate may, if circumstances favour it, result in precipitation of calcium salts in the urine: the patient will present with *renal calculi*, and these may occur without significant renal parenchymal damage. All patients with renal stones should have plasma calcium estimated on more than one occasion.

2. *On neuromuscular excitability.*—High ionized calcium levels depress neuromuscular excitability in both voluntary and involuntary muscle. The patient may complain of *constipation* and *abdominal pain*. He may also show *hypotonia* of voluntary muscles. The *anorexia*, *nausea* and *vomiting* of hypercalcaemia are more probably due to a central effect.

3. *On the heart.*—Hypercalcaemia causes changes in the electrocardiogram. If severe (as a rough guide, more than 15 mg/100 ml) it carries the risk of sudden *cardiac arrest*, and for this reason should be treated as a matter of urgency.

Clinical Effects of Reduced Ionized Calcium Levels

Low ionized calcium levels (including those associated with a normal total calcium in alkalosis, p. 176) cause increased neuromuscular activity leading to *tetany*.

Prolonged hypocalcaemia, even when mild, interferes with the metabolism of the lens and causes *cataracts*: it may also cause mental depression and other *psychological symptoms*. Because of the danger of cataracts, asymptomatic hypocalcaemia should be sought when there has been a known risk of damage to the parathyroid glands (e.g. after partial or total thyroidectomy).

Effects of High Parathyroid Hormone Levels on Bone

1. **High PTH levels with a normal supply of vitamin D and calcium** (for example, primary hyperparathyroidism).—Parathyroid hormone acts on the osteoclasts of bone, increasing their activity. In cases in which the supply of vitamin D and calcium is normal and in which PTH has been circulating in excess over a long period of time the effects are as follows:

Clinical:
Bone pains.
Bony swellings.

Radiological:
Generalized decalcification.
Subperiosteal erosions.
Cysts in the bone.

Histological:
Increased number of osteoclasts.

A secondary osteoblastic reaction may occur: osteoblasts manufacture the enzyme alkaline phosphatase which, when these cells are overactive, is released into the extracellular fluid in abnormal amounts and leads to a *rise in plasma alkaline phosphatase activity*.

The effects of excess parathyroid hormone on bone are only evident in long-standing cases. In disease of short duration (for instance, when the excess of PTH is due to malignant disease, or to early primary hyperparathyroidism) they are absent. Osteoblastic reaction is a late manifestation and plasma alkaline phosphatase levels are usually normal or only moderately raised in primary hyperparathyroidism.

2. **High PTH levels in vitamin D and calcium deficiency** (for example, rickets and osteomalacia).—Vitamin D must be present in adequate amounts for the complete action of PTH on bone. In cases of vitamin D deficiency PTH levels may be very high, but the effects described above are seen to only a minor degree. Calcium deficiency means that osteoblastic reaction is ineffective, and uncalcified osteoid is a characteristic histological finding: this osteoblastic activity is marked and increases plasma alkaline phosphatase levels.

The effects are therefore as follows:

Clinical:
   Bone pains.
   Rarely bony swelling.

Radiological:
   Generalized decalcification.
   Pseudofractures.
   Rarely subperiosteal erosions or cysts in bone.

Histological:
   Uncalcified osteoid: wide osteoid seams.
   Occasionally increased numbers of osteoclasts.

In the Plasma:
   Raised alkaline phosphatase activity.

These changes in the bone are also seen in certain inborn errors of renal tubular reabsorption of phosphate (p. 187).

Diseases of Calcium Metabolism

Diseases Associated with High Circulating Parathyroid Hormone Levels

Diseases due to inappropriate secretion of parathyroid hormone.—The term "inappropriate secretion of parathyroid hormone" is used here to mean the production of the hormone under circumstances in which it should normally be absent (i.e. in the presence of normal or high ionized calcium concentrations). This syndrome should be compared with that of "inappropriate" ADH secretion (p. 379).

Such inappropriate secretion occurs in three circumstances:

1. Primary hyperparathyroidism.
2. Tertiary hyperparathyroidism.

(In these two cases the hormone is produced by the parathyroid gland.)

3. Ectopic production of PTH.

The findings, if renal function is normal, are those of excess PTH production, that is a raised serum calcium concentration, with a normal or low serum phosphate level. With the onset of renal damage, usually due to hypercalcaemia, both these tend to return to normal, the phosphate because of the inability of the kidney to respond to the phosphaturic effect of PTH and the calcium because of the lowering of plasma calcium in renal failure (p. 183). Diagnosis at this stage may be very difficult.

The *clinical features* of these cases are due to:—

1. Excess of circulating ionized calcium (p. 178).
2. The effect of PTH on bone (p. 179).

Differences between these syndromes depend on the duration of the disease more than any other factor.

Primary hyperparathyroidism.—Primary overaction of the parathyroid glands is usually due to a benign adenoma, which may occasionally be present in an ectopic gland. Parathyroid adenomata are almost always benign, but very rarely primary hyperparathyroidism is due to parathyroid carcinoma. Occasionally it results from diffuse hyperplasia of the glands.

In this country primary hyperparathyroidism presents most commonly with signs and symptoms associated with high ionized calcium levels, such as nausea, anorexia and abdominal pain, or with renal changes (calculi, polyuria or even renal failure). In many of these cases bone changes are absent and the plasma alkaline phosphatase concentration is normal or only slightly elevated. Patients presenting with overt bony lesions, on the other hand, often show no renal changes. It may be that when conditions in the urine are favourable for calcium precipitation (for instance an alkaline pH), or when a patient complains of symptoms early, the disease is usually diagnosed before bony changes occur: if these warning signs are absent the patient presents with the overt picture of bone disease. However, it should be pointed out that some of the renal cases have not developed bone disease after remaining untreated for many years: the reason for the two types of presentation is not fully understood.

Occasionally, as with hypercalcaemia due to any cause, the patient is admitted as an emergency with abdominal pain, vomiting and constipation due to severe hypercalcaemia.

Tertiary hyperparathyroidism.—Tertiary hyperparathyroidism is the name given to the disease in which the parathyroid has been under prolonged feed-back stimulation by low ionized calcium levels, and the resulting hypersecretion has become autonomous. Except for the history of previous hypocalcaemia, the disease is identical with primary hyperparathyroidism. It is usually diagnosed when the cause of the original hypocalcaemia is removed (e.g. by renal transplantation or correction of a calcium deficiency). The typical biochemical findings of excess PTH are superimposed on those of osteomalacia, and because the condition is of long duration the plasma alkaline phosphatase level is usually very high.

Ectopic production of parathyroid hormone.—Sometimes malignant tumours of non-endocrine tissues manufacture peptides foreign to them: PTH can be one of these. The production of hormone at these sites is not subject to feed-back control, and the initial findings are those of inappropriate PTH excess. Because of the nature of the underlying disease the condition is rarely of long standing, and the bony lesions due to excess circulating PTH are not evident: the alkaline phosphatase, however, may be raised because of bony or hepatic metastases, or both.

The subject of ectopic hormone production is discussed more fully in Chapter XX.

Secondary hyperparathyroidism ("appropriate" secretion of parathyroid hormone).—In secondary hyperparathyroidism, the parathyroids are stimulated to produce hormone in response to low plasma ionized calcium levels. This secretion is therefore "appropriate" in that it is necessary to restore ionized calcium levels to normal. If it is effective in doing so the stimulus to production is removed, and the glands are "switched off". In secondary hyperparathyroidism, therefore, plasma calcium concentration is low (if the increased production of hormone is inadequate to correct the hypocalcaemia) or normal: it is *never* high. Hypercalcaemia, or a plasma calcium level in the upper normal range, suggests either a diagnosis of primary hyperparathyroidism (and this may be a *cause* of renal failure), or that prolonged calcium deficiency has led to tertiary hyperparathyroidism.

If renal function is normal the high PTH levels cause phosphaturia with hypophosphataemia. In all cases of secondary hyperparathyroidism, except that due to renal failure, both the plasma calcium and phosphate levels tend to be low.

The effects of excess PTH on bone when vitamin D and calcium levels are low are described on p. 180. The alkaline phosphatase concentration tends to rise, and very high levels can be reached in long-standing disease.

Any factor tending to lower ionized calcium levels (except of course, hypoparathyroidism) causes secondary hyperparathyroidism.

The causes of secondary hyperparathyroidism are:

1. Calcium deficiency.
2. Renal failure.
3. (Pseudohypoparathyroidism.)

The *clinical features* of these cases are due to:

1. The effect of PTH on bone when vitamin D and calcium is deficient.
2. The reduced ionized calcium concentration (p. 179).

Calcium and vitamin D deficiency.—Vitamin D is essential for normal absorption of calcium from the intestinal tract and calcium depletion is more commonly the result of deficiency of intake of this factor than of calcium itself. The commonest cause of calcium and vitamin D deficiency in this country is the malabsorption syndrome: dietary deficiency is more important in the world as a whole. In the presence of steatorrhoea, vitamin D, which is fat soluble, is poorly absorbed. In addition calcium combines with the excess of fatty acids in the intestine to form insoluble soaps. The resulting low plasma ionized calcium concentration stimulates PTH production, with the consequences described above. This syndrome of calcium deficiency is known as *rickets* in children and *osteomalacia* in adults.

Malnutrition is rarely selective, and protein deficiency may lead to a reduction of the protein bound fraction of the calcium. The ionized calcium level may not, therefore, be as low as that of total calcium would indicate.

Renal failure.—Renal failure is usually accompanied by significant hypocalcaemia. No single explanation of this finding fits all the facts. Uraemic patients show resistance to the action of vitamin D, and the resultant malabsorption of calcium is undoubtedly an important contributory factor; it cannot explain the development of hypocalcaemia within a few days of the onset of acute renal failure. Low protein levels sometimes contribute to the reduction of those of total calcium, but, although tetany is rarely present in renal failure, the development of secondary hyperparathyroidism suggests that ionized calcium levels are low and direct measurement confirms this. The cause is probably multifactorial.

The consequences are those of secondary hyperparathyroidism due to any cause, but, because of the renal failure, there is hyperphosphataemia. In chronic renal failure progressive decalcification of bone (aggravated by acidosis) leads to rising plasma alkaline phosphatase levels and, in long-standing cases, to clinical evidence of osteomalacia.

Pseudohypoparathyroidism.—In this rare inborn error circulating levels of parathormone are high. However, because the kidney and bone cannot respond to the hormone, the biochemical changes of hypoparathyroidism, rather than hyperparathyroidism, are present.

Acute pancreatitis.—Acute pancreatitis causes temporary hypocalcaemia because of the precipitation of calcium soaps (calcium salts of fatty acids) following the local release of excess fatty acids from fats by the liberated lipase. Stimulation of PTH production rapidly restores levels to normal. Although this disease rarely presents as a problem of differential diagnosis of hypocalcaemia, the finding may be of use in the diagnosis of acute pancreatitis after serum amylase levels have returned to normal (p. 216).

Diseases Associated with Low Circulating Parathyroid Hormone Levels

A low level or absence of circulating PTH leads to the changes described on p. 177.

Primary parathyroid hormone deficiency (hypoparathyroidism).—Primary hypoparathyroidism may be due to primary atrophy of the parathyroid glands (probably of autoimmune origin—compare Hashimoto's disease, p. 161), or more commonly to surgical damage, either directly to the glands or to their blood supply during partial thyroidectomy (during total thyroidectomy removal of the glands is inevitable). Evidence for asymptomatic hypocalcaemia should always be sought after partial thyroidectomy because of the danger of cataracts (p. 179): early post-operative parathyroid insufficiency may recover, but a low calcium level persisting more than a few weeks should be treated. Even with highly skilled surgery there is a danger of parathyroid damage during this operation. Recent work has, however, suggested that post-thyroidectomy hypocalcaemia may not always be due to parathyroid damage, but may be due to the rapid entry of calcium into depleted bone when the thyroid hormone levels fall to normal (see p. 178): it may be these cases that appear to recover from hypoparathyroidism.

The clinical symptoms are those due to a low ionized calcium concentration (p. 179).

Secondary suppression of parathyroid hormone secretion.—Just as hypocalcaemia from any cause leads to secondary hyperparathyroidism, so hypercalcaemia (unless due to inappropriate PTH secretion) suppresses PTH secretion, with the consequences described on p. 177.

The causes of hypercalcaemia with suppression of PTH secretion are:

1. Vitamin D excess.
2. Idiopathic hypercalcaemia of infancy.

3. Sarcoidosis.
4. Thyrotoxicosis.
5. Malignant disease of bone (possibly).
6. Milk-alkali syndrome.

The *clinical picture* in these cases is due to the high ionized calcium level (p. 178). Decalcification of bone only occurs in this group in the hypercalcaemia of thyrotoxicosis. The alkaline phosphatase level is usually normal in the other conditions.

Hypercalcaemia due to vitamin D excess.—Overdosage with vitamin D increases calcium absorption and may cause dangerous hypercalcaemia. PTH secretion is suppressed, and phosphate levels are usually normal. However, as vitamin D has a phosphaturic effect (p. 178) plasma phosphate levels may occasionally be in the low normal range.

Such overdosage may be caused by over-vigorous treatment of hypocalcaemia, and this therapy should always be controlled by frequent plasma calcium and alkaline phosphatase estimations.

Occasionally patients overdose themselves with vitamin D. In any obscure case of hypercalcaemia a drug history should be taken.

The hypercalcaemia associated with two diseases is thought to be due to oversensitivity to the action of vitamin D. These diseases are:

1. Idiopathic hypercalcaemia of infancy.
2. Hypercalcaemia of sarcoidosis.

Idiopathic hypercalcaemia of infancy.—In these days of milk and vitamin supplements rickets is a rare disease in Great Britain. By contrast, the number of infants presenting with hypercalcaemia of obscure origin increased during the 1950's. The incidence of this syndrome has declined since the recommended dosage of vitamin D for infants was reduced in 1957, although the correlation between these two variables is uncertain. This is still a rare disease.

Hypercalcaemia of sarcoidosis.—Hypercalcaemia as a complication of sarcoidosis may also be due to vitamin D sensitivity. *Chronic beryllium poisoning* produces a granulomatous reaction very similar to that of sarcoidosis, and may also be associated with hypercalcaemia: beryllium is used in the manufacture of fluorescent lamps and in several other industrial processes.

Other diseases associated with hypercalcaemia are:

Hypercalcaemia of thyrotoxicosis.—Thyroid hormone probably has a direct action on bone (p. 178). In rare cases of very severe thyrotoxicosis significant hypercalcaemia may occur. If the hypercalcaemia fails to respond when hyperthyroidism is controlled, the possibility of coexistent hyperparathyroidism should be borne in mind, since some patients show multiple endocrine abnormalities.

Malignant disease of bone.—The hypercalcaemia due to ectopic PTH production by malignant tumours has been described on p. 182. A different syndrome has been reported in cases with multiple bony metastases, or with myeloma: in these the parallel rise of phosphate is said to indicate that the hypercalcaemia is caused by direct breakdown of bone by the local action of malignant deposits. Critical examination of the findings in most of these cases shows a rise of plasma urea accompanying that of phosphate, and such findings are compatible with the action of excess PTH with renal failure. Moreover, there is little correlation between the incidence of hypercalcaemia and the extent of the bony lesions. Probably most, if not all, such cases are due to ectopic PTH production.

The raised alkaline phosphatase level associated with bony secondary deposits is due to the resultant stimulation of local osteoblastic reaction (p. 179). This osteoblastic reaction does not occur in myelomatosis, and the bony alkaline phosphatase level is therefore normal. This fact may be a useful pointer to the diagnosis of myeloma in the presence of extensive bony deposits of unknown origin.

The paraproteins of myeloma probably do not bind calcium to any significant extent, and are unlikely to account for hypercalcaemia in these cases.

Milk-alkali syndrome.—Hypercalcaemia has been reported due to massive intake of calcium in milk, when alkalis are also being taken, during treatment of peptic ulcer. The hypercalcaemia is probably the consequence of the very high calcium intake, and the alkalis, by causing glomerular damage, may temporarily aggravate the hypercalcaemia by delaying excretion of the excess ion.

This is an exceedingly rare cause of hypercalcaemia nowadays. Most modern antacids are acid absorbents rather than alkalis, and do not cause alkalosis. The syndrome should not be diagnosed in the absence of alkalosis, and until other causes have been excluded. In true milk-alkali syndrome the calcium level falls rapidly when therapy is stopped.

There is a well-documented association between peptic ulceration and parathyroid adenomata: the association of hypercalcaemia with medication for dyspepsia should be assumed to be due to primary hyperparathyroidism until proved otherwise.

Disease of Bone Not Affecting Plasma Calcium Levels

Diseases producing biochemical abnormalities, or important in the differential diagnosis from those already mentioned, are:

Osteoporosis.—In this disease the primary lesion is a reduction in the mass of bone matrix with a secondary loss of calcium. Clinically it may resemble osteomalacia, but normal plasma calcium, phosphate and alkaline phosphatase concentrations (especially the latter) are more in favour of osteoporosis.

Paget's disease of bone.—Calcium and phosphate levels are rarely affected in Paget's disease. The alkaline phosphatase level is typically very high.

Renal tubular disorders of phosphate reabsorption.—This group of diseases comprises a number of inborn errors of renal tubular function in which phosphate is not reabsorbed normally from the glomerular filtrate. These usually present as cases of rickets or osteomalacia, but, unlike the usual form of this disease, response to vitamin D therapy is poor: very large doses may be needed to produce an effect. The syndrome has, therefore, been called *"resistant rickets"*. The defect in phosphate reabsorption may be an isolated one, as in *Familial Hypophosphataemia*, or part of a more general reabsorption defect as seen in the *Fanconi Syndrome* (p. 12). In these cases phosphate deficiency is the primary lesion, and failure to calcify bone may be due to this. Plasma levels of phosphate are usually very low and fail to rise when vitamin D is given: there is a relative phosphaturia. The osteomalacia is reflected in the high plasma alkaline phosphatase levels. Plasma calcium concentration is usually normal, and in this way the findings differ from those of classical osteomalacia; because of the normocalcaemia there is rarely evidence in the bone of hyperparathyroidism.

DIFFERENTIAL DIAGNOSIS

In the preceding sections diseases of calcium metabolism have been discussed according to their aetiology, in an attempt to explain biochemical and clinical findings. Clinically they more often present as a problem of differential diagnosis of the causes of an abnormal plasma calcium concentration.

THE DIAGNOSIS OF PRIMARY HYPERPARATHYROIDISM AND TESTS USED IN THE DIFFERENTIAL DIAGNOSIS OF HYPERCALCAEMIA

Primary hyperparathyroidism must, in its early stages, exist with serum calcium levels within the normal range, but diagnosis at this time is almost impossible. A plasma calcium concentration in the upper normal range, with that of phosphate in the low normal range in a patient with recurrent, calcium containing, renal calculi is suggestive of primary hyperparathyroidism: in such a case plasma calcium levels should be estimated at three-monthly intervals, and, if primary hyperparathyroidism is present, these will eventually become unequivocally raised.

In the presence of hypercalcaemia the causes must be differentiated.

Plasma Levels

Raised protein bound calcium.—Apparent mild hypercalcaemia may be due to a raised albumin concentration, with no change in that of ionized calcium (p. 176). The only *in vivo* cause of this is dehydration with haemoconcentration (p. 27), and in such cases the clinical state of the patient, and the raised plasma *protein* and *haemoglobin* levels, should provide the clue. Such hypercalcaemia will disappear when the patient is rehydrated.

A more common cause of a raised protein bound calcium is the artefactual one caused by prolonged stasis during venesection (p. 393). When hypercalcaemia is found, especially if mild, the analysis should be repeated on a specimen taken without stasis.

In both the *in vivo* and artefactual causes of a raised protein bound calcium, plasma phosphate tends to rise because of leakage of this radical from cells (compare potassium).

Calcium levels, especially serial ones, should never be interpreted without an accompanying protein level. If the cause of a change in protein concentration is uncertain, the serum albumin should be estimated, as this is the calcium binding fraction. In most cases, however, total protein estimation is adequate.

Raised ionized calcium.—Hypercalcaemia found in a specimen taken without stasis from a well-hydrated patient can be assumed to be due to a rise in the physiologically active ionized calcium. It should be noted that a normal total plasma calcium in the presence of significant hypoproteinaemia also suggests an increase in the ionized fraction.

An accompanying low plasma *phosphate* is suggestive of inappropriate PTH secretion due to primary or tertiary hyperparathyroidism, or to ectopic hormone production. In the presence of a high plasma urea the presence of hyperphosphataemia does not exclude these causes, and because uraemia also tends to lower calcium levels the plasma urea, as well as phosphate and protein, should always be estimated when calcium metabolism is being investigated. If this estimation is normal an increase of both calcium and phosphate suggests that these three causes are unlikely.

In primary hyperparathyroidism the plasma *alkaline phosphatase* concentrations rise significantly only at a relatively late stage of the disease. A finding of a very high level with no clinical evidence of severe bone disease makes the diagnosis improbable. In the hypercalcaemia of malignant disease this enzyme may rise because of bony or hepatic metastases, and other signs of these should be sought. The alkaline phosphatase concentration is normal in myelomatosis (p. 242) unless there is a plasma cell deposit in the liver: in such a relatively rare case the enzyme can be shown to be of hepatic origin (p. 291). In sarcoidosis, as in malignant disease, the plasma alkaline phosphatase level may increase because of bony or hepatic infiltration. In the rare hypercalcaemia of severe thyrotoxicosis there may be some elevation of plasma concentrations of the enzyme, but in all other uncomplicated causes of hypercalcaemia it is normal.

A marked increase in plasma *protein* level, in the absence of clinical dehydration or of stasis in taking the blood, suggests myelomatosis as a cause, and this will often be evident on the electrophoretic pattern. If this cause is considered, *sternal puncture* must be performed, even in the presence of normal serum protein fractions.

Steroid Suppression Test

This test is by far the most useful one in the differential diagnosis of hypercalcaemia of obscure origin. In most cases it differentiates primary or tertiary hyperparathyroidism from any other cause. Large doses of hydrocortisone (or cortisone) result in a fall of high plasma calcium levels to those within the normal range in almost all cases *except primary hyperparathyroidism*. Exceptions do occasionally occur, but in most of them the clinical diagnosis is clear and the test unnecessary (for instance in very advanced malignant disease of bone or very severe hyperthyroidism). Details of the test are given in the Appendix (p. 198).

The reason for this difference in reaction to steroids is not clear. It is particularly interesting that the calcium level in many cases of ectopic parathormone production does suppress, whereas it fails to do so in those in which the hormone is produced in the parathyroid glands.

Urinary Calcium

This frequently requested estimation is of little diagnostic value in the differential diagnosis of hypercalcaemia. In the presence of normal renal function, hypercalcaemia from any cause, by increasing the load on the glomerulus, causes hypercalcuria. Urinary calcium excretion may also be increased in the so-called "*idiopathic hypercalcuria*" which is a cause of renal calculi, but not of hypercalcaemia, and in osteoporosis, when calcium cannot be deposited in normal amounts in bone because of a deficient matrix.

Calcium excretion may be normal or low if renal function is diminished, even in the presence of hypercalcaemia (whether due to hyperparathyroidism or to other causes).

Phosphate Excretion Tests

It was hoped that the phosphaturic effect of parathormone might help to differentiate hypercalcaemia due to excess of hormone from that due to other causes. Various tests were devised in which renal

TABLE XIII

DIFFERENTIAL DIAGNOSIS OF HYPERCALCAEMIA

Diagnosis	Plasma			Steroid suppression	Comments
	Phosphate	Proteins	Alk. Phos.		
Due to Raised Ionized Calcium					
Group 1. *Inappropriate Parathyroid Hormone*					
Primary or tertiary hyperparathyroidism	N or ↓	N	N or ↑	No	Calcium and phosphate changes masked in uraemia.
Malignancy with ectopic hormone production	N or ↓	N (↑ myeloma)	N or ↑ (N in myeloma)	Yes (usually)	
Group 2. *Vitamin D*					
Vitamin D overdosage	Variable	N	N	Yes	Rare
Sarcoidosis	Variable	γ glob. ↑	N or ↑	Yes	
Idiopathic hypercalcaemia of infancy	Variable	N	N	Yes	
Group 3. *Milk–Alkali Syndrome*	N or ↑	N	N or ↑	Yes	Very rare. HCO_3 ↑
Group 4. *Thyrotoxicosis*	N or ↑	N	N or ↑	Yes (usually)	Severe thyrotoxicosis. Thyroid function tests abnormal.
Due to Raised Protein Bound Calcium					
1. Dehydration	N or ↑	↑	N		Clinical signs of dehydration. Urea ↑ Corrected by rehydration.
2. Artefactual (excess stasis)	N or ↑	↑	N		Specimen taken without stasis gives normal values.

Hypercalcaemia due to raised protein bound calcium should *NOT* be treated.

phosphate clearance was compared with that of creatinine: the effect of renal failure in reducing phosphate excretion was thus allowed for. Results were disappointing, and the overlap between normals and abnormals so great that these tests have been abandoned.

Tests Used in the Differential Diagnosis of Hypocalcaemia

Plasma Levels

Reduced protein bound calcium.—As in the case of hypercalcaemia, hypocalcaemia due to a low protein bound fraction must be distinguished from that due to a low ionized fraction.

Just as protein bound calcium concentrations may be raised in haemoconcentration due to dehydration, so they may be reduced in overhydration. In such cases the protein and calcium levels will return to normal as hydration is restored.

In any condition associated with significant hypoalbuminaemia (p. 232) the protein bound calcium may be reduced. In malnutrition, whether due to malabsorption or to a deficient diet, there may be an accompanying reduction of ionized calcium due to associated vitamin D and calcium deficiency. In such cases treatment should not aim to restore the total calcium level to normal, but to maintain that of alkaline phosphatase within the normal range (i.e. to prevent osteomalacia).

Reduced ionized calcium levels.—If plasma albumin levels are normal, or only slightly reduced, a significant reduction in total calcium concentration can be assumed to be due to that of ionized calcium.

Accompanying high *phosphate* levels suggest either reduced circulating parathormone, or the failure of bone and kidney to respond to it in the rare pseudohypoparathyroidism. Hypophosphataemia with hypocalcaemia is associated with calcium and vitamin D deficiency.

High plasma *alkaline phosphatase* levels also suggest that calcium deficiency is the primary abnormality, which has led to increased parathormone secretion and resultant decalcification of bone (secondary hyperparathyroidism). This is most commonly due to malabsorption or to dietary deficiency, but may rarely be due to excessive renal loss consequent on renal tubular defects of phosphate absorption. A dietary history should be taken, tests for malabsorption (p. 223) performed if indicated by the bowel history, and if a renal defect is suspected, other evidence of tubular defects (e.g. glycosuria, aminoaciduria, failure to acidify the urine) sought.

A high plasma *urea* suggests that the hypocalcaemia is due to renal failure, and caution should be exercised in basing treatment on plasma calcium levels alone.

TABLE XIV
DIFFERENTIAL DIAGNOSIS OF HYPOCALCAEMIA

Diagnosis	Plasma				Ellsworth-Howard Test	Comments
	Phosphate	Proteins	Urea	Alk. Phos.		
Due to Low Ionized Calcium						
1. Hypoparathyroidism	↑	N	N	N	Increased response to PTH	
2. Calcium and vitamin D deficiency	↓	N or ↓	N	↑		May be accompanied by low protein bound calcium.
3. Renal failure	↑	N or ↓	↑	N or ↑		Should be treated with caution in absence of bone disease.
4. Pseudohypoparathyroidism	↑	N	N	N	Reduced response to PTH	Very rare.
Due to Low Protein Bound Calcium						
1. Overhydration	N or ↓	↓	N or ↓	N or ↓		Responds to fluid restriction.
2. Isolated protein deficiency	N	↓	N or ↓	N		

Hypocalcaemia due to lowered protein bound calcium should *NOT* be treated.

The Ellsworth-Howard Test

This test distinguishes between hypoparathyroidism and pseudo-hypoparathyroidism by measuring the increases in phosphate excretion in reponse to administered PTH. In true hypoparathyroidism the tubular cells can respond by producing a phosphaturia: in pseudohypopara-thyroidism they cannot; nor can the bone respond by releasing calcium into the plasma, and thus correcting hypocalcaemia (Appendix, p. 198).

BIOCHEMICAL BASIS OF TREATMENT

Hypercalcaemia

Mild hypercalcaemia.—If raised calcium levels of less than about 15 mg/100 ml are presented in a patient without serious symptoms of hypercalcaemia, there is no *immediate* need for urgent therapy. However, treatment should be instituted as soon as a diagnosis is made because of the danger of renal damage.

If possible the cause should be removed (e.g. a parathyroid adenoma, a primary malignant lesion, hyperthyroidism). If this is not possible hydrocortisone will reduce the levels within a day or two in many cases except that of primary (or tertiary) hyperparathyroidism (see "Steroid Suppression Test", p. 189). It may sometimes be relatively ineffective in malignant hypercalcaemia.

Oral sodium phosphate will tend to precipitate calcium phosphate in the intestine and remove calcium from the body. This treatment may be preferable to steroid therapy in many cases. It may be used, in conjunction with steroids, to treat intractable hypercalcaemia of late malignancy. The effect of oral phosphate, like that of steroids, is only manifested after 24 hours.

Severe hypercalcaemia.—If plasma calcium levels exceed about 15 mg/100 ml treatment is indicated as a matter of urgency, because of the danger of cardiac arrest.

Most measures available for lowering plasma calcium acutely (i.e. within a few hours) depend, partially at least, on precipitation of insoluble calcium salts. Since some of this precipitation may occur in the kidney, the treatment carries a slight risk of initiating or aggravating renal failure, and this risk should always be weighed against the danger of cardiac arrest. It is small in subjects with normal or only slightly raised plasma urea levels: although many cases show a transient rise of plasma urea at the start of treatment, this usually subsides rapidly.

Solutions which have been used for intravenous administration are either a mixture of sodium and potassium phosphates (see Appendix, p. 199) or sodium sulphate. The latter, though somewhat less effective, increases calcium loss in the urine with less theoretical danger of ectopic calcification: an effective dose of sulphate must be dissolved in relatively large volumes of water, and it should not be used in patients in whom there is a danger of fluid overloading. In practice intravenous phosphate is usually satisfactory (Appendix, p. 199).

Ethylene diamine tetraacetate (EDTA, sequestrene), a substance which chelates calcium, has been used, but has been shown to be nephrotoxic.

As with most other extracellular constituents, rapid changes in calcium level may be dangerous because time is not allowed for equilibration across cell membranes (see e.g. urea, p. 18 and sodium, p. 33). The aim of emergency treatment should be to lower calcium temporarily to safe levels, while initiating treatment for mild hypercalcaemia. A too rapid reduction of calcium concentration may induce tetany, or, more seriously, hypotension, even though the calcium is within or above normal levels. (Tetany in the presence of normocalcaemia may also occur during the rapid fall of serum calcium concentration after removal of a parathyroid adenoma.) A partial reduction of calcium also reduces the risk of renal calcification.

Hypocalcaemia

Asymptomatic hypocalcaemia.—Hypocalcaemia, whatever the cause, if asymptomatic or accompanied by only mild clinical symptoms, is usually treated with large doses of vitamin D by mouth. It is difficult to give enough oral calcium, by itself, to make a significant difference to plasma calcium levels and vitamin D, by increasing absorption of calcium, is usually adequate without calcium supplementation.

Therapy should be carefully controlled by very frequent plasma calcium estimations (daily in some cases). Even after stabilization the required dosage may vary, and because of the very real danger of precipitating hypercalcaemia the patient should be kept under regular observation so long as treatment continues. Treatment of calcium deficiency should also be monitored by frequent estimations of plasma alkaline phosphatase concentrations. As these approach normal, indicating that recalcification of bone is almost complete, the dose of vitamin D should be reduced: at this stage the serum calcium may rise suddenly if high dosage treatment is continued.

The hypocalcaemia of renal failure should be treated with caution in the absence of signs of osteomalacia (raised alkaline phosphatase, etc.), because of the danger of ectopic calcification in the presence of hyperphosphataemia. Hypocalcaemia associated with low protein levels should not be treated.

Hypocalcaemia with severe tetany.—In the presence of severe tetany hypocalcaemia should be treated, as an emergency, with intravenous calcium (usually as the gluconate).

MAGNESIUM METABOLISM

Magnesium is present with calcium in bone salts, and tends to move in and out of bone with calcium. It is also present in all cells of the body in much higher concentrations than those in the extracellular fluid, and therefore tends to enter and leave cells under the same conditions as do potassium and phosphate.

Magnesium can be lost in large quantities in the faeces in diarrhoea.

PLASMA MAGNESIUM AND ITS CONTROL

Probably some of the plasma magnesium, like calcium, is protein bound. However, less is known about the importance of this than in the case of calcium.

The mechanism of control of magnesium levels is poorly understood, but may involve the action of aldosterone and PTH.

CLINICAL EFFECT OF ABNORMAL PLASMA MAGNESIUM LEVELS

Hypomagnesaemia

This causes symptoms very similar to those of hypocalcaemia. If a patient with tetany has normal calcium, protein and bicarbonate (or, more accurately, blood pH) levels, blood should be taken for magnesium estimation. If there is good reason to suspect magnesium deficiency (e.g. in the presence of severe diarrhoea), and if it is not possible to get the result of the estimation reasonably quickly, intravenous magnesium should be administered as a therapeutic test (see Appendix, p. 200). Less severe magnesium deficiency should be treated orally (Appendix, p. 201).

Hypermagnesaemia

This causes muscular hypotonia, but as this condition is rarely seen in isolation, symptoms are difficult to distinguish from those of co-existent abnormalities (e.g. hypercalcaemia).

CAUSES OF ABNORMAL PLASMA MAGNESIUM LEVELS

Hypomagnesaemia

1. **Excessive loss of magnesium.**—Excessive loss of magnesium occurs in severe diarrhoea, and this is by far the most important cause of a clinical disturbance of magnesium metabolism requiring treatment.

2. **Hypomagnesaemia accompanied by hypocalcaemia.**—Magnesium tends to move in and out of bones in association with calcium, and hypocalcaemia is often accompanied by hypomagnesaemia. This may occur in hypoparathyroidism, or during the fall of calcium after the removal of a parathyroid adenoma, especially if severe bone disease is present.

3. **Hypomagnesaemia accompanied by hypokalaemia.**—Since magnesium moves in and out of cells with potassium, hypomagnesaemia tends to occur in association with hypokalaemia. These conditions include diuretic therapy and primary aldosteronism (p. 48). Such hypomagnesaemia is rarely of clinical importance.

Hypermagnesaemia

The commonest cause of hypermagnesaemia is probably renal failure (when serum potassium is also high). It rarely, if ever, requires treatment on its own, and it responds to measures to treat the underlying condition (e.g. haemodialysis). Magnesium salts should never be administered in renal failure.

SUMMARY

Calcium Metabolism

1. About half the calcium in plasma is bound to protein, and half is in the ionized form.

2. The ionized calcium is the physiologically important fraction and calcium levels should be interpreted with protein levels in mind.

3. Plasma calcium levels are controlled by parathyroid hormone. Parathyroid hormone secretion is increased if ionized calcium concentrations are reduced.

4. Parathyroid hormone acts:

(*a*) On bone, releasing calcium and phosphate into the plasma. Prolonged action increases osteoblastic activity and increases plasma alkaline phosphatase levels.

(*b*) On kidneys, causing phosphaturia, which lowers the serum phosphate.

5. Symptoms and findings in diseases of calcium metabolism can be related to circulating levels of ionized calcium, to levels of parathyroid hormone, and to renal function.

6. Excessive "inappropriate" levels of parathyroid hormone are present in primary parathyroid disease, or if the hormone is produced at ectopic sites. In these circumstances serum calcium is high.

7. Increased "appropriate" levels of parathyroid hormone are present whenever serum calcium levels fall.

8. Parathyroid hormone levels are low in hypoparathyroidism (associated with a low serum calcium), or in the presence of hypercalcaemia other than that of inappropriate parathyroid hormone production. The causes and differential diagnosis of hypercalcaemia and hypocalcaemia are summarized in Tables XIII and XIV.

Magnesium Metabolism

1. Hypomagnesaemia may cause tetany in the absence of hypocalcaemia.

2. The commonest cause of significant hypomagnesaemia is severe diarrhoea.

3. Magnesium levels tend to follow those of calcium (in and out of bone) and potassium (in and out of cells).

FURTHER READING

FOURMAN, P., and ROYER, P. (1968). *Calcium Metabolism and the Bone* 2nd edit. Oxford: Blackwell Scientific Publications.

APPENDIX TO CHAPTER VIII

DIAGNOSIS

STEROID SUPPRESSION TEST IN DIFFERENTIAL DIAGNOSIS OF HYPERCALCAEMIA
(Dent, C. E., and Watson, L. *Lancet*, 1968, **2**, 662)

All specimens for calcium estimation should be taken without venous stasis (p. 188).

Procedure

1. At least two specimens are taken on two different days before the test starts for estimation of plasma calcium, protein and urea concentrations.

2. The patient takes 120 mg of oral hydrocortisone a day in divided doses (40 mg, 8-hourly), for 10 days.

3. Blood is taken for estimation of plasma calcium, protein and urea concentration on the 5th, 8th and 10th day.

4. After the 10th day the dose of hydrocortisone is gradually reduced, as usual after steroid therapy.

Calculations

During administration of steroids there may be significant fluid retention. This will dilute the protein bound calcium and may lead to an apparent fall of calcium. To correct this it is desirable to "correct" total calcium results for changes in protein concentration, and a "standard" total protein of 7·2 g/100 ml is used in the calculation.

For every 0·3 g/100 ml that the protein concentration is *below* 7·2 g/100 ml, 0·25 mg/100 ml is *added* to the calcium level.

For every 0·3 g/100 ml that the protein concentration is *above* 7·2 g/100 ml, 0·25 mg/100 ml is *subtracted* from the calcium level.

This correction is a rough one, and is inaccurate in the presence of very abnormal plasma protein concentrations.

Interpretation

Failure of plasma calcium concentration to fall to within the normal range by the end of the test is strongly suggestive of *primary hyperparathyroidism*. For exceptions see p. 189.

ELLSWORTH-HOWARD TEST FOR HYPOPARATHYROIDISM

Caution

There is a diurnal variation in urinary phosphate excretion. It is therefore important that control collections are made at the same time of day as the test ones.

Collection bottles should contain acid to keep phosphate salts in solution.

Procedure

1. Parathyroid extract varies in potency. Each batch should be tested on a normal subject (as below) to ensure that it is capable of producing an adequate response.

2. The patient should fast overnight to eliminate variations due to diet.

3. *Control Day—6 a.m.* The patient empties his bladder and the specimen is discarded. All urine passed between this time and 9 a.m. should be put in collection bottle 1.

9 a.m. (1) Blood is taken for plasma calcium and protein estimation.
       (2) The patient empties his bladder and the specimen is added to collection bottle 1, which is now complete.
       All urine passed between this time and 12 noon should be put in collection bottle 2.

12 noon (1) The patient empties his bladder and the specimen is added to collection bottle 2, which is now complete.
       (2) Blood is taken for plasma calcium and protein estimation.

4. *Test Day—*6 a.m. to 9 a.m. as on control day.
9 a.m. 2 ml (200 units U.S.P.) parathyroid extract are given intravenously.
9 a.m. to 12 noon. Collection as on control day.

All four specimens (two from the control day and two from the test day) are analysed for total phosphate excretion per 3 hours.

Interpretation

The two urine collections on the control day are used to check that a spontaneous rise of phosphate excretion does not occur between the two specimens.

1. A significant rise of plasma calcium on the second, but not the first day indicates that the bone can respond to parathyroid hormone.

2. **Urinary phosphate.**—The *normal subject* should show a five- to six-fold increase in phosphate excretion in the 9 a.m. to 12 noon specimen over the 6 a.m. to 9 a.m. specimen on the test day.

A *hypoparathyroid* patient should show a 10-fold increase in the second specimen.

A patient with *pseudohypoparathyroidism* should show, at most, a two-fold increase in the second specimen.

TREATMENT

EMERGENCY TREATMENT OF HYPERCALCAEMIA

Solution for intravenous infusion contains

Na_2HPO_4 (anhydrous)—11·50 g ⎱
KH_2PO_4 (anhydrous)— 2·58 g ⎰ made up to 1 litre with water.

500 ml of this should be infused over 4–6 hours. This 500 ml will contain a total of 81 mEq of sodium and 9·5 mEq of potassium.

C.C.   8

Long-Term Oral Phosphate Treatment for Hypercalcaemia

Oral phosphate is given as the disodium or dipotassium salt. The choice depends on the serum potassium level.

1. The solution should contain 1 g phosphorus per 100 ml.

This is   46 g/litre of Na_2HPO_4 (anhydrous)
or   56 g/litre of K_2HPO_4 (anhydrous)

The dose is 100–300 ml per day in divided doses. 100 ml contains approximately 65 mEq of sodium or potassium respectively.

2. Phosphate Sandoz Effervescent tablets contain:

Phosphorus	500 mg	
Sodium	21 mEq	per tablet
Potassium	3 mEq	

The dose is 1–6 tablets daily.

3. Alternatively the phosphate can be given as sodium cellulose phosphate (Whatman) 5 g (the contents of one sachet), three times a day.

Note that hypokalaemia is a common accompaniment of hypercalcaemia. When this is present the phosphate preparation of choice is the K_2HPO_4.

Emergency Treatment of Hypocalcaemia

Calcium Gluconate Injection (B.P.)—9 mg calcium/ml.
Dose—10 ml intravenously in the first instance.

Oral Calcium Tablets

Calcium Gluconate (B.P.C.) (600 mg) = 54 mg of calcium per tablet.
Calcium Gluconate Effervescent (B.P.C.) (1000 mg) = 90 mg of calcium per tablet.
"Sandocal" Effervescent (4·5 g calcium gluconate) = 400 mg of calcium per tablet.
Calcium Sandoz Chocolate (1·5 g calcium gluconate) = 135 mg of calcium per tablet.
Calcium Lactate (B.P.) (300 mg) = 40 mg of calcium per tablet.
Calcium Lactate (B.P.) (600 mg) = 80 mg of calcium per tablet.

Emergency Treatment of Magnesium Deficiency

Magnesium Chloride ($MgCl_2.6H_2O$)—20 g/100 ml.
This contains 200 mEq of magnesium/100 ml and may be added to other intravenous fluid. If renal function is normal, up to 80 mEq (40 ml) may be infused in 24 hours.

ORAL MAGNESIUM THERAPY

Magnesium Chloride ($MgCl_2.6H_2O$)—20 g/100 ml.
The dose is 5–10 ml, q.d.s. Each 5 ml contains 10 mEq of magnesium. Note, however, that magnesium is poorly absorbed.

Chapter IX

INTESTINAL ABSORPTION: PANCREATIC AND GASTRIC FUNCTION

THE most important function of the gastro-intestinal tract is the digestion and absorption of nutrients. Many substances which are absorbed from the food also enter the intestinal tract via the mucosal cells so that net absorption may be less than true absorption (insorption): for instance, dietary fat is nearly completely absorbed under physiological circumstances, and almost all that found in normal faeces is of endogenous origin—a fact of importance in interpretation of faecal fat values (p. 224).

Digestion of larger molecules involves the action of intestinal enzymes: if these are to act under optimal conditions the nutrient molecules must be dispersed as much as possible, firstly by mechanical action such as chewing, and secondly by mixture of the food with fluid. Enzymes act best in the presence of certain electrolytes and at certain pH values; the fluid secreted contains these ions and varying amounts of hydrogen ion. Before the smaller water-soluble molecules can pass through the intestinal cells they must be in solution and this, too, requires fluid at the correct pH. The very large amounts of electrolyte and water secreted into the gastro-intestinal tract have already been mentioned, and it has been pointed out that normally about 99 per cent of the sodium and water are reabsorbed (p. 26). In this context the gastro-intestinal tract acts in much the same way as the kidney (if we consider that gastro-intestinal secretions are in some ways analogous with the glomerular filtrate): water, sodium and potassium are reabsorbed throughout the small intestine, as they are in the proximal renal tubule. Final adjustment is made in the colon where, for instance, aldosterone stimulates sodium reabsorption and potassium secretion as it does in the distal renal tubule, and where final water reabsorption occurs. Disturbances of water and electrolyte metabolism and of acid-base balance are therefore common in diarrhoea due to extensive small intestinal or colonic disease, or when there is direct loss of fluid and electrolyte from the upper intestinal tract through vomiting or fistulae. They also occur if absorption from the upper intestinal cells is so grossly impaired that the amounts of fluid and electrolyte entering distal parts exceed the reabsorptive capacity: this effect is similar to that of an increased glomerular filtration rate and of osmotic diuretics on the volume and composition of urine (p. 35 and p. 7). These disturbances of electrolyte, water and acid-base metabolism have been discussed in Chapters II and III.

In this chapter we are concerned with disturbances of the absorptive mechanisms, either due to abnormality of absorptive cells of the small intestine, or to failure of normal digestion of food. Unless malabsorption is gross, causing severe intestinal hurry, water, electrolyte and acid-base disturbances are relatively unimportant in malabsorptive syndromes. The effects are largely those of disturbed nutrition, since nutrient cannot pass through the intestinal cells.

NORMAL DIGESTION AND CONVERSION
OF NUTRIENT TO AN ABSORBABLE FORM

Complex molecules such as those of protein, polysaccharides and fat are usually broken down by digestive enzymes. This process starts in the mouth, where food is mechanically broken down by chewing and is mixed with saliva containing *amylase*. In the stomach further fluid is added and the low pH initiates protein digestion by *pepsin*. The stomach also secretes *intrinsic factor* necessary for absorption of vitamin B_{12}. However, quantitatively by far the most important digestion takes place in the duodenum and upper jejunum, where large volumes of alkaline fluid are added to the already liquid food. Pancreatic enzymes in this fluid convert protein to amino-acids and small peptides, polysaccharides to mono- and disaccharides and oligosaccharides (consisting of a small number of monosaccharide units), and fat to monoglycerides and fatty acids. From the pathological point of view, severe generalized malabsorption due to failure of *digestion* is most commonly due to pancreatic disease.

NORMAL ABSORPTION

Normal absorption depends on:

1. The integrity and normal surface area of absorptive cells.

2. The presence of the substance to be absorbed in an absorbable form (and therefore on normal digestion).

3. A normal ratio of speed of absorption to speed of passage of contents through the intestinal tract.

The *absorptive area* of the intestine is normally very large. Macroscopically the mucosa forms *folds*, increasing the area considerably. Microscopically, these folds are further folded into *villi*, lined with absorptive cells: this further increases the area about eight-fold.

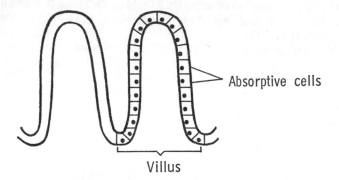

Absorptive cells

Villus

If these villi are flattened, as they are, for instance, in idiopathic steatorrhoea, the absorptive area is much reduced.

Each intestinal absorptive cell has on its surface a large number of minute projections (*microvilli*) detectable with the electron microscope, further increasing absorptive area by about 20-fold.

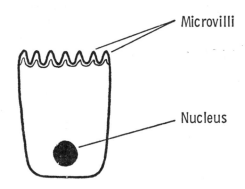

Microvilli

Nucleus

Minute passages exist between the microvilli (*microvillous spaces*).

To be absorbable, the substances must be in the form of relatively *small molecules*, such as result from normal digestion. Absorption may be dependent on the formation of a *complex* (such as that of vitamin B_{12} with intrinsic factor) that can attach to the intestinal cells and bring the substance in a spatially advantageous position for absorption. The method of absorption depends on whether the molecule is *water soluble* or *lipid soluble*. Lipid soluble nutrients frequently share the mechanisms for fat absorption. Absorption may be *active*, in which case it can occur against a physicochemical gradient, or *passive* when it passes along physicochemical gradients (for a more complete definition of these processes see p. 2).

LIPID ABSORPTION

Digestion of Neutral Fats

Neutral fats (triglycerides) contain glycerol with three fatty acids. These fatty acids are usually three different ones (R_1, R_2, R_3).

$$CH_2OR_1$$
$$|$$
$$CHOR_2$$
$$|$$
$$CH_2OR_3$$

In shorthand notation this can be written

The *lipase* of pancreatic juice releases the fatty acids from glycerol by hydrolysis and has a predilection for the fatty acids in positions 1 and 3. The end result is production of some diglycerides, but mainly the 2-monoglycerides together with free fatty acids.

Before lipase can act efficiently *bile salts* emulsify the fat to small droplets, allowing easier access of the enzyme to the fat molecules.

Micelle Formation

The resultant monoglyceride and fatty acids aggregate with bile salts to form a *micelle*: the micelle also contains free *cholesterol* (liberated by hydrolysis in the lumen from cholesterol esters) and *phospholipids*, as well as *fat soluble vitamins* (A, D and K). The diameter of the micelle is between 100 and 1000 times as small as that of the emulsion particle and is small enough to pass through the microvillous spaces: it is also negatively charged, which is necessary if it is to pass through these spaces.

Lipids in the Intestinal Cell

In the intestinal cell monoglycerides and fatty acids are resynthesized to triglycerides. Cholesterol is reesterified. The triglycerides, cholesterol esters and phospholipids, together with the fat soluble vitamins, are coated with a layer of lipoprotein (manufactured in the cell) to form *chylomicrons* (p. 253). These are readily suspended in water and probably pass through the cell wall into the lymphatic circulation.

Absorption of Free Fatty Acids

A significant proportion of free fatty acids pass through the intestinal cell into the portal blood stream.

From this account it will be seen that absorption of the following constituents of food,

> Neutral fat
> Cholesterol
> Phospholipids
> Fat soluble vitamins,

depends on:

1. Normal emulsification of fats, and therefore the presence of *bile salts*.

2. Normal digestion of neutral fat by *lipase* and therefore normal pancreatic function.

3. Normal *intestinal mucosa* for formation of the chylomicron and a normal absorptive area.

Bile salts are synthesized in the liver from cholesterol. They enter the intestinal tract in the bile and are reabsorbed in the distal ileum. They are recirculated to the liver and resecreted into the bile (the "enterohepatic circulation"). Resection of the distal ileum may prevent reabsorption and re-use of bile salts, and stimulate their resynthesis from cholesterol. The plasma cholesterol concentration may fall as a result, but this is probably of little clinical importance.

Some intestinal bacteria convert bile salts to bile acids and thus inactivate them: some of the bile acids formed may be toxic.

CARBOHYDRATE ABSORPTION

Polysaccharides such as starch and glycogen are hydrolyzed by amylase (salivary and pancreatic, the latter being of the greater importance) to disaccharides such as maltose (glucose + glucose).

Disaccharides (maltose, sucrose (glucose + fructose) and lactose (glucose + galactose)) are hydrolyzed to their constituent monosaccharides by the appropriate disaccharidase (maltase, sucrase or lactase): these enzymes are not secreted in intestinal juices, but are present on the surface of the intestinal cell where the hydrolysis takes place.

Monosaccharides are absorbed in the duodenum. Glucose and galactose are probably absorbed by a common active process, while fructose is absorbed by a different mechanism apparently not requiring metabolic energy.

Thus carbohydrate absorption depends on:

1. The presence of *amylase*, and therefore on normal pancreatic function (polysaccharides only).

2. The presence of *disaccharidases* on the intestinal cell (disaccharides).

3. Normal *intestinal cells* with normal active transport mechanisms (monosaccharides).

Note that absorption of polysaccharides requires normal function of all three mechanisms.

PROTEIN ABSORPTION

Protein is broken down by pepsin, followed by trypsin and the other proteolytic enzymes of pancreatic juice. The products are amino-acids and small peptides.

Amino-acids are actively absorbed in the small intestine.

Small peptides may be hydrolyzed on the cell surface (compare disaccharide absorption), or be absorbed into the cell intact and hydrolyzed intracellularly. It is not yet clear which of these mechanisms is responsible for peptide absorption.

Protein absorption therefore depends on:

1. The presence of *pancreatic proteolytic enzymes* and therefore on normal pancreatic function.

2. Normal *intestinal cells* with normal active transport mechanisms.

VITAMIN B_{12} ABSORPTION

Vitamin B_{12} can be absorbed only when it has formed a complex with *intrinsic factor*, a mucopolysaccharide secreted by the stomach: in this form it can bind to the intestinal cell where it is absorbed, mainly in the lower ileum. Its absorption therefore depends on:

1. Normal *gastric secretion*.
2. Normal *intestinal cells* in the *lower ileum*.

Some intestinal bacteria require vitamin B_{12} for growth and prevent its absorption by mechanisms probably involving competition with the intestinal cells for it. Normal absorption therefore also depends on:
    3. Normal *intestinal flora.*

ABSORPTION OF OTHER WATER SOLUBLE VITAMINS

Most of the water soluble vitamins (C and all those of the B group except B_{12}) are absorbed, probably by passive mechanisms, mainly in the upper small intestine. Since their absorption does not require an active process and is not dependent on fat absorption, clinical deficiencies of these (with the exception of folate) are relatively uncommon in malabsorption syndromes.

ELECTROLYTE AND WATER ABSORPTION

Much electrolyte and water absorption is really reabsorption of the contents of intestinal secretions.

Sodium and potassium are probably absorbed by an active process throughout the small intestine, much as they are in the renal tubule: many other active transport mechanisms depend on metabolic energy provided by the sodium pump. In the colon sodium-potassium exchange is stimulated by aldosterone.

Chloride absorption in the small intestine probably follows the electrochemical gradient created by absorption of sodium and other cations. In the colon chloride is absorbed in exchange for bicarbonate (see p. 76).

Water is probably absorbed passively, as in the proximal renal tubule, along an osmotic gradient created by absorption of sodium, sugars, amino-acids and other solutes. If these solutes cannot be absorbed normally water is "held" in the intestinal lumen (see "dumping syndrome" p. 214 and disaccharidase deficiency p. 218). Final water absorption occurs in the colon.

CALCIUM AND MAGNESIUM ABSORPTION

Calcium is actively absorbed in the upper small intestine, particularly the duodenum and upper jejunum. Normal calcium absorption depends on its presence in an ionized form (it is inhibited by the formation of insoluble salts with phosphate, fatty acids and phytate), and on the presence of vitamin D. Much of the faecal calcium is endogenous and derived from calcium in intestinal secretions.

Magnesium is also absorbed by an active process and may share in the calcium pathway.

Normal calcium and magnesium absorption depends on:

1. A *low concentration of fatty acids*, phosphate and phytate in the intestine.
2. The absorption of *vitamin D* and therefore on normal fat absorption.
3. Normal *intestinal cells*.

IRON ABSORPTION

Iron is absorbed by an active process in the duodenum and upper jejunum, and absorption is stimulated by anaemia (p. 309). Some of the iron absorbed into the intestinal cell enters the blood but some stays in the cell and is lost into the intestine when this is desquamated (p. 308). Pancreatic juice inhibits iron absorption.

We are now in a position to understand the consequences of disorders of digestion and absorption. From the above account it should be noted that:

1. *Pancreatic failure* affects absorption of large molecules only (fats, polysaccharides and protein).
2. *Disease of the intestinal cells* affects absorption of small molecules and products of digestion of large molecules.
3. Absence of *bile salts* causes malabsorption of fats and of those substances sharing mechanisms for fat absorption.

MALABSORPTION SYNDROMES

From the clinical point of view the malabsorption syndromes can be divided into those associated with generalized malabsorption of fat, protein and carbohydrate and those associated with failure to absorb one or more specific substances.

GENERALIZED MALABSORPTION (ASSOCIATED WITH STEATORRHOEA)

Intestinal Disease

1. Reduction of absorptive surface or general impairment of transport mechanisms.

> Gluten sensitivity causing:
> > Coeliac disease (in children)
> > Idiopathic steatorrhoea (in adults)
> Tropical sprue
> Extensive surgical resection of small intestine.

2. Extensive infiltration or inflammation of small intestinal wall (for example, Crohn's disease, amyloidosis, scleroderma).

3. Increased rate of passage through the small intestine:
Post-gastrectomy
Carcinoid syndrome.

Pancreatic Disease (Failure of Digestion)
Chronic pancreatitis
Fibrocystic disease of the pancreas.

FAILURE OF ABSORPTION OF SPECIFIC SUBSTANCES

1. Altered bacterial flora (fat, p. 206; vitamin B_{12}, p. 207):
Blind loop syndrome
Diverticula
Surgery
Antibiotic therapy.

2. Biliary obstruction (fat and substances dependent on fat absorption, p. 206).
3. Local disease or surgery (for instance, disease of the terminal ileum affects vitamin B_{12} absorption).
4. Pernicious anaemia (vitamin B_{12}).
5. Disaccharidase deficiency:
Congenital
Acquired.
6. Protein-losing enteropathy.
7. Isolated transport defects resulting from inborn metabolic errors (p. 338).

GENERALIZED MALABSORPTION

Coeliac disease and idiopathic steatorrhoea are by far the commonest causes of generalized malabsorption in moderate climates. In these diseases sensitivity to gluten (in wheat germ) causes flattening of intestinal villi and considerable reduction in absorptive area. The flattening of the villi may be demonstrated on intestinal biopsy specimens. Most of these cases respond to treatment with a gluten-free diet, but this improvement may not be evident for some months.

In **tropical sprue** there is also flattening of the villi, but these cases do not respond to a gluten-free diet. They do respond to broad spectrum antibiotics, suggesting that bacterial infection is an important aetiological factor in the disease.

Extensive surgical resection of the small intestine may so reduce the absorptive area as to cause malabsorption.

Extensive infiltration and inflammation of small intestinal mucosa may damage its ability to carry out absorptive processes. This may be aggravated by the presence of altered bacterial flora in these conditions.

After gastrectomy normal mixing of food with fluid, acid and pepsin does not occur in the stomach, so that the activity of enzymes in the small intestine is less efficient than usual. Passage of intestinal contents through the duodenum is also more rapid than usual. In spite of this, post-gastrectomy malabsorption is rarely severe, and clinically "dumping" and hypoglycaemic attacks are more troublesome (p. 214).

The carcinoid syndrome (p. 371) is due to the excessive production of 5-hydroxytryptamine (5HT) by tumours of argentaffin cells usually arising in the small intestine, and by their metastases, usually in the liver. This is a rare disease which even more rarely presents a problem of differential diagnosis of malabsorption. The malabsorption is probably the result of increased intestinal motility induced by 5HT. Diagnosis depends on the presence of the other clinical features of the disease, and on an increased excretion of 5-hydroxyindole acetic acid in the urine.

In pancreatic disease (due most commonly to *chronic pancreatitis*) failure of absorption is due to failure of digestion and predominantly affects large molecules. *Fibrocystic disease of the pancreas* (*cystic fibrosis: mucoviscidosis*) is an inherited disease, usually presenting in early childhood but, more rarely, first recognized in the adult patient. Pancreatic and bronchial secretions are viscid, and by blocking pancreatic ducts and bronchi cause obstructive disease of these organs. Sweat glands are also affected and the diagnosis depends on the demonstration of an *increase in concentration of sweat electrolytes*, often to about twice normal (p. 38). The patient may present with pulmonary disease, or with malabsorption. In the latter case this syndrome must be differentiated from coeliac disease.

Results of Generalized Malabsorption

The most obvious finding common to generalized intestinal and pancreatic malabsorption is *steatorrhoea* (more than 5–6 g of fat in the stools per day—see Appendix, p. 223). In gross steatorrhoea the stools are usually pale, greasy and bulky and, if the condition is extensive, there may be diarrhoea. In intestinal malabsorption fat can be acted on by lipase, but the products cannot be absorbed normally. In pancreatic steatorrhoea the intestinal wall is normal but fat cannot be digested. The collections of specimens for faecal fat estimation must be carefully controlled if a reliable answer is to be obtained (Appendix, p. 223).

Malabsorption of fat is always accompanied by malabsorption of the substances listed on p. 206. *Vitamin D deficiency* impairs calcium absorption and this is one of the causes of a low level of circulating ionized calcium and of osteomalacia in malabsorption syndromes. *Vitamin K* is required for prothrombin formation in the liver, and severe cases of malabsorption may develop a haemorrhagic diathesis associated with a prolonged prothrombin time: this prothrombin deficiency, unlike that of liver disease, can be reversed by parenteral administration of vitamin K. *Vitamin A* deficiency is rarely clinically evident, although malabsorption of an oral dose of vitamin A can be demonstrated. Malabsorption of lipids causes low plasma *cholesterol* levels—an incidental finding of no diagnostic importance.

The *low ionized calcium level and osteomalacia* due to vitamin D malabsorption is aggravated by the formation of insoluble calcium soaps with unabsorbed fatty acids in intestinal malabsorption. If ionized calcium levels have been low for a sufficiently long time to cause osteomalacia the *plasma alkaline phosphatase* concentration will rise. Secondary hyperparathyroidism due to the low ionized calcium level causes phosphaturia with a low plasma phosphate (p. 182). If the ionized calcium levels fall very low *tetany* may result.

Protein malabsorption occurs in intestinal disease because intestinal transport mechanisms are impaired: in pancreatic disease protein cannot be completely hydrolyzed to amino-acids. In either case prolonged disease causes generalized *muscle and tissue wasting* and *osteoporosis* (p. 186), and a lowering of all protein fractions in the blood. The low albumin may cause oedema (p. 46) and results in a reduction of *protein bound calcium* (p. 191). The total calcium level may therefore give a false idea of the severity of the hypocalcaemia. Reduced *antibody formation* (γ globulins) predisposes to infection.

Thus in generalized malabsorption, whether pancreatic or intestinal, the *clinical picture* may be as follows:

Bulky, fatty stools, with or without diarrhoea.
General wasting and malnutrition (protein deficiency).
Osteoporosis and osteomalacia (protein and calcium deficiency).
Oedema (albumin deficiency).
Haemorrhages (vitamin K deficiency).
Tetany (calcium deficiency).
Recurrent infections (γ globulin deficiency).

The *laboratory findings* are:

Increased excretion of fat in the stools.
Hypocalcaemia (ionized and protein bound)—with hypophosphataemia.

Raised alkaline phosphatase levels in cases with osteomalacia.
Generalized lowering of the concentration of all protein fractions.
Possibly a low urea (due to decreased production from amino-acids).
Hypocholesterolaemia.
Prolonged prothrombin time.

The complete picture is only seen in advanced cases of the syndrome. It is important to realize that generalized malabsorption may present as osteomalacia, with bone pains.

Differential Diagnosis of Generalized Intestinal and Pancreatic Malabsorption

Tests of pancreatic function are generally unsatisfactory (see below), and the differential diagnosis of steatorrhoea is usually made on indirect evidence. Remember that pancreatic malabsorption affects large molecules predominantly.

Malabsorption of fat occurs in both types of disease. Theoretically, in pancreatic malabsorption fat should be predominantly present as triglyceride (neutral fat), while in intestinal disease free fatty acids should be present. However, the estimation of so-called "split" and "unsplit" fat in the stools has been abandoned as it provides no useful information because of the action of fat-splitting bacteria in the lower intestinal tract: if a small amount of stool is emulsified on a micro-scopic slide the presence of many fat globules (triglyceride) suggests a pancreatic cause. Similarly, the presence of many undigested meat fibres (striated muscle) in the stool is suggestive of a pancreatic rather than intestinal origin. This examination requires experience, and is rarely helpful if other estimations are available.

Differences in carbohydrate metabolism.—Polysaccharide absorption is impaired in both conditions. However, some of the carbohydrate in the diet is in the form of mono- and disaccharides and these can be absorbed in pancreatic disease when neither intestinal disaccharidase activity nor active monosaccharide absorption is affected. Hypo-glycaemia is rare in either condition, but is probably more common in intestinal malabsorption: however, in this type of malabsorption im-paired absorption of a glucose load is often evident in a "flat" *glucose tolerance curve* (but see p. 140). In pancreatic disease this curve may be normal, but as insulin is of pancreatic origin the curve may even be diabetic in type.

Because glucose is rapidly metabolized in the body, interpretation of the glucose tolerance curve as an index of the type of malabsorption may be difficult. *Xylose* is a pentose, not rapidly metabolized in mam-malian tissues and filtered by the renal glomerulus. There is an active transport mechanism for xylose in the intestinal mucosa, although this is relatively inefficient (p. 224). If an oral dose of xylose is given, and if the intestinal mucosa is normal, it will be absorbed and appear in the urine: if, however, there is disease of intestinal cells it will not be absorbed normally and less will appear in the blood and urine. This is the basis of the *xylose absorption test* which is usually normal in pancreatic malabsorption and abnormal in intestinal disease.

Anaemia is more common in intestinal than in pancreatic malabsorption since iron, vitamin B_{12} and folate are not digested by pancreatic enzymes before absorption; iron absorption may even be increased in pancreatic disease, because pancreatic juice inhibits iron absorption. In intestinal malabsorption the blood and bone marrow films typically show a mixed iron deficiency and megaloblastic picture. Malabsorption of iron, vitamin B_{12} and folate may be demonstrable and the absorption of vitamin B_{12} is not increased by the simultaneous administration of intrinsic factor, as it is in pernicious anaemia (see p. 217). Anaemia may be aggravated by protein deficiency.

The differential diagnosis is summarized in Table XV.

The Post-Gastrectomy Syndrome

Malabsorption after gastrectomy is usually mild. However, rapid passage of the contents of the small gastric remnant into the duodenum may have two clinical consequences:

1. **The "dumping syndrome".**—Soon after a meal the patient may experience abdominal discomfort and feel faint and sick. The syndrome is thought to be due to the sudden passage of fluid of high osmotic content into the duodenum. Before this abnormally large load can be absorbed, water passes along the osmotic gradient from the extracellular fluid into the lumen of the intestine. The reduction in plasma volume causes faintness and the large volume of duodenal fluid causes abdominal discomfort.

2. **Post-gastrectomy hypoglycaemia.**—If a meal containing much glucose passes more rapidly than normal into the duodenum glucose absorption is very rapid. The blood glucose level rises suddenly and causes an outpouring of insulin. The resultant "over-swing" of blood glucose concentration may cause hypoglycaemic symptoms which typically occur at about two hours after a meal. The glucose tolerance curve in this type of case is "lag storage" in type.

Both these disabilities can be improved if meals low in carbohydrate content are taken "little and often".

Tests of Exocrine Pancreatic Function

It is convenient to digress here to discuss tests of the ability of the pancreas to secrete digestive juices. Unfortunately such tests of pancreatic function are very unsatisfactory. In chronic pancreatic hypo-function the diagnosis is usually made by the indirect methods described above. Carcinoma of the pancreas is very difficult to diagnose unless the lesion is in the head of the organ, and causes obstructive jaundice: extensive gland destruction may cause late onset diabetes. Acute pancreatitis, however, may usually be diagnosed by estimation of plasma amylase levels.

Plasma enzymes.—Measurements of plasma *amylase* levels usually show little change from normal in pancreatic disease except in acute pancreatitis (see below), when they may be raised. In chronic pancreatic hypofunction low levels can rarely be demonstrated, possibly because of the presence of amylase of hepatic and salivary gland origin, and the estimation is useless. Plasma *lipase* estimation is technically not very suitable for routine use.

Faecal trypsin levels are extremely variable, probably because of bacterial action. The estimation is of no value in diagnosis of pancreatic hypofunction in adults. In infants with diarrhoea its absence is suggestive of fibrocystic disease of the pancreas.

Duodenal enzymes.—Measurement of pancreatic enzymes and bicarbonate in duodenal aspirate before and after stimulation of the pancreas with secretin or pancreozymin (hormones stimulating the pancreas which are normally secreted during digestion) is not very suitable for routine use because of difficulty in positioning the duodenal tube correctly and in quantitative sampling of the secretions.

Acute Pancreatitis

In acute pancreatitis necrosis of the cells of the organ results in release of their enzymes into the peritoneal cavity and blood stream. The presence of pancreatic juice in the peritoneal cavity causes *severe abdominal pain* and *shock*: this picture is common to many acute abdominal emergencies. A vicious circle is set up as more pancreatic cells are digested by the released enzymes.

Acute pancreatitis is most commonly the result of obstruction of the pancreatic duct, or of regurgitation of bile along this duct. The most important predisposing factors are *alcoholism* and *biliary tract disease*. *Trauma* to the pancreas by damaging the cells may also initiate the vicious circle.

Typically plasma amylase values reach more than 1000 Somogyi units (the "normal" value is less than 200 Somogyi units). However, it is important to realize that concentrations of up to, and even above, this value may be reached in any acute abdominal emergency, but especially after gastric perforation into the lesser sac: very high levels may occur in renal failure when the enzyme cannot be excreted normally, and these are usually asymptomatic. Conversely, levels in acute pancreatitis may not reach very high levels, and usually fall very rapidly as the enzyme is lost in the urine. High plasma amylase levels are therefore only a rough guide to the presence of acute pancreatitis.

As the released fatty acids form soaps with calcium, plasma calcium levels may fall. This may be a useful sign when amylase concentrations have fallen to normal (a few days after the acute attack).

Malabsorption probably does occur during acute pancreatitis but is of little importance in the acute phase. Chronic pancreatic failure may follow a severe attack and is especially probable following repeated attacks.

FAILURE OF ABSORPTION OF SPECIFIC SUBSTANCES

1. Altered Bacterial Flora (Malabsorption of Vitamin B_{12} and Fat)

The "Blind Loop syndrome".—This syndrome is associated with stagnation of intestinal contents with a consequent alteration of bacterial flora, and occurs when the loops are the result of surgery, or in the presence of *diverticula*.

Treatment with broad spectrum antibiotics, by altering bacterial flora, may cause a similar syndrome.

Many intestinal bacteria require vitamin B_{12} and folate for metabolism, and *macrocytic anaemia* is common in the syndrome. Bile salts may be metabolized to bile acids with resultant *steatorrhoea* and malabsorption of all those substances associated with fat absorption (p. 206). Protein and carbohydrate are usually normally absorbed.

2. Biliary Obstruction (Malabsorption of Fat)

Bile salts are synthesized and secreted by the liver. In biliary obstruction these cannot reach the intestinal lumen in normal amounts, and *steatorrhoea* results with the usual consequences (p. 206). Because of extreme jaundice there is rarely any difficulty in the differential diagnosis.

Differential Diagnosis of Steatorrhoea

The malabsorptive conditions described so far are all associated with steatorrhoea. As has been mentioned, biliary obstruction is rarely a problem of diagnosis. The important points in laboratory findings in differential diagnosis of the other conditions are summarized in Table XV.

3. Local Disease or Surgery

As a few substances are absorbed in significant amounts only in certain areas of the small intestine, local disease or resection of such an area will cause selective malabsorption. The lower ileum is concerned

TABLE XV

DIFFERENTIAL DIAGNOSIS OF STEATORRHOEA

	Intestinal	Pancreatic	Blind Loop Syndrome
Xylose absorption	Reduced	Normal	Normal
Glucose Tolerance Test	Flat (except post-gastrectomy)	Normal or diabetic	Normal
Anaemia	Mixed macrocytic and iron deficiency common	Rare	Macrocytic common
Intestinal Biopsy	May show flattened villi or other cause	Normal	Normal

with vitamin B_{12} absorption and with reabsorption of bile salts, and re-section or disease of this area (for example, Crohn's disease), may cause macrocytic anaemia.

4. Pernicious Anaemia

Vitamin B_{12} cannot be absorbed in the absence of intrinsic factor (p. 207). In pernicious anaemia the stomach cannot secrete this substance and significant deficiency may occur after total gastrectomy or with extensive malignant infiltration of the stomach.

The Schilling test.—In such subjects malabsorption of vitamin B_{12} can be demonstrated if a small dose of the radioactive vitamin is given and its excretion in the urine measured (compare xylose absorption test, p. 214). If the malabsorption is due to pernicious anaemia, administration of the labelled vitamin together with intrinsic factor results in normal absorption: if it is due to intestinal disease malabsorption persists. To ensure that the labelled vitamin is quantitatively excreted in the urine, stores should be "saturated" before the start of the test by giving a large dose of non-radioactive vitamin B_{12}. Haematological tests such as examination of blood and marrow films should have been completed before the vitamin B_{12} is given.

5. Disaccharidase Deficiency

Generalized disease of the intestinal wall usually causes a non-selective disaccharidase deficiency, because these enzymes are located on the surface of the absorptive cells: this is relatively unimportant compared with the general malabsorption and tests for this syndrome are therefore useful only in the absence of steatorrhoea when a selective rather than a generalized malabsorption of carbohydrate may be present.

The *symptoms* of disaccharidase deficiency are those of the effects of unabsorbed, osmotically active sugars in the intestinal tract, and include faintness, abdominal discomfort and severe diarrhoea after ingestion of the offending disaccharide. (Compare the "dumping syndrome", p. 214.)

Lactase deficiency occurs in the following conditions:

1. *Congenital lactase deficiency.*—This is very rare. Infants present soon after birth with severe diarrhoea. Stools are typically acid because of bacterial production of lactic acid from lactose. The syndrome is cured by removal of milk and milk products from the diet.

2. *Lactase deficiency associated with prematurity.*—In premature infants lactase may not be present in normal amounts in intestinal cells. Initially these cases resemble the last group. However, the sensitivity to milk usually disappears within a few days of birth.

3. *Acquired lactase deficiency* is much more common than the congenital form and is probably the commonest type of disaccharidase deficiency: it presents in later life. It may be due to a sensitivity reaction.

Congenital sucrase deficiency is more common than congenital lactase deficiency.

Acquired sucrase deficiency and *maltase deficiency* of any kind are very rare.

The *diagnosis* of all types of disaccharidase deficiency depends on oral administration of the relevant disaccharide, and measurement of blood glucose levels, as in the glucose tolerance test. If the disaccharide cannot be hydrolyzed the constituent glucose cannot be absorbed and the curve is flat. The result should be compared with a glucose tolerance curve performed with an equivalent amount of glucose (in the case of lactose, which consists of one mole of glucose combined with one mole of galactose, the equivalent dose of glucose in grams is half that of lactose).

The most reliable test for deficiency is estimation of disaccharidases in intestinal biopsy tissue.

Radiological examination may assist in the diagnosis of disaccharidase deficiency. Barium is administered without, and then with, the disaccharide. When the sugar is not absorbed the flocculation pattern of barium is altered by its osmotic effect.

6. Protein Losing Enteropathy

This is a very rare syndrome in which the intestinal wall is abnormally permeable to large molecules (as the glomerulus is in the nephrotic syndrome). This is not strictly speaking a malabsorptive syndrome, but is due to excessive loss of protein from the body into the gut. It occurs in a variety of conditions in which there is ulceration of the bowel, lymphatic obstruction and intestinal lymphangiectasis, or hypertrophic lesions of the bowel. Typically it is only rarely associated with steatorrhoea, and the clinical picture, like that of the nephrotic syndrome (p. 11), is due to hypoalbuminaemia: protein is not usually found in the urine.

In this syndrome the hypoproteinaemia is probably not entirely due to loss from the body, because some of the protein which passes into the intestinal tract is digested and the amino-acids reabsorbed. However, the rate of protein breakdown probably exceeds the rate at which the reabsorbed amino-acids can be resynthesized into protein.

Diagnosis can be made by measuring the loss into the bowel after intravenous injection of a substance of a molecular weight approximating that of albumin: substances that have been used are radioactive polyvinylpyrrolidone (PVP) or albumin. Typically the electrophoretic pattern is similar to that found in the nephrotic syndrome: as in that syndrome the relatively high molecular weight α_2 fraction is retained in the blood stream while all other fractions are lost from the body.

GASTRIC FUNCTION

The important components of gastric secretion are *hydrochloric acid, pepsin* and *intrinsic factor*. All these factors have already been mentioned as being of importance in digestion and absorption, and loss of hydrochloric acid in pyloric stenosis has been discussed as a cause of metabolic alkalosis (p. 77).

Stimulation of gastric secretion occurs by two main pathways:

1. Through the *vagus nerve*, which in turn responds to stimuli from the cerebral cortex, normally resulting from the sight, smell and taste of food. Hypoglycaemia can stimulate this pathway and this fact can be used to assess the completeness of vagotomy.

2. By *gastrin*, a hormone normally produced by the pyloric glands in response to the presence of food, and carried by the blood stream to the stomach where it stimulates secretion.

HYPERSECRETION

Hypersecretion of gastric juice may be associated with *duodenal ulceration*, when it may be neurogenic in origin.

In the *Zollinger-Ellison syndrome* non-β cell tumours of the pancreatic islets produce large amounts of gastrin: of these tumours about 60 per cent are malignant; of the remaining 40 per cent two-thirds are multiple and only one-third (17 per cent of the total) are single, resectable adenomata. Acid secretion by the stomach in this condition is very high. The consequent ulceration of the stomach and upper small intestine may cause severe diarrhoea. Benign adenomata may be found in other endocrine glands, such as the parathyroid, pituitary, thyroid and adrenal (multiple endocrine adenomatosis): these are only occasionally functional.

HYPOSECRETION

Hyposecretion of gastric juice occurs in *pernicious anaemia* (p. 217) and is possibly the result of antibodies to intrinsic factor: this is by far the commonest cause, and the achlorhydria is usually "histamine fast" (p. 221). In extensive *carcinoma of the stomach* and in *chronic gastritis* there may also be gastric hyposecretion.

TESTS OF GASTRIC FUNCTION

Most routine tests of gastric function involve measurement of the acid secretion by the stomach, either at rest or in response to stimuli.

"Tubeless" Gastric Analysis

This depends on oral administration of a substance in which hydrogen ions can replace another cation in the molecule. The released cation (usually a dye) is excreted in the urine and measured. Caffeine, which can act as a gastric stimulant, is usually included in the tablets. Unfortunately results of this test have been disappointing and this is, at best, a screening procedure. Excretion of any dye during the test probably excludes complete achlorhydria.

All other tests involve the passage of a tube into the stomach. This is unpleasant for the patient: moreover valuable results will only be obtained when the operator is skilled and able to recognize when the specimens obtained are incomplete, either because of blockage or malpositioning of the tube. For these reasons the tests should only be carried out when really necessary for diagnosis and management, and only by a skilled operator.

Resting Juice or Overnight Secretion

Gastric contents may be aspirated overnight and the total night secretion measured, or a timed specimen may be obtained without a stimulus and the hourly secretion determined. Both these secretions will usually be high in volume and acid content in duodenal ulceration. In the Zollinger-Ellison syndrome diagnosis depends on finding a very high rate of secretion in a one-hour basal collection (more than 15 mEq/hour) (see Appendix).

Stimulation of Gastric Secretion

1. Direct stimulation of parietal cells is used to demonstrate achlorhydria, which is typically "histamine fast" in pernicious anaemia.

Histamine or "Histalog" (ametazole hydrochloride).—Histamine acts directly on parietal cells and stimulates secretion. Because of the undesirable side-effects of histamine it should be given with antihistamine cover: antihistamines do not block the gastric stimulatory effect of histamine. "Histalog" is a synthetic analogue of histamine, said to have fewer undesirable side-effects than the parent substance.

Pentagastrin is a pentapeptide consisting of the physiologically active part of the gastrin molecule. It can be used in the same way as histamine. It has fewer undesirable side-effects, but is relatively expensive.

2. Vagal stimulation of gastric secretion is used before vagotomy to test the therapeutic prospects of this operation in treatment of peptic ulcer, and after vagotomy to test completeness of the section of the nerve. The stimulus used is insulin induced hypoglycaemia (compare the use of insulin to stimulate cortisol secretion). If vagotomy is complete there should be no acid secretion even when the blood glucose level falls below 40 mg/100 ml, and when there is clinical evidence of hypoglycaemia.

SUMMARY

Intestinal Absorption

1. Normal intestinal absorption depends on adequate digestion of food (and therefore on normal pancreatic function), and on a normal area of functioning intestinal cells.

2. Normal digestion and absorption of fat depends on the presence of bile salts as well as of lipase.

3. Absorption of cholesterol, phospholipids and fat soluble vitamins depends on normal neutral fat absorption.

4. In *intestinal* malabsorption there is malabsorption of small molecules, usually due to a reduced absorptive area.

5. In *pancreatic* malabsorption there is malabsorption of fats, proteins and polysaccharides, but small molecules are usually absorbed normally.

6. An *abnormal bacterial flora* may cause steatorrhoea (because of competition for bile salts), and macrocytic anaemia (because of competition for vitamin B_{12}).

7. There may be steatorrhoea in biliary obstruction (because of lack of bile salts).

8. Selective malabsorption of vitamin B_{12} occurs in pernicious anaemia (lack of intrinsic factor).

9. Selective disaccharidase deficiencies cause malabsorption of disaccharide. These deficiencies are more commonly acquired than congenital in origin.

Pancreatic Function

1. Direct tests for pancreatic hypofunction are unsatisfactory.

2. Acute pancreatitis is associated with a transient rise in plasma amylase levels. This enzyme can also reach high concentrations in many acute abdominal emergencies and in renal failure.

Gastric Function

1. Hypersecretion of acid occurs in:
   - (*a*) Duodenal ulceration.
   - (*b*) The Zollinger-Ellison syndrome.

2. Hyposecretion of acid (histamine fast) occurs in:
   - (*a*) Pernicious anaemia.
   - (*b*) Extensive gastric infiltration.

3. The parietal cells can be directly tested by stimulation with histamine (or its analogue), or pentagastrin.

4. The vagal stimulation of gastric secretion can be tested by producing insulin induced hypoglycaemia.

APPENDIX TO CHAPTER IX

TESTS OF MALABSORPTION

COLLECTION OF SPECIMENS FOR FAECAL FAT ESTIMATION

When we estimate faecal fat output we are measuring the difference between the fat absorbed and that entering the intestinal tract from the diet and from the body (p. 202). Absorption of fat and addition of fat to the intestinal contents occurs throughout the small intestine. For two reasons a single 24-hour collection of faeces will usually give inaccurate results.

1. The transit time from the duodenum to the rectum is variable.
2. Rectal emptying is variable and may not be complete.

It has been shown that consecutive 24-hour collections yield answers which may vary by several hundred per cent, and which are therefore useless as an estimate of daily excretion from the body into the gut. The longer the period of collection, the nearer does the calculated daily mean value approach the "true" one.

For obvious reasons patients cannot be kept in hospital indefinitely. A usual compromise is to collect *at least a 3-day* and preferably a 5-day specimen of stools. Precision may be increased by collecting between "markers"— usually dyes which can be taken orally and which colour the stool.

Procedure

Day 0.—The first "marker" (usually two capsules of carmine) is given.

As soon as the "marker" appears in the stool the collection is started. This "marker" will gradually disappear.

Day 5.—The second "marker" is given.

As soon as the second "marker" appears in the stool the collection is stopped.

The estimation is made on all the specimens passed between the appearance of the two "markers" and including one of the marked stools.

Important.—1. It is very important that *all* stools should be collected during this period. To ensure that none is missing it is best to label each specimen with the following information:

> Name of Patient
> Ward
> Date of Specimen
> *Time* of specimen   ⎫ A record of these should also be kept on the
> *Number* in the series ⎭ ward.

The patient should not be allowed to go to the toilet, and should be impressed with the importance of a complete collection.

2. The time for collection of specimens will be about a week (including the time for appearance of the marker). Before starting the test try to make sure that during this time the patient is *not to be discharged*, is *not going to be*

operated on (except in emergency), does *not receive enemas or aperients*: any patient requiring aperients to keep his bowels open is most unlikely to have significant steatorrhoea at that time. *Neither barium enemas nor barium meals* should be performed during this time as the barium interferes with the estimation.

The collection and estimation of faecal fat excretion is time consuming and unpleasant for all concerned (including the patient). It is important that specimen collection is carefully controlled so that the answer may be meaningful.

Interpretation

A *mean* daily fat excretion of more than 5–6 g indicates steatorrhoea. Since, in the normal person, almost all the faecal fat is of endogenous origin, it is not affected by diet within very wide limits.

XYLOSE ABSORPTION TEST

Until recently it was customary to give an oral dose of 25 g of xylose for this test. However, the absorption of xylose is relatively inefficient and the presence of this large dose in the intestine may, by its osmotic effect, cause unpleasant symptoms and further interfere with absorption. For this reason a 5 g dose is preferable.

Warning. In the presence of poor renal function the test is invalid. In patients over 65 who often have a reduced GFR a low excretion does not necessarily indicate intestinal disease.

Procedure

The patient is fasted overnight.

8 a.m.—The bladder is emptied and the *specimen discarded.* 5 g of xylose dissolved in a glass of water is given orally.

All specimens passed between 8 a.m. and 10 a.m. are put into Bottle 1.

10 a.m.—The bladder is emptied and *the specimen put into Bottle 1* which is now complete.

All specimens passed between 10 a.m. and 1 p.m. are put into Bottle 2.

1 p.m.—The bladder is emptied and *the specimen is put into Bottle 2*, which is now complete.

Both bottles are sent to the laboratory for analysis.

Interpretation

In the normal person more than 23 per cent of the dose (1·44 g) should be excreted during the five hours of the test. Fifty per cent or more of the total excretion should occur during the first two hours. In mild intestinal malabsorption the total 5-hour excretion may be normal, but delayed absorption is reflected in a 2- to 5-hour excretion ratio of less than one.

In pancreatic malabsorption the result should be normal (p. 214).

TESTS OF GASTRIC FUNCTION

"Histalog" or Pentagastrin Test

Procedure (applies to all types of test meal)

The patient fasts from 10 p.m. on the evening before the test. On the morning of the test a radio-opaque Levin tube is passed into the stomach (preferably under x-ray control) until it lies in the pyloric antrum: the tube is attached to the side of the face with plaster.

8 a.m.—All the gastric juice is aspirated from the stomach and is put in a bottle marked *"Resting Juice"*.

8 a.m. to 9 a.m.—Gastric juice is aspirated continuously for the next hour and put in a bottle marked *"Basal Secretion"*.

9 a.m.—"Histalog" 100 mg, *or* pentagastrin 6 μg/kg body weight, is injected intramuscularly.

9 a.m. to 9.15 a.m.
9.15 a.m. to 9.30 a.m. } Four 15-minute samples are aspirated and put
9.30 a.m. to 9.45 a.m. into bottles marked with the appropriate times.
9.45 a.m. to 10 a.m.

All specimens are sent to the laboratory for analysis.

Interpretation

1. In histamine fast *achlorhydria* no specimen has a pH as low as 3·5.

2. A *basal* acid secretion of greater than 15 mEq of hydrogen ion in the hour, with no further response to "Histalog", is suggestive of the *Zollinger-Ellison syndrome*.

3. If any specimen is of pH 3·5 or less the hydrogen ion secretion is checked by titration. In *hyperchlorhydria* the highest mean acid secretion (calculated by adding the results of the two consecutive specimens of highest acidity and by multiplying by two, to give an hourly secretion), is greater than 40 mEq/hour.

The resting juice is inspected for *blood*. A large quantity of altered blood is suggestive of carcinoma. Small flecks may be due to trauma during aspiration.

Insulin Test Meal (p. 221)

This test is usually carried out at about six months after vagotomy. Insulin induced hypoglycaemia stimulates gastric secretion via the vagus nerve.

Procedure

The preparation of the patient and positioning of the tube is described under "'Histalog' Test Meal".

8 a.m.—The stomach is emptied and the specimen discarded.

8 a.m. to 9 a.m.—A 1-hour "basal secretion" is collected.

9 a.m.—Soluble insulin (0·2 units/kg) is injected intravenously.

9 a.m. to 11 a.m.—Specimens are collected for blood glucose estimation every 30 minutes for two hours. During this time gastric juice is aspirated every 15 minutes.

The specimens are sent to the laboratory for analysis.

Interpretation

Analysis of gastric samples is only useful if the blood glucose has fallen to levels below 40 mg/100 ml and if clinical hypoglycaemia is present.

If more than 2 mEq of hydrogen ion is present in any 60-minute sample the response is positive, suggesting the presence of intact vagal fibres.

Chapter X

PLASMA PROTEINS AND IMMUNOGLOBULINS

PLASMA PROTEINS

GENERAL

PLASMA contains a complex mixture of proteins at a concentration of about 7 g/100 ml. This includes simple proteins as well as those incorporating carbohydrates and lipids. These different proteins have different functions and originate from several different cell types. Changes in disease are frequently non-specific, but in a limited number of conditions are of diagnostic value.

Functions

The following is an outline of the main functions of the plasma proteins.

1. *Distribution of extracellular fluid* (*ECF*).—Although the total plasma osmolarity is mostly due to sodium and its associated anions, the effective osmotic pressure (colloid osmotic pressure) is due to plasma proteins. The intravascular protein concentration is much higher than that of the extravascular ECF and the difference is sufficient to keep fluid in the blood vessels despite the higher hydrostatic pressure on this side of the capillary wall (see p. 32). Albumin, because of its lower molecular weight and its consequent greater contribution to osmolarity, is much more active than globulin in this respect.

2. *Antibodies* are proteins (p. 236).

3. Many hormones (for example, cortisol (p. 91) and thyroxine (p. 159), vitamins, lipids (p. 249), calcium, trace metals and drugs are, at least partly, *carried* in combination with plasma proteins.

4. Most of the *blood clotting factors are proteins*.

5. Circulating protein, as part of the general protein pool, can form a source of *nutrient* protein for the tissues.

6. Proteins form a minor part of the *plasma buffering* system (p. 64).

7. *Enzymes* are proteins.

Source of Plasma Proteins

Many of the proteins, notably albumin, some of the coagulation factors, the special carrier proteins and the lipoproteins are synthesized in the liver. Plasma proteins alter in hepatic disease (p. 271). The anti-bodies are synthesized in the reticulo-endothelial system by plasma cells and lymphocytes.

Control of Plasma Protein Levels

The factors controlling the normal levels of plasma proteins are poorly understood. Loss of a particular fraction, such as albumin, is followed by increased synthesis of that fraction, suggesting a feed-back stimula-tion of synthesis. The nature of the feed-back mechanism is unknown and it does not seem to be a specific one. The increased synthesis of albumin that occurs following its loss in the nephrotic syndrome may be accompanied by increased synthesis of other proteins of hepatic origin.

Plasma protein synthesis is at all times dependent on an adequate supply of amino-acids and in malnutrition lowered levels occur because of dietary protein deficiency.

Value of Total Protein Estimations

Because of the large number of its components, total protein estima-tions have a limited place in diagnosis of protein abnormalities. Changes in one fraction may be masked by opposite changes in another as, for instance, in chronic inflammation in which a low albumin is frequently accompanied by a raised γ globulin level. Only with extreme abnormal-ities is a total protein estimation of value in the study of protein meta-bolism. The following list outlines the conditions in which an abnormal protein concentration may be found. The fraction most affected is given in brackets in each case.

Causes of Raised Total Protein Concentration

1. Artefactual (all fractions).
    (a) Dehydration (p. 27).
    (b) Stasis during venepuncture (see below).
2. Paraproteinaemia (paraprotein, p. 240).
3. Certain chronic diseases (γ globulin).
    (a) Sarcoidosis.
    (b) Some cases of cirrhosis.
    (c) Some collagen diseases, for example, systemic lupus erythematosis.
    (d) Certain chronic inflammatory conditions (p. 234).

Causes of Reduced Total Protein Concentration

1. Artefactual (all fractions).
    Overhydration.

2. Excessive loss of lower molecular weight proteins; for example, in the nephrotic syndrome.

3. Decreased synthesis of protein.

(*a*) Dietary protein deficiency, for instance in kwashiorkor (all fractions).

(*b*) Severe malabsorption (all fractions).

(*c*) Liver disease (mainly albumin).

One clinical situation in which total protein estimations are of value is in assessing hydration. Because of their large size the plasma proteins are virtually confined to the vascular space and changes in the fluid content of the blood will show as a change in total protein concentration (and in haematocrit). Serial estimations are useful in following the hydration of a patient on intravenous fluids.

Stasis induced by keeping the tourniquet on too long during venesection causes fluid to escape into the extravascular compartment with haemoconcentration and a falsely raised protein concentration. This artefact is one of the commonest causes of a high total protein level.

INDIRECT TESTS OF ALTERED PLASMA PROTEINS

(*a*) **Flocculation tests.**—Although more commonly used as tests of liver function, the flocculation tests merely reflect changes in the proportions of different plasma proteins. The subject is fully discussed on p. 271 and only the main points will be reviewed here. The tests are based on the observation that flocculation occurs on the addition of certain agents to the serum of persons with protein disturbances. Albumin inhibits flocculation of, for example, thymol, and raised levels of γ globulin enhance it. The interpretation of the different flocculation tests is discussed on p. 271. In myeloma "dissociated" flocculation tests (that is a normal thymol turbidy with a very high reading of one of the other turbidities) are common because of the rise in the γ fraction without a concomitant fall in albumin.

(*b*) **Erythrocyte sedimentation rate (ESR).**—Among the multitude of factors affecting the ESR, the main one is the extent of rouleaux formation. This, in turn, is influenced largely by levels of plasma fibrinogen and to a lesser extent by levels of α_2 and γ globulin. The raised ESR in infective, neoplastic and degenerative diseases reflects the increase in fibrinogen and α globulins. Very high ESR readings are encountered in cases of myelomatosis due, most probably, to the abnormal γ globulin.

Serial ESR estimations are used for following the course of and assessing activity in a number of chronic diseases, such as rheumatoid arthritis and tuberculosis.

FRACTIONATION OF PLASMA PROTEINS

More valuable information may be obtained if the plasma proteins are separated into fractions. An early method, still practised today, was to precipitate out all or part of the globulins by salt fractionation (usually with sodium or ammonium sulphate) and to estimate albumin in the filtrate. In most laboratories this has been replaced by zone electrophoresis on paper or cellulose acetate and by more sophisticated methods. The following methods will be considered briefly:

(a) Zone electrophoresis.
(b) Immunoelectrophoresis.
(c) Specific methods.

Zone electrophoresis.—The basic principle of electrophoresis is that a charged particle in a buffered electrolyte solution will move towards one or other of the electrodes if a current is passed through the solution.

At the pH commonly used (pH 8·6) the plasma proteins are mostly negatively charged and move towards the anode at rates depending on the amount of charge they carry. In outline the technique is as follows:

A few microlitres of serum (used instead of plasma—see below) is applied as a narrow band at one end of a strip of paper or cellulose acetate soaked in buffer—this includes the charged protein particles suspended in an electrolyte solution. A current is passed through the strip and the various proteins move at rates dependent mainly on their charge. After a period of time the different fractions separate into different bands across the strip. The strip may then be stained to render the protein fractions visible and they may be proportioned by their ability to transmit or reflect light. This results in the electrophoretic scan which shows five fractions (Fig. 15).

Serum is used in preference to plasma to avoid the extra band of fibrinogen (between β and γ globulin) which makes separation of these two difficult and which may mask a paraprotein.

The technique is simple, but because it is subject to a number of variables rigid control is necessary. Results may vary between different laboratories using different methods, and each laboratory should issue its own normal range based on the technique in use. As a guide to approximate values, serum from a normal person might give the following results:

Albumin	—	4·0 g/100 ml.
α_1 globulin	—	0·3 g/100 ml.
α_2 globulin	—	0·7 g/100 ml.
β globulin	—	0·9 g/100 ml.
γ globulin	—	1·3 g/100 ml.

Zone electrophoresis in other media such as starch gel or agar gel allows separation of a greater number of bands, but is rarely used for routine diagnostic purposes.

Immunoelectrophoresis.—The separation achieved by zone electrophoresis may be improved by the sensitivity and specificity of the antigen-antibody reaction. After initial electrophoresis, usually in agar gel rather than cellulose acetate, an antiserum to human serum proteins is allowed to diffuse into the gel from a trough in the agar next to the separated protein fractions and parallel to the direction of migration. As this antiserum contains antibodies to the individual proteins of human serum a line of precipitation occurs where each reacts with its

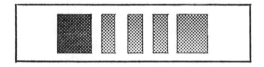

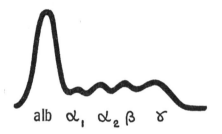

FIG. 15.—Normal electrophoretic strip and scan.

specific antibody. Many more fractions are detectable using this method than using zone electrophoresis.

By using a specific antiserum a single fraction may be identified. Specific antisera are also used for quantitation of individual protein fractions using the method of radial diffusion.

Specific methods.—Proteins of especial clinical significance are often estimated by other methods. Examples of such proteins include transferrin (p. 313), caeruloplasmin (p. 345) and lipoproteins.

ALTERATION OF PLASMA PROTEIN FRACTIONS IN DISEASE

As most laboratories use zone electrophoresis on paper or cellulose acetate the changes in plasma proteins will be further considered according to the findings by this method.

Albumin

There are two rare congenital anomalies of albumin synthesis. In the first, *bisalbuminaemia,* two albumin types are present. This is a curiosity only as there are no clinical consequences. In the second condition, *analbuminaemia,* there is deficient synthesis of the protein. Clinical consequences are slight, and oedema, though present, is surprisingly mild.

An abnormally high albumin level is seen only with dehydration and all clinical interest centres on low albumin levels.

Consequences of a low serum albumin.—The role of plasma proteins in fluid distribution has been discussed. As albumin is the most important fraction in this respect one of the consequences of a reduced level is *oedema.* The critical level varies, but oedema is almost always present if the plasma albumin is below 2 g/100 ml. The surprising exception of analbuminaemia has been mentioned above.

About half the plasma calcium is bound to albumin (p. 176) and hypoalbuminaemia is accompanied by *hypocalcaemia.* As this involves only the protein bound (inactive) half, symptoms of tetany do not develop and calcium or vitamin D supplements are not indicated. As a rough guide there is about 1 mg of calcium per 0·8 g albumin.

Albumin also binds bilirubin, free fatty acids, and a number of drugs such as salicylates. Normally a small proportion of circulating thyroxine and cortisol is bound to albumin, and although the major portion is carried by specific binding proteins, when these hormones are present in excess there is an increase in the proportion bound to albumin.

Causes of hypoalbuminaemia.—There are three main causes of hypoalbuminaemia.

(*a*) *Decreased synthesis.*—Albumin is catabolized at a steady rate of about 4 per cent of the body pool daily, so that any impairment of synthesis soon causes hypoalbuminaemia. As albumin is synthesized in the liver, liver disease, whether acute or chronic, results in lowered levels. Malabsorption and malnutrition may also cause low albumin levels because of amino-acid deficiency.

(*b*) *Loss.*—Albumin is a relatively small molecule with a molecular weight of about 67,000 and so is lost in protein-losing states such as the nephrotic syndrome (p. 11), protein-losing enteropathy (p. 218) or by exudation as in extensive burns. The lowest levels are usually reached in this category of disease.

(*c*) *Non-specific.*—One of the commonest reasons for a low serum albumin is less easily explained. In many acute conditions, including apparently minor illnesses such as colds and boils, the serum albumin level falls. The answer cannot lie entirely in decreased synthesis or increased breakdown as there is a rapid return to normal on recovery. It could be partly due to a switch to synthesis of other fractions, because the total protein level often remains the same. This phenomenon is seen commonly in hospitalized patients, and changes of concentration of up to 0·5–1 g/100 ml may be a completely non-specific finding. The effect of posture on albumin levels (p. 404) may contribute to this syndrome. Low levels are seen in the newborn and in the late stages of pregnancy, probably due to increased blood volume with dilution of albumin.

In summary, the causes of a low serum albumin are:

1. Acute or chronic illness of any nature (usually not marked).
2. Liver disease, both acute and chronic.
3. Nephrotic syndrome.
4. Gastro-intestinal loss.
5. Extensive burns.
6. Malabsorption.
7. Malnutrition.

α_1 and α_2 Globulins

The major components of the α_1 and α_2 globulins are a group of proteins, synthesized in the liver, and increased in states of *tissue destruction or proliferation*. These include the glycoproteins (protein with attached carbohydrate), α_2 macroglobulin and haptoglobins. The mechanism of this non-specific response is not known but it is seen in a wide variety of conditions.

Raised values therefore occur in:

1. Inflammation.
2. Neoplasm.
3. Trauma.
4. Collagen diseases.

The α_2 globulin may also be raised in the *nephrotic syndrome.*

Low levels are seen in hepatic parenchymal disease, in malabsorption syndromes and in malnutrition, due to decreased synthesis.

The copper-binding protein, caeruloplasmin (p. 345) is an α_2 globulin and some lipoproteins (p. 249) are found in this region.

Mucoprotein (seromucoid).—This group of proteins represents a fraction of the α_1 glycoproteins that can be measured chemically. Normally the serum concentration is about 80 mg/100 ml. Not unexpectedly, raised levels occur with the non-specific stimuli listed above and low levels with liver disease. As an index of inflammatory response a changed level has the same significance as a raised ESR. The estimation has been used to distinguish hepatitis (low levels) from obstructive jaundice (raised levels), but it is no more successful than similar liver function tests.

β Globulins

The major components of the β fraction are the iron-carrying protein transferrin (p. 309) and β lipoprotein (p. 251). Changes in transferrin concentration are not usually evident on the electrophoretic strip. In general, raised β globulins reflect an increase in β lipoprotein. This may occur in the nephrotic syndrome and in obstructive jaundice, but on routine electrophoresis the rise is rarely detectable.

γ Globulins

This group is considered more fully in the section on immuno-globulins (p. 236). The γ fraction contains the circulating antibodies and increased levels are seen with chronic inflammatory processes. It is important to distinguish between a *diffuse* increase due to an increase in all antibodies and the *localized* band of a paraprotein. This is discussed on p. 240.

A diffusely raised γ globulin occurs in:

1. Cirrhosis.
2. Chronic infections, including subacute bacterial endocarditis. In the tropical diseases kala-azar and lymphogranuloma venereum very high values may be found.
3. Sarcoidosis.
4. Systemic lupus erythematosis (SLE).
5. Rheumatoid arthritis.

Discrete *bands* in the γ region occur with:

1. Myelomatosis (p. 241).
2. Macroglobulinaemia (p. 243).
3. Non-malignant (essential) and transient paraproteinaemia (p. 244).

Decreased γ globulins occur in:

1. Nephrotic syndrome.
2. Malabsorption and malnutrition.
3. Hypogammaglobulinaemia—Congenital.
                              —Acquired.

ELECTROPHORETIC PATTERNS

Protein electrophoresis is a commonly requested investigation although there are few conditions where it is of diagnostic value. Several patterns may be recognized (refer to numbers in Fig. 16 in which the normal pattern is represented by a dotted line).

1. Parallel changes in all fractions (not shown in Fig. 16).—An increase in all protein fractions may be seen in dehydration or with stasis during venepuncture. Conversely, a lowering of all fractions is seen in overhydration and severe protein malnutrition and malabsorption.

2. Non-specific patterns.—These occur in a variety of illnesses and are no more important in diagnosis than a raised ESR.

(*a*) A *low albumin level* only occurs in many acute illnesses. This may occur even with such mild infections as bad colds. (Levels up to 0·5 g/100 ml below the normal range may be due to this factor.) Total protein levels usually remain within the normal range.

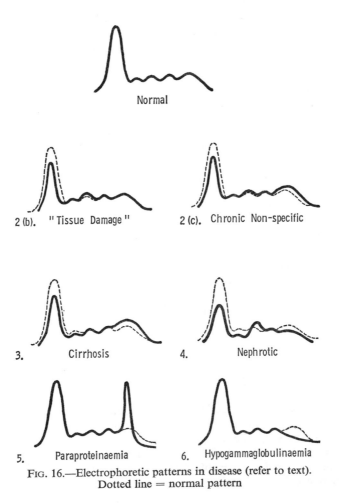

Fig. 16.—Electrophoretic patterns in disease (refer to text). Dotted line = normal pattern

(b) A *low albumin and raised* α_2 *globulin* concentration occurs in more severe acute infections, inflammation and neoplasia ("tissue damage" pattern).

(c) A *low albumin with raised* γ *and often* α_2 *globulin* levels occurs in chronic infections. This pattern (without a rise in α_2 globulin) may also be seen in liver disease, which is discussed more fully below.

3. **Liver disease.**—In *acute hepatitis* there are lowered levels of albumin and α globulins, as both are synthesized in the liver. γ globulins may be slightly increased. Occasionally this disturbance of the albumin/globulin ratio may be detected by the flocculation tests before it is evident on the electrophoretic strip.

If the hepatic changes persist γ globulin increases further, and in *cirrhosis* is markedly raised. As there is an increase in fast-moving fractions, apparent fusion of β and γ globulins produces a characteristic pattern.

4. **Nephrotic syndrome.**—The plasma protein changes depend on the severity of the renal lesion. In early cases albumin may be the only protein lost, but in most established cases all fractions are lost except some of the larger α_2 and β globulins. The typical pattern is therefore a lowering of all fractions except the α_2 globulin (the rise in β-lipoprotein is not usually detectable by routine methods). The α_2 globulin fraction may actually be increased in absolute amounts possibly due to non-specific stimulus to synthesis by low albumin levels (p. 228). This rise is associated with an increase in the lipids carried in this region. If the nephrotic syndrome is due to systemic lupus erythematosis the γ globulin may be normal or raised.

A similar pattern may be seen in some cases of protein-losing enteropathy.

5. **Paraproteinaemia.**—A sharp band, usually in the γ region, is seen with myelomatosis and macroglobulinaemia, and in essential (benign) paraproteinaemia.

6. **Hypogammaglobulinaemia.**—This is shown by a decreased density in the γ globulin region.

IMMUNOGLOBULINS

GENERAL

It has long been recognized that the γ globulins have antibody activity, but as some antibodies are found in the β and even α_2 positions of the electrophoretic strip, the term immunoglobulins (Ig) is a preferable one. The term also includes proteins found in cases of myelomatosis which may not possess demonstrable antibody activity, and the structurally related Bence-Jones protein.

There are three major classes of immunoglobulins called IgG, IgM and IgA. In addition two recently described minor classes IgD and IgE will be mentioned.

Structure of Immunoglobulins

All the immunoglobulin classes have the same basic molecular structure, shown schematically in Fig. 17. Each unit contains four polypeptide chains, two light (L) and two heavy (H) chains, held together by inter-chain disulphide bonds. Both H and L chains are required for antibody activity (there is a maximum of two binding sites per molecule). Many other features of the immunoglobulin molecule, such as complement fixation and the reaction with rheumatoid factor, are properties of the H chain.

Classification of Immunoglobulins

There are five different H chains and it is on this difference that the naming of the immunoglobulin classes is based. The chains are referred to as γ (in IgG), μ (in IgM), α (in IgA), δ (in IgD) and ϵ (in IgE). The L chains too may be of two types: κ and λ.

Both L chains in a single molecule are of the same type but each class of immunoglobulins has molecules of both types. The *class* of immunoglobulins depends on the H chain, the *type* depends on the L chain.

In routine clinical work only IgG, IgA, and IgM are measured, regardless of the L chain present.

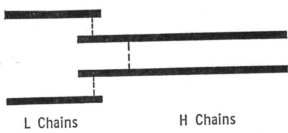

L Chains   H Chains

FIG. 17.—Schematic representation of Ig subunit.

Other classifications.—The simplified account of the immunoglobulin unit presented above does not take into account the fact that more than one unit may be present in a molecule. IgM, for example, contains five basic four chain units and so is much larger than IgG composed of a single unit. Circulating IgA molecules vary in size depending on the number of units present. These other differences have led to the other classifications and terminologies which appear in text-books and publications. These are based on:

(*a*) *Density*.—The immunoglobulins may be separated on a basis of density, in the *ultracentrifuge*. The unit used is a Svedberg unit (S) and the S value of a protein (although S is strictly a measurement of time) increases with increasing molecular size. IgG for example sediments as 7S, IgM as 19S and IgA varies between 7S and 13S depending on the number of basic units present.

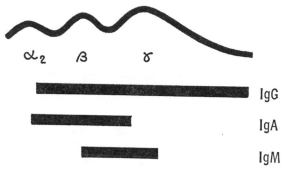

FIG. 18.—Electrophoretic distribution of major Ig classes.

(*b*) *Electrophoretic mobility*.—Because of the difference in charge and other physicochemical differences the electrophoretic mobilities of the immunoglobulins vary and offer yet another way of classifying them. The position of the various classes is shown in Fig. 18 and the names are given in Table XVI.

TABLE XVI

CLASSIFICATION AND NOMENCLATURE OF THE IMMUNOGLOBULINS

Class	Approximate concentration (mg/100 ml)	Other terminology based on	
		ultracentrifuge	electrophoresis
IgG (γG)	700–1400	6·6S ; 7S	γ_2
IgA (γA)	140–260	7–13S	β_2A
IgM (γM)	70–130	19S	γ_1M : β_2M

Physiology of the Immunoglobulins

Most of the immunoglobulins have been shown to have antibody activity. The different classes respond to different stimuli and together provide a range of response. For example, IgM appears relatively rapidly in response to a stimulus (about 15 days) and reacts with particulate antigens. IgG reacts with soluble antigens and appears more slowly (about 30 days).

IgG.—This group of proteins forms about 75 per cent of the immuno-globulin population and contains most of the normal human plasma antibodies. Deficiency is accompanied by recurrent pyogenic infections. It is synthesized by plasma cells in response to many bacterial and viral antigens, and in these conditions there is often an increased number of plasma cells in the bone marrow. These proteins may be transported across the placenta and are the damaging antibodies in haemolytic disease of the newborn. The antinuclear factor found in cases of systemic lupus erythematosis belongs to this group. In the infant IgG synthesis begins at the age of about three months and adult levels are reached after one year.

Primary *excess* of IgG is seen in *myelomatosis* (p. 241) and inherited *deficiency* causes one form of *hypogammaglobulinaemia* (p. 245).

IgA.—This group forms about 20 per cent of the total serum immuno-globulins. Some IgA appears to be synthesized mainly beneath the mucosa of the gut and respiratory tract where it has important local antibody activity. Deficiency of IgA may be associated with respiratory tract infection and intestinal disease. IgA also appears in saliva, tears and milk.

Primary *excess* of IgA is seen in some cases of *myelomatosis* and deficiency can occur.

IgA does not cross the placenta. It may not reach adult levels until the age of 15.

IgM.—This group forms about 7 per cent of serum immunoglobulins. It is synthesized by lymphocytes. The primary response to an antigen is IgM production, and this is stimulated mainly by particulate antigens such as organisms in the blood stream. In IgM deficiency septicaemia is common. The major blood group isohaemagglutinins (anti-A and anti-B) belong to this group, as does rheumatoid factor. This group does not cross the placenta, but they are the first antibodies to be made by the infant and reach adult levels at 6–12 weeks after birth.

IgD and IgE.—These proteins are normally present in very low con-centrations. The reagins (antibodies of passive cutaneous hypersensi-tivity) are IgE. The function of IgD is doubtful. Very rarely a myeloma protein is IgD or IgE.

BENCE-JONES PROTEIN (BJP)

This protein, named after Bence-Jones who first studied it, is found in the urine of some patients with myeloma and macroglobulinaemia. It has peculiar heat properties. If a sample of urine at the correct pH (usually pH 4·9) is heated, the protein precipitates at a temperature below 60°C and redissolves on further heating, only to reappear on subsequent cooling. It is now known that Bence-Jones protein consists of L chains (p. 237) synthesized in excess. Because of their relatively low molecular weight (20–40,000) they pass the glomerular filter and do not usually accumulate in the plasma unless there is glomerular failure. If present in high enough concentration they may be demonstrated by the heat test outlined above (for details see Appendix). If not detected by this method a 24-hour collection of urine may be concentrated and the protein identified by zone or immunoelectrophoresis. It is held by some that the name "Bence-Jones protein" can only be applied to a urine with the described heat characteristics, but from a diagnostic point of view an excess of L chains in the urine, however identified, suggests malignant proliferation of protein producing cells—usually myelomatosis or macroglobulinaemia. It is worth noting that the rapid tests for urinary proteins—precipitation with salicylsulphonic acid and use of "Albustix"—may be negative despite the presence of BJP.

DISORDERS OF IMMUNOGLOBULIN SYNTHESIS

The following conditions will be considered:

(a) Increased synthesis
1. Myelomatosis
2. Macroglobulinaemia
3. Heavy Chain Disease
4. Cryoglobulinaemia
5. "Essential" Paraproteinaemia

(b) Decreased synthesis
1. Congenital
2. Acquired

These conditions are uncommon but not rare and have evoked a great deal of interest—particularly the group associated with increased synthesis. These have been described under a wide variety of names, such as plasma cell dyscrasias, monoclonal gammopathies, paraproteinaemias. A *paraprotein* is a protein (other than fibrinogen) that appears as a *sharp narrow band* on the electrophoretic strip anywhere from α to γ globulin region inclusive, and which on further testing proves to be a single type of immune globulin. It must be realized that paraproteinaemia is not a disease in itself but may be a sign of disease.

A diffusely raised γ globulin is due to many different plasma cells synthesizing many different antibodies. It is presumed that in myelomatosis and similar conditions a single cell becomes malignant, and it and its offspring (a clone) produce increased amounts of a single protein—hence the term *monoclonal gammopathy*. The protein cannot strictly be called abnormal as it may merely be large amounts of a "normal" antibody. The relevant antigen—if any—has not been identified.

A term which can be confusing is "M-band". This means simply a paraprotein and does not necessarily imply the presence of IgM.

Myelomatosis (*Synonyms:* multiple myeloma; plasma cell myeloma)

This disease may present in a number of ways. In the commonest form there is generalized malignant proliferation of plasma cells throughout the bone marrow and occasionally in the soft tissues. Microscopically there is a gradation of cell types from normal plasma cells through to multinucleate and abnormal forms with large nucleoli (myeloma cells). In most cases these cells produce globulins.

The clinical and laboratory features are due to these two processes:

(*a*) Malignant proliferation of plasma cells.

(*b*) Globulin production.

(*a*) *Malignant proliferation of cells* in the bone marrow causes severe bone pain and this is the commonest presenting feature. On x-ray discrete *punched out areas* of radiotransparency may be seen, most frequently in the skull, vertebrae, ribs and pelvis: there may be generalized *osteoporosis*. There is little, if any, compensatory osteoblastic activity around the lesions (p. 186). *Pathological fractures* may occur, especially of the vertebrae.

Replacement of normal marrow elements leads to *anaemia* (the next most common feature), and occasionally to leucopenia and thrombocytopenia. As the levels of other immunoglobulins are frequently low there may be a history of recurrent bacterial infections.

(*b*) *Excess globulin production.*—In some cases there are very high levels of circulating protein which may produce symptoms in various ways. Increased serum viscosity results in *impaired circulation*, clinically most commonly affecting the central nervous system or causing *retinal thrombosis*. Paradoxically there may also be *haemorrhagic* manifestations due to the myeloma protein forming complexes with coagulation factors. Certain myeloma proteins are cryoglobulins (p. 243), and produce symptoms of *cold sensitivity*. In cases with Bence-Jones proteinuria (see below) there may be renal damage and *renal failure* due to precipitation of protein in the renal tubules. *Amyloidosis* may be associated with this type of myeloma.

Occasional cases are being diagnosed in the presymptomatic stage with only a few abnormal laboratory findings.

Rarely, single tumours of plasma cells (solitary plasmacytoma) occur in the soft tissues, particularly in the nasopharyngeal region. Plasma protein abnormalities are uncommon in these cases and the relationship to myelomatosis is uncertain.

In summary, myelomatosis may present:

(*a*) With generalized bone pain or fractures.

(*b*) With anaemia.

(*c*) With renal failure.

(*d*) Rarely as—Cryoglobulinaemia with Raynaud's phenomenon.
Haemorrhagic manifestations.
Amyloidosis.
(*e*) Asymptomatic—Accidenta discovery.

Laboratory Findings and Diagnosis

As in macroglobulinaemia, the first clue to the diagnosis may be noticed during venepuncture. The blood may be very viscous and may clot in the syringe. Preparation of blood films can be extremely difficult.

1. *Serum protein changes.*—Frequently the total protein concentration is raised and may even be higher than 10 g/100 ml. On electrophoresis the increase of protein appears as a narrow band, usually in the γ region (paraprotein), and there are usually reduced levels of normal γ globulins. The raised protein is usually IgG; less commonly IgA (about 3:1) and rarely Bence-Jones protein (if renal failure is present). Very occasionally IgD or IgE is found.

Rarely no abnormal protein band is seen. This happens if the malignant cells are very undifferentiated and fail to produce protein, or if they are only producing Bence-Jones protein. In the first group there is usually a low normal γ globulin level, and in the second Bence-Jones protein is found in the urine.

2. *Bence-Jones proteinuria.*—In over half of the cases of myelomatosis BJP may be identified by electrophoresis of a concentrated 24-hour collection of urine. The heat test is positive in only 10 per cent or less of proven cases and should not be relied on to make the diagnosis.

If present, BJP is of diagnostic value.

3. *Hypercalcaemia* may be present (p. 186). High levels usually suppress with cortisone (see cortisone suppression test, p. 198) and this fact can be used in treatment.

As there is little osteoblastic activity the *alkaline phosphatase is normal* unless there is liver involvement. In this case the raised level is accompanied by a raised level of 5'-nucleotidase, indicating its hepatic origin (p. 291).

4. Depending on the presence or degree of renal damage, the biochemical *features of renal failure* (p. 14) such as a raised blood urea, uric acid or phosphate may be present.

5. The *erythrocyte sedimentation rate* (ESR) is usually raised and may be very high. This may be the first indication of the disease and is probably due to the increased γ globulin concentration.

6. *Haematological abnormalities.*—There is usually anaemia. The leucocyte and platelet counts are usually normal, but may be low. Rarely, large numbers of plasma cells appear in the peripheral blood (plasma cell leukaemia).

7. Bone marrow.—The diagnosis of myelomatosis can only be made with certainty by demonstrating malignant plasma cells ("myeloma cells") in bone marrow aspirate (or biopsy). This may be the only abnormality and without this finding the diagnosis can only be presumptive.

Macroglobulinaemia (Waldenström's Macroglobulinaemia)

This condition is commoner in males than in females.

The disease differs from myelomatosis in that the proliferating cells resemble lymphocytes rather than plasma cells. These cells produce large amounts of IgM and as this protein has a much higher viscosity than IgG, symptoms due to vascular changes predominate. Haemorrhagic manifestations are common, particularly in the retina and this, together with vascular sludging, produces a high incidence of visual disturbances. Anaemia is common and there is often lymphadenopathy. In contradistinction to myelomatosis, skeletal manifestations are not seen.

Laboratory Findings and Diagnosis

1. *Serum protein changes.*—As in myelomatosis there is usually a raised total protein concentration and electrophoresis shows a paraprotein in the γ region. This can be identified as IgM. A useful screening test is the *Sia Test* (see Appendix).

As in myelomatosis there may be reduced levels of the normal immunoglobulins.

2. *Bence-Jones protein* can be identified in the urine by electrophoresis in about 10 per cent of cases.

3. *Haematological findings.*—Anaemia is common and is due to several factors including bleeding, marrow replacement and haemolysis.

The bone marrow aspirate or lymph node biopsy contains atypical lymphocytic cells.

Heavy Chain Disease (Franklin's Disease)

This is a rare group of disorders characterized by the presence of an abnormal protein identifiable as part of the H chain (α, γ or μ). The clinical picture is that of a malignant lymphoma or chronic lymphatic leukaemia. Bone lesions are rare.

Cryoglobulinaemia

In several diseases cryoglobulins occur. These are plasma proteins that precipitate on being cooled to below body temperature—either *in vitro*, or in the superficial capillaries on being exposed to cold. The latter may give rise to Raynaud's phenomenon, superficial ulceration of the skin, or purpura.

Cryoglobulins have been described as occurring in:

1. Myelomatosis.
2. Collagen diseases.
3. Lymphomas.
4. Any disease associated with raised levels of γ globulin; for example, cirrhosis, chronic infections.
5. Essential cryoglobulinaemia. This category is diagnosed by excluding all the others.

The severity of vascular symptoms tend to increase with increasing cryoglobulin levels.

Frequently the abnormal protein is not detected on routine testing because it precipitates as the blood specimen clots on cooling. If the clinical history suggests cryoglobulinaemia blood should be taken into a warm syringe and tests, including electrophoresis, performed at 37°C without cooling the specimen.

Essential (Benign) Paraproteinaemia

It has become increasingly apparent that between 10 and 30 per cent of all paraproteins are not due to malignancy of immunoglobulin producing cells. These "essential paraproteinaemias" may be associated with a variety of diseases, and the clinical features are those of the underlying disease. Any of the Ig classes may be involved, most commonly IgG. The level of the paraprotein is not as high as that commonly found in myelomatosis or macroglobulinaemia and tends to remain constant for long periods (several years). Bence-Jones proteinuria is not found.

Assessment of Paraproteinaemia

Occasionally a paraprotein is discovered on an electrophoretic strip done for some unrelated condition. The possible causes include:

1. Myelomatosis (p. 241).
2. Macroglobulinaemia (p. 243).
3. Rarely, other malignant lymphoproliferative disorders such as lymphosarcoma, chronic lymphatic leukaemia and Hodgkin's disease.
4. Franklin's disease (p. 243).
5. Cryoglobulinaemia (p. 243).
6. Essential paraproteinaemia.

If there are no relevant clinical findings the question arises of whether this is an early myelomatosis or macroglobulinaemia, or whether it is benign. In many cases only time will tell, but the following points indicate malignancy:

1. Bence-Jones proteinuria.
2. Reduced levels of normal immunoglobulins.
3. Increasing level of paraprotein.

   In myelomatosis or macroglobulinaemia the level usually doubles in less than two years.
4. The initial level of the paraprotein.

   A level of IgG above 2 g/100 ml (or above 1 g in the case of IgA or IgM) is strongly suggestive of malignancy.

Hypogammaglobulinaemia

There is a group of diseases characterized by primary immunological deficiency. The cases usually present in infancy, most commonly with recurrent infections. Most of them have decreased levels of circulating immunoglobulins and others have impaired cellular immunity. Detailed classification of these syndromes is beyond the scope of this book and they will be considered in broad groups only.

1. *Transient Hypogammaglobulinaemia*

At birth, the circulating IgG present is derived from the mother, and levels decrease progressively, reaching their lowest at two to three months. At about this time the infant begins to synthesize its own IgG and the level rises to adult levels between six months and one year. In a few cases synthesis is delayed and low levels persist for several months. Diagnosis at this stage is extremely difficult.

2. *Congenital Hypogammaglobulinaemia*

(*a*) *Congenital sex-linked type.*—This occurs in males and is characterized by absence of plasma cells. Levels of all classes of immunoglobulins are extremely low, but circulating lymphocytes are present in normal numbers. Cellular immunity is normal and graft rejection occurs. Bacterial infections are common.

(*b*) *Alymphocytic types.*—This abnormality is usually inherited as autosomal recessive and so occurs in both sexes. There is hypoplasia of the thymus and lymphoid tissues with low numbers of circulating lymphocytes. There is usually deficiency of all classes of immunoglobulins and cellular immunity is impaired. Most affected individuals do not survive beyond the age of two.

3. *Acquired Hypogammaglobulinaemia*

This may occur at any age in both sexes. Deficient antibody formation may occur in a number of conditions such as lymphomas, thymoma and myelomatosis. Impaired cellular immunity, without depressed immunoglobulin synthesis, may occur in tuberculosis, sarcoidosis and following the use of a number of cytotoxic drugs.

Diagnosis of Hypogammaglobulinaemia

Diagnosis depends on demonstrating low levels (less than 0·2 g/ 100 ml) of γ globulin by electrophoresis, or low levels of specific immunoglobulins by immunological methods. The presence or absence of lymphocytes may be detected in the peripheral blood.

If the sibling of an affected child is being investigated it is important to remember that "physiologically" low levels occur at about three months.

SUMMARY

Plasma Proteins

1. The proteins of normal plasma have a variety of functions (p. 227).

2. The antibodies are synthesized in the reticulo-endothelial system while the liver is the source of most of the other proteins (p. 227).

3. Total protein estimations are of limited use in the diagnosis of protein abnormalities (p. 228).

4. Fractionation of serum protein is usually made by zone electrophoresis on cellulose acetate (p. 230). Five fractions are recognized by this method—albumin, α_1, α_2, β and γ globulins. These fractions are affected in different ways by disease (p. 231).

5. A non-specific pattern is seen in many inflammatory diseases, including liver disease and in conditions characterized by tissue damage. Specific patterns may be seen in the nephrotic syndrome, the paraproteinaemias, hypogammaglobulinaemias and in some cases of cirrhosis.

Immunoglobulins

1. The immunoglobulins (Ig) are a group of proteins that are structurally related. They include the normal antibodies, the myeloma proteins and Bence-Jones protein. Five classes of Ig are described. The main ones are IgG, IgA and IgM.

2. The immunoglobulin molecule consists of heavy (H) and light (L) chains. Classification is made on the basis of the H chains.

3. Bence-Jones protein consists of L chains. It has peculiar heat properties and is diagnostic of malignant proliferation of Ig-producing cells (p. 239).

4. A paraprotein is a narrow band usually found in the γ region of the electrophoretic strip. It may signify a malignant process of Ig-producing cells (such as myelomatosis) or it may be benign (p. 240).

5. The most frequently encountered disease with a paraprotein is myelomatosis. It may present in a variety of ways and is diagnosed by bone marrow examination and protein abnormalities in the plasma and urine (p. 241).

6. Grossly reduced levels of γ globulin are found in hypogammaglobulinaemia. The cause may be congenital or acquired (p. 245).

7. Cryoglobulins are proteins that precipitate at low temperatures. They occur in a number of diseases and produce symptoms on exposure to cold (p. 243).

APPENDIX TO CHAPTER X

1. Blood for protein estimation should be taken with a minimum of stasis otherwise falsely high results may be obtained (p. 229). Blood for protein fractionation should be taken without anticoagulant, since fibrinogen interferes with the interpretation of the results.

2. Simple tests for Bence-Jones protein (BJP).—*N.B.* Negative results with the salicylsulphonic test or "Albustix" do not exclude the presence of BJP (p. 240).

Urine for BJP tests should be fresh. An old specimen containing albumin may give apparently positive results due to breakdown products. A fresh, early morning specimen offers the greatest chance of success as it is usually concentrated.

(*a*) *Bradshaw's test.*—Urine is layered carefully on to a few millilitres of concentrated HCl in a test-tube. A thick white precipitate at the interface indicates the presence of globulin in the urine (most commonly, but not necessarily BJP). Albumin does not give this reaction. This test can be positive in the nephrotic syndrome when globulins are being lost in the urine.

(*b*) *Heat test.*—There are many variants of tests designed to show the heat properties of Bence-Jones protein. The best results are obtained in buffered urine at a pH of 4·9, but a simple and effective test is the *three tube test.*

Three small glass tubes containing 1–2 ml of urine are attached to a thermometer with a rubber band. To the first and second of these tubes, one and two drops of 33 per cent acetic acid are added respectively, while the third has no added acid. This provides a range of pH. The tubes and thermometer are held in a beaker of water which is slowly heated while the urine is stirred. If protein precipitation (clouding) occurs in any of the tubes below 60°C one of the properties of BJP is satisfied. This tube is then further heated to see if the precipitate redissolves (p. 239).

If protein other than BJP is present in the urine this may mask the disappearance of BJP on further heating. If the boiling urine is filtered other protein will be removed: BJP will then reappear in the filtrate on cooling.

Failure to detect BJP by these tests is not conclusive evidence of its absence. Electrophoresis after concentration of a 24-hour urine specimen may demonstrate it.

3. Sia test for macroglobulins.—Once again best results are obtained with properly buffered solutions, but a simple, if less accurate test may be adequate. Serum is dropped into previously boiled distilled water. Macroglobulins form a dense white flocculum which settles rapidly: other immunoglobulins do not.

Chapter XI

PLASMA LIPIDS AND LIPOPROTEINS

INTRODUCTION

THE study of plasma lipids is of growing importance but understanding of the subject is hindered by the different terminologies used. These are based on:

Chemical Analysis

There are four chemical groups of lipids in the plasma—cholesterol, fatty acids, phospholipids and triglycerides.

Lipoprotein Electrophoresis

The lipids are carried in the plasma bound to protein, which can therefore be separated by electrophoresis into α, β, pre-β lipoproteins and chylomicrons.

Ultracentrifugation

This separates the fractions on the basis of density. High density and low density lipoproteins (HDL and LDL) and chylomicrons are described.

The first section of this chapter is devoted to a description and correlation of these terminologies. Of the three methods, chemical analysis is the most widely available. Lipoprotein electrophoresis offers a good system of classification of lipid disorders but the description of this will be supplemented by reference to chemical changes. Ultracentrifugation is available in only a few specialized centres.

TERMINOLOGY AND CLASSIFICATION

CHEMICAL CLASSIFICATION

The four forms of lipid present in plasma are illustrated diagrammatically in Fig. 19. Although they appear structurally diverse they are all insoluble in water and soluble in such organic solvents as ether or chloroform.

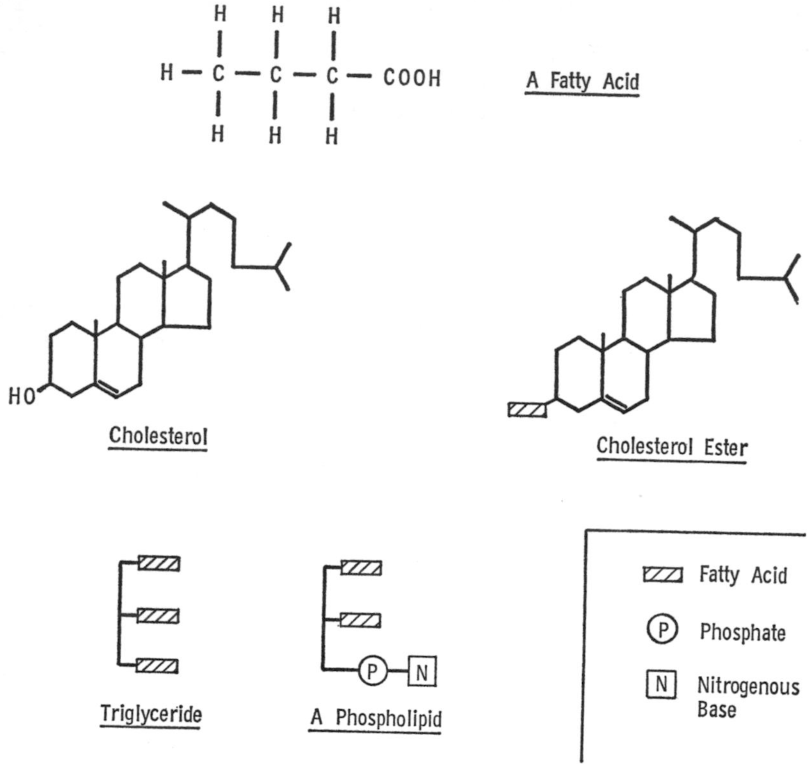

Fig. 19.—Plasma lipids.

(a) Fatty Acids

These are straight chain compounds, the chain varying in length depending on the number of carbon atoms in the molecule. Fatty acids may be *saturated* (containing no double bonds), or *unsaturated* (with one or more double bonds). The two most important saturated fatty acids in plasma are palmitic and stearic acids which contain 16 and 18 carbon atoms respectively. A further subdivision is used in clinical practice: fatty acids may be *esterified* with glycerol (an ester is the compound formed by chemical combination of an acid and an alcohol) to form glycerides, or they may be free, when they are called *free fatty acids* (FFA) or *non-esterified fatty acids* (NEFA).

(b) Triglycerides

Triglycerides consist of glycerol, each molecule of which is esterified with three fatty acids. 95 per cent of the lipids of adipose tissue are triglycerides (also referred to as neutral fat).

(c) Phospholipids

These complex lipids are so called because they also contain phosphate and a nitrogenous base. The major phospholipids in plasma are *lecithin* and *sphingomyelin*. The phosphate and nitrogenous bases are water soluble, a fact that is important in lipid transport.

(d) Cholesterol

This lipid has a steroid structure and other steroids are derived from cholesterol. In the plasma, cholesterol occurs in two forms. About 75 per cent is esterified with a fatty acid (Fig. 19) to form a *cholesterol ester*, and the remainder is free. The two fractions are usually measured together as *total cholesterol*.

The normal concentrations of these substances in plasma taken when the subject is *fasting* are:

NEFA	5– 20 mg/100 ml.
Triglycerides	0–150 mg/100 ml.
Phospholipids	175–250 mg/100 ml.
Total cholesterol	150–250 mg/100 ml.

Non-fasting specimens give variable results, and should not be collected for this purpose.

LIPOPROTEINS

Lipids are insoluble in water and so in plasma. Nevertheless plasma lipids are in solution because they are combined with a protein carrier. The resultant large molecule, a *lipoprotein*, is water soluble. The mechanism of lipoprotein formation is not entirely understood. All lipoproteins contain protein and phospholipid as well as cholesterol and triglycerides. It is probable that the large molecule is so arranged that the protein and water miscible groups of the phospholipids are on the outside, in contact with the aqueous plasma, while the insoluble lipids are in the centre.

Because of the protein moiety lipoproteins can be separated by electrophoresis. The technique is basically the same as that of other protein electrophoresis (p. 230) except that a different stain is used to render the lipid visible. Four zones may be recognized (Fig. 20):

α lipoproteins—these contain mostly cholesterol and phospholipids
pre-β lipoproteins—these contain mostly triglycerides
β lipoproteins—these contain mostly cholesterol
chylomicrons—these contain mostly triglycerides.

In normal fasting plasma the α and β bands are usually the only ones visible. Pre-β lipoproteins are visible only when there is excessive endogenous triglyceride synthesis (p. 256) and may be seen in persons on a high carbohydrate diet. Triglycerides at normal levels are probably carried mostly in the β and to some extent in the pre-β lipoproteins : the latter are not always detectable. Chylomicrons appear after a fatty meal.

The levels of α lipoproteins are constant throughout life and are higher in women (about 320 mg/100 ml) than men (about 260 mg/ 100 ml). They do not vary with dietary changes. The concentration of β lipoproteins tends to increase with age and is generally higher in men than women during the reproductive years. It is influenced by the diet.

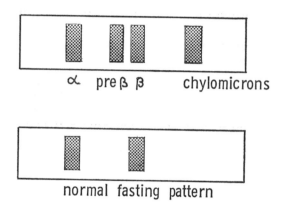

Fig. 20.—Lipoprotein electrophoretic strips (diagrammatic).

ULTRACENTRIFUGATION

Like other proteins (p. 238), lipoproteins may be separated on the basis of molecular density. When suspended in salt solution of specific gravity 1·063 some of the lipoproteins sediment together with the other plasma proteins. These are the high density lipoproteins (HDL), which correspond to the α lipoproteins in the electrophoretic pattern. The remainder, because of their greater lipid content, have a lower density and tend to float, and are referred to as low density lipoproteins. There are two major subdivisions in this group depending on the flotation rate, which is expressed in S_f (Svedberg flotation) units. The greater the content of triglycerides, the lower the density and the greater the S_f number. The major subdivisions are:

(a) S_f 0–20

These are referred to as *low density lipoproteins* (LDL) and consist mostly of cholesterol and phospholipids. They correspond to the β lipoproteins.

(b) S_f 20–400

These are referred to as *very low density lipoproteins* (VLDL). They have a much higher proportion of triglycerides and correspond to the pre-β lipoproteins.

Chylomicrons are usually separated before ultracentrifugation, but may also be considered here.

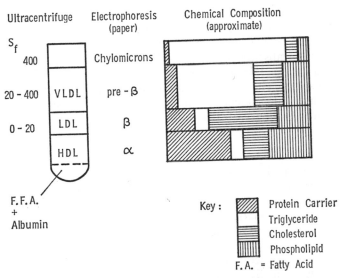

FIG. 21.—Correlation of plasma lipid and lipoprotein nomenclature.

(c) S_f 10^3–10^5

These chylomicrons are extremely large molecules that appear in the plasma after a fatty meal (p. 254). They consist almost entirely of triglycerides and remain at the origin on electrophoresis.

These nomenclatures are correlated in Fig. 21.

METABOLISM AND FUNCTIONS OF LIPIDS

TRIGLYCERIDES AND FATTY ACIDS

Only an outline of the metabolism of fat can be given and discussion will be confined to points of clinical importance. The most logical sequence is to follow the fate of ingested lipid. Almost all the lipid in a normal diet is in the form of neutral fat (triglycerides). Animal products also contribute cholesterol.

254 CLINICAL CHEMISTRY

Digestion and Absorption

In the small intestine triglycerides are hydrolyzed by *pancreatic lipase*. This process is aided by *bile salts* which emulsify the fat globules. Only about a quarter of the triglycerides are completely hydrolyzed to glycerol and FFA and the major end product is monoglyceride. Small amounts of diglyceride are also present. With the aid of bile salts this mixture of hydrolyzed and partly hydrolyzed fat is absorbed (see p. 205 for further details).

Adequate digestion of fat is dependent on adequate amounts of pancreatic lipase and bile salts. Pancreatic disease, such as chronic pancreatitis, or absence of bile salts due to biliary obstruction, may be associated with malabsorption of fat.

The fat soluble vitamins A, D and K are absorbed at this stage. They are particularly dependent on bile salts for absorption and deficiencies may occur with biliary obstruction.

Transport

In the intestinal mucosa FFA and glycerol are resynthesized into triglycerides and combined with small amounts of carrier protein, cholesterol and phospholipid to form *chylomicrons*. These large aggregates enter the lymphatics and pass via the thoracic duct into the blood stream. Here, because of their large size, they scatter light and account for the turbidity of plasma seen after a fatty meal.

Some short and medium-chain fatty acids enter the portal system and pass directly to the liver. They are, however, a minor component of the usual diet.

Removal of Chylomicrons

Although several tissues are capable of handling chylomicrons the major site of removal is adipose tissue. Here an enzyme called *lipoprotein lipase* hydrolyzes the chylomicron triglycerides and releases FFA which are taken up by the fat cells. This reduces the size of the molecule and the plasma clears.

Lipoprotein lipase is a mysterious enzyme that is probably situated in capillary walls. It is not normally detectable in the blood stream except after an injection of heparin: consequently heparin can clear lipaemic plasma *in vivo* but not *in vitro*. The relationship between heparin and lipoprotein lipase is not clear. There is a rare condition in which lipoprotein lipase activity is congenitally absent (p. 259). This is characterized by the presence of circulating chylomicrons in the fasting state because they cannot be broken down.

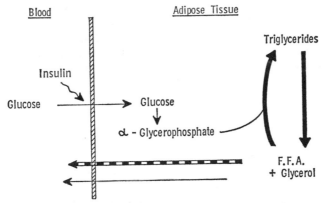

FIG. 22.—Metabolism of adipose tissue with (━━) and without (▨▬▨) adequate intracellular glucose.

Metabolism of Adipose Tissue

Contrary to earlier belief, adipose tissue is metabolically highly active. It consists almost entirely of triglyceride which is subject to continual breakdown and resynthesis. As this process is central to many metabolic problems it will be considered in some detail. The essential features are outlined in Fig. 22.

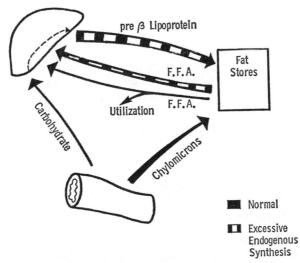

FIG. 23.—Normal and abnormal triglyceride and F.F.A. metabolism.

Triglycerides are hydrolyzed by *adipolytic lipase* to FFA and glycerol. Adipose tissue lacks the necessary enzymes for resynthesis of triglyceride from glycerol; instead, the FFA are combined with α glycerophosphate. This in turn is derived from intracellular glucose so that the most crucial factor in this reaction is the availability of intracellular glucose. If intracellular glucose is not available, as in fasting, starvation, or insulin lack (diabetes mellitus), breakdown exceeds synthesis and FFA accumulate and pass into the blood stream. Plasma FFA levels are raised in these conditions.

Metabolism of FFA

Free fatty acids in the plasma are transported bound to albumin. The half-life of circulating FFA is a matter of minutes because of their rapid removal from the plasma by one of two routes: (*a*) FFA are a major source of body fuel in the fasting state (p. 131); (*b*) excess FFA may be taken up by the liver, re-esterified into triglycerides and released as *endogenous triglycerides* (as opposed to *exogenous triglyceride* derived from the diet). These triglycerides form the VLDL or pre-β lipoproteins and are metabolized in the adipose tissue in the same way as those from chylomicrons. When very large amounts of FFA reach the liver a proportion is converted to ketone bodies.

This account of the metabolism of adipose tissue and FFA has been greatly simplified. Many other hormones influence the release of FFA from fat by altering the balance of synthesis and breakdown of triglyceride, but it is beyond the scope of this book to consider them further.

Summary of Triglyceride and FFA Metabolism (Fig. 23)

1. The triglycerides in plasma are derived from the diet (after a fatty meal) or from the liver in the post-absorptive state. Depending on their origin they appear in the lipoprotein pattern in one of the following ways:

(*a*) Normal amounts are probably carried in the β lipoprotein.

(*b*) Exogenous triglycerides appear as chylomicrons and represent dietary triglycerides in transit to fat stores. Assimilation into adipose tissue is dependent on lipoprotein lipase.

(*c*) Excess endogenous triglycerides are carried as pre-β lipoproteins. They are synthesized in the liver from excess FFA derived from fat stores, or from dietary carbohydrate.

2. FFA are the most metabolically active lipid fraction. Accumulation in the plasma occurs when intracellular glucose levels are low, for instance in fasting, starvation and diabetes mellitus. Plasma FFA

are used as fuel by most tissues of the body and any excess is converted by the liver to endogenous triglyceride.

3. Lipid and carbohydrate metabolism are intimately related. This relationship is considered more fully in the section on carbohydrate metabolism (p. 131). The relevant points so far discussed are:

(a) Adipose tissue metabolism and FFA levels in the blood are dependent largely on the availability of glucose.

(b) Glucose may be converted by the liver to fatty acids and incorporated into triglycerides.

METABOLISM OF CHOLESTEROL

Dietary cholesterol is derived almost exclusively from animal products. Meat, dairy products and particularly egg yolk are the main sources of it. However, much of the cholesterol in the body (about 1 g a day) arises by synthesis, largely in the liver, and only about 0·3 g a day is absorbed from the intestine.

There is considerable controversy as to the effect of dietary cholesterol on plasma cholesterol levels and on arterial disease. There is little difference between the fasting cholesterol level and that in a random specimen. Several studies have shown that subjects on a long-term high cholesterol diet do have higher levels than those on a cholesterol-free diet: the effect of intermediate diets is not so clear. Most recent work points to the fact that intestinal absorption over a wide range of cholesterol intake (0·5–10 g) is constant at about 0·3 g/day and that at these levels the dietary cholesterol produces about 25 per cent of the plasma cholesterol. Further study is needed in the range of intake of 0–0·3 g cholesterol a day, a level which is below that of the average affluent population.

Cholesterol is found in all the lipoproteins of plasma, but mainly in the β lipoprotein of LDL. About 75 per cent is present as cholesterol ester (p. 251) and esterification takes place in the intestinal mucosa during absorption, in the liver, and possibly to some extent, in the plasma. In parenchymal liver disease the percentage of esterified cholesterol falls.

The amount of cholesterol that is added daily to the body pool is balanced by an equivalent excretion in the bile. Part is excreted as sterol and may be reabsorbed, while part is degraded by the liver to bile acids and bile salts. The role of bile salts in fat absorption has been mentioned (p. 254). In biliary obstruction cholesterol levels may be very high.

Cholesterol is the precursor of the steroid hormones (p. 94) but has little quantitative effect on their production as there is always surplus available for this purpose.

METABOLISM OF PHOSPHOLIPIDS

Phospholipids are widely distributed in all tissues and are closely concerned with mitochondrial metabolism. Dietary phospholipids may be absorbed as such because of their relative solubility but the phospholipids of plasma are derived mainly from synthesis in the liver.

The role of plasma phospholipids is uncertain. They are concerned with blood coagulation (the lipid portion of thromboplastin) and their role in lipoproteins has been mentioned (p. 251). They are probably concerned, like other binding proteins, with transport of lipids.

ROLE OF THE LIVER IN FAT METABOLISM

This may be summarized briefly:

1. Synthesis and esterification of cholesterol. Excretion of cholesterol as sterol and bile acids (p. 257).

2. Synthesis of lipoproteins (p. 256).

3. Synthesis of FFA *de novo* and conversion of excess FFA to endogenous triglyceride.

4. Synthesis of phospholipids.

ABNORMALITIES OF PLASMA LIPIDS

A much clearer understanding of lipid abnormalities has been developed recently by classifying them in terms of lipoprotein patterns. This approach will be used with constant reference to the corresponding chemical fractions. Both hyperlipoproteinaemias and hypolipoproteinaemias have been described.

HYPERLIPAEMIA

(*Synonyms:* hyperlipidaemia, hyperlipoproteinaemia)

Clinical interest in the hyperlipaemias is centred on the association with cardiovascular disease and the development of xanthomata.

Xanthomatosis

Xanthomata are yellowish deposits of lipids in the tissues of the body. Several different types exist and usually seem to be correlated with elevations of different lipid fractions in the plasma, although this correlation is not a constant one.

(*a*) **Eruptive xanthomata** are crops of small itchy yellow nodules that occur in association with raised triglycerides (either endogenous or exogenous).

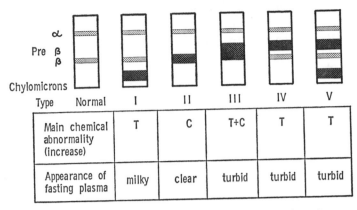

	Normal	I	II	III	IV	V
Main chemical abnormality (increase)		T	C	T+C	T	T
Appearance of fasting plasma		milky	clear	turbid	turbid	turbid

T - Triglycerides   C - Cholesterol

FIG. 24.—Classification of hyperlipoproteinaemia by lipoprotein electrophoresis (Fredrickson).

(b) **Xanthomata tuberosum** are flat yellow plaques found over elbows, buttocks and knees and which are seen with elevated endogenous triglycerides.

(c) Deposits in tendons (**xanthoma tendinosum**), eyelids (**xanthelasma**) and cornea (**corneal arcus**) are seen with raised cholesterol levels.

PATTERNS OF HYPERLIPOPROTEINAEMIA

Five basic patterns have been described by Frederickson's group (Fig. 24). These may be secondary to another disease or primary. If primary, there may be a familial pattern.

Type I

This is a rare familial condition usually seen before the age of 10. It is characterized clinically by eruptive xanthomata, hepatomegaly and attacks of abdominal pain. The fasting plasma is milky because of raised chylomicron levels. In many of these patients there is a deficiency of lipoprotein lipase (p. 254). If fat is removed from the diet, the plasma clears within a few days (*fat-induced hyperlipaemia*). There is *no* increased incidence of cardiovascular complications.

Type II (Hypercholesterolaemia)

This is the commonest group and is characterized by a raised cholesterol concentration with clear plasma. Hypercholesterolaemia may be primary or secondary.

Secondary hypercholesterolaemia.—This is seen in:
1. Diabetes mellitus (p. 135).
2. Hypothyroidism (p. 170).
3. Biliary obstruction (p. 275).
4. Nephrotic syndrome (p. 11).
5. Normal pregnancy (to a lesser degree) (p. 368).

If the triglycerides are also raised, this is a Type III pattern.

Primary hypercholesterolaemia.—A raised plasma cholesterol concentration with no apparent cause is not uncommon, particularly among affluent population groups. There is, however, a well-recognized entity, familial hypercholesterolaemia, which is characterized clinically by atheromatosis and cardiovascular disease, sometimes at an early age. Xanthomata are common in this condition.

Types III, IV and V

Because of their similar clinical features these types will be considered together.

Type III is characterized by a broad β-lipoprotein band. Both cholesterol and triglyceride levels are raised.

Type IV is characterized by a pre-β-lipoprotein band and raised triglyceride levels.

Type V is characterized by a pre-β-lipoprotein band and the presence of circulating chylomicrons in the fasting state. The increase in triglycerides is of both endogenous and exogenous origin.

The chemical feature linking these groups is the presence of increased endogenous triglycerides. The fasting plasma is therefore turbid. There are several clinical features common to the three groups.

1. Impaired glucose tolerance is frequent in all groups.
2. Obesity and cardiovascular disease are common in all groups.
3. Reduction of carbohydrate in the diet frequently lowers the triglyceride levels (*carbohydrate-induced hyperlipaemia*), although this does not occur significantly in Type V.

The patterns described above may be primary (with or without a family history) or secondary to other disease.

Secondary Causes of Raised Triglyceride Levels

1. Diabetes mellitus (p. 135).
2. Pancreatitis (p. 215).
3. Excessive alcohol intake.
4. Glycogen storage disease (p. 148).
5. Hypothyroidism (p. 170).
6. Severe nephrotic syndrome (p. 11).
7. Pregnancy (p. 368).
8. Oral contraceptives (p. 368).

Approach to the Diagnosis of Hyperlipoproteinaemia

The presence of hyperlipoproteinaemia may be suggested by a number of clinical findings such as cardiovascular disease at an early age, xanthomata, or a family history of either condition. As has been discussed, the most logical classification at present is based on lipoprotein electrophoretic patterns. If this estimation is not available routine chemical tests will, in most cases, indicate the type of abnormality.

(a) Blood is taken after a fast of 14–16 hours and is centrifuged. The supernatant plasma or serum is examined. Visible turbidity in a fresh specimen indicates raised triglyceride levels. The distinction between exogenous and endogenous triglycerides may be made by allowing the separated plasma to stand overnight. Chylomicrons (exogenous triglycerides) form a creamy layer on the surface, whereas pre-β lipoproteins (endogenous triglycerides, VLDL) remain dispersed. It must be emphasized that fasting chylomicronaemia is very rare and the vast majority of turbid fasting sera contain raised VLDL levels.

(b) Cholesterol is estimated chemically.

These two observations will indicate the type of abnormality in most cases of hyperlipoproteinaemia. A clear plasma with raised cholesterol levels will almost certainly have a type II pattern (hyperbetalipoproteinaemia). If triglyceride estimations are also available further differentiation is possible, but because of overlap between the groups some cases may still remain unclassified.

It must be remembered that all the lipoprotein groups contain cholesterol and triglycerides (as well as protein and phospholipid), and elevation of triglyceride is usually accompanied by some elevation of cholesterol levels and vice versa. It is for this reason that a classification based on lipoprotein changes is of more value than one based on chemical analysis only.

Once the type of hyperlipoproteinaemia is identified by electrophoresis or by the above scheme, the next step is to decide if it is a primary or secondary phenomenon. The main causes of secondary hyperlipoproteinaemia have been listed. If primary, the relatives should be investigated to establish a familial incidence.

HYPOLIPOPROTEINAEMIA

There are two interesting but very rare inherited lipoprotein deficiencies.

Low Density Lipoprotein Deficiency (Abetalipoproteinaemia)

The clinical syndrome is characterized by intestinal malabsorption with steatorrhoea, progressive ataxia, retinitis pigmentosa and acanthocytosis (crenation of red blood cells). Plasma levels of cholesterol and phospholipids are low (often below 60 mg/100 ml) and triglycerides are virtually absent. Chylomicrons do not appear in the blood after a fatty meal.

High Density Lipoprotein Deficiency (Tangier disease)

This condition is characterized by the presence of large quantities of cholesterol esters in certain tissues. There is consequent tonsillar enlargement, hepatosplenomegaly and lymphadenopathy. Plasma cholesterol and phospholipid levels are low but triglyceride levels are raised.

The pathogenic mechanisms of these two syndromes are unknown, but defective synthesis of the lipoprotein is a possible cause.

SUMMARY

1. Lipids in plasma are carried in the form of lipoproteins and chylomicrons (p. 251).

2. Plasma lipids may be classified according to their chemical structure, or as lipoproteins by electrophoresis or ultracentrifugation. Chemical estimations are most frequently available but lipoprotein analysis offers the best understanding of abnormalities (p. 251).

3. The chemical lipid fractions are cholesterol, triglycerides, phospholipids and free fatty acids (p. 250).

4. Triglyceride and free fatty acid metabolism is intimately connected with carbohydrate metabolism (Summary, p. 256).

5. The functions of plasma cholesterol and phospholipids are uncertain. Both are an integral part of all lipoprotein molecules (p. 251).

6. Hyperlipoproteinaemias may be classified according to electrophoretic patterns. The clinical associations of these conditions include cardiovascular disease, xanthomatosis, carbohydrate intolerance and obesity (p. 259).

7. Hyperlipoproteinaemias may be primary or secondary in origin. Primary hyperlipoproteinaemias often have a familial incidence (p. 259).

8. The commonest form of hyperlipoproteinaemia is type II (hyperbetalipoproteinaemia), characterized by a raised plasma cholesterol concentration. It may be primary, or secondary to other disease (p. 259).

9. Two rare familial lipoprotein deficiency syndromes exist.

10. If lipoprotein electrophoresis is not available, most cases of hyperlipaemia may be classified on the basis of chemical estimation and inspection of fasting plasma.

Chapter XII

LIVER DISEASE AND GALL STONES

LIVER DISEASE

Outline of Functions of the Liver

THE liver plays an important role in many metabolic processes. It receives blood from the portal vein and so all nutrient from the gut, with the exception of fats (p. 206), reaches the liver before entering the systemic circulation.

1. **Carbohydrate metabolism.**—Glycogen is synthesized and stored in the liver during periods of carbohydrate availability. During fasting, blood glucose levels are maintained within normal limits by breakdown of stored glycogen (glycogenolysis) and conversion of amino-acids and fatty acids into glucose (gluconeogenesis). This takes place in the liver (see p. 127 for further discussion).

2. **Lipid metabolism.**—Synthesis of lipoproteins, phospholipids, cholesterol and endogenous triglyceride occurs largely, but not exclusively, in the liver. Furthermore cholesterol is esterified in the liver and the breakdown products of cholesterol are excreted in bile.

3. **Protein synthesis.**—Many of the plasma proteins, including special carrier proteins and most of the coagulation factors, but with the notable exception of the γ globulins, are synthesized in the liver (see p. 227). Prothrombin and factors VII, IX and X require vitamin K for their synthesis.

4. **Storage functions.**—In addition to glycogen, many vitamins such as vitamins D and B_{12} are stored in the liver (p. 354) and it is a major site of iron storage (p. 307).

5. **Excretion and detoxication.**—Bile pigments and cholesterol (p. 264) are excreted in the bile. Numerous drugs are detoxicated by the liver and some are excreted in bile. Ammonia, derived from protein and amino-acid metabolism or produced in the bowel by bacteria, is converted to urea and rendered non-toxic. Steroid hormones are inactivated by conjugation with glucuronic acid and sulphate in the liver and excreted in the urine.

6. **Reticulo-endothelial function.**—The Kupffer cells lining the sinusoids of the liver form part of the reticulo-endothelial system.

BILE PIGMENT METABOLISM

At the end of their life span circulating red cells are broken down in the reticulo-endothelial system, mainly in the spleen. The released haemoglobin is split into globin, which enters the general protein pool, and haem which is converted to bilirubin after removal of the iron molecule. The iron is reutilized.

The bilirubin formed by this process is carried to the liver and accounts for about 80 per cent of the bilirubin metabolized daily. Other sources include the breakdown of immature red cells in the bone marrow and of compounds chemically related to haemoglobin, such as myoglobin and cytochromes. In all about 300 mg of bilirubin is carried daily to the liver. Healthy hepatic cells are capable of handling much greater loads than this.

Bilirubin in transit to the liver is bound to plasma albumin and is not soluble in water. It is referred to as *unconjugated bilirubin* (or simply as *bilirubin*) and, because of its binding to albumin and water insolubility does not appear in the urine. Most of the "normal" plasma bilirubin is in this form.

Bilirubin is transported into the liver cell and is conjugated with glucuronic acid to form bilirubin glucuronide or *conjugated bilirubin*. This takes place in the hepatic microsomes under the influence of the enzyme uridyl diphosphate (UDP) glucuronyl transferase. Conjugated bilirubin is transported out of the liver cell into the bile canaliculi and excreted in the bile.

Conjugated bilirubin is present in normal plasma in very small quantities, if at all, and routine methods of estimation are inaccurate at this level. Conjugated bilirubin at pathologically high concentration may also be bound to plasma albumin. This form of bilirubin is water-soluble and appears in the urine.

The conjugated bilirubin enters the gut in bile. In the colon it is broken down by bacteria to a group of products known collectively as *stercobilinogen* (often referred to as *faecal urobilinogen*). These are oxidized to *stercobilin*, a pigment that contributes to the brown colour of the stool. A small amount is absorbed into the portal circulation and most of this is re-excreted in bile: a very small fraction appears in the urine as *urobilinogen* which in turn can be oxidized to *urobilin*. These amounts are usually below the limits of detection of the routine urine tests (p. 270). The sequence of events is outlined in Fig. 25.

Bile salts are one of the end products of cholesterol breakdown

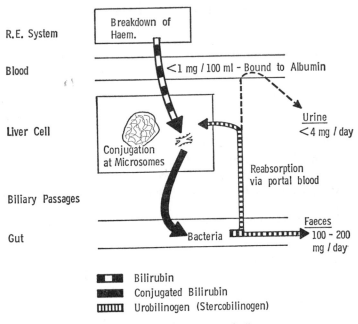

Bilirubin
Conjugated Bilirubin
Urobilinogen (Stercobilinogen)

FIG. 25.—Bile pigment metabolism.

(p. 206). Their role in fat absorption has been mentioned (p. 254). In biliary obstruction failure of bile salts to reach the bowel may result in malabsorption of fat and fat soluble vitamins (p. 206). In addition bile salts accumulate in the plasma and appear in the urine. As no accurate simple method of measurement of these compounds exists, their place in routine diagnosis is limited.

The term *bile pigments* is used to include bilirubin and its breakdown products. With the exception of urobilinogen and stercobilinogen all are coloured.

Other terminology for bile pigments.—An early test used in the investigation of jaundice was the van den Bergh reaction. In some cases of jaundice plasma bilirubin reacted directly with the colour reagent used (direct reaction) whereas in others the addition of methanol was required (indirect reaction). These terms are still sometimes used in expressing the results of quantitative tests and total plasma bilirubin may be subdivided into *direct* and *indirect* fractions. These correspond approximately to *conjugated bilirubin* and *bilirubin* respectively. The latter terms are preferable and will be used in this book.

DISORDERS OF BILE PIGMENT METABOLISM

AND THE CLASSIFICATION OF JAUNDICE

Numerous classifications of jaundice exist. Most are based on the mechanism or site of production of the excess bilirubin, but these are not of great diagnostic value. Many cases of jaundice overlap more than one category. The scheme outlined below is based on the work of Sherlock and offers an approach to diagnosis rather than an attempt at theoretical classification.

The metabolism of bilirubin may be considered in four stages:

1. Formation of bilirubin and transport to the liver.
2. Passage of bilirubin into the liver cell.
3. Conjugation of bilirubin by glucuronyl transferase in the liver cell microsomes.
4. Passage of conjugated bilirubin out of the liver cell and excretion in the bile.

Interference at stages 1–3 would result in a rise of unconjugated bilirubin levels while interference with stage 4 would result in a rise of the concentration of conjugated bilirubin. Congenital abnormalities of many stages of the excretion of bilirubin exist and have helped outline the steps of normal bile pigment metabolism. They are uncommon but will be considered briefly below and on p. 277.

Based on this scheme jaundice may be due to:

1. **An increased load of bilirubin arriving at the liver cell.**—The main cause in this category is increased red cell destruction as in *haemolysis* or breakdown of early red cells in the marrow. Absorption of a *large haematoma* has the same result and may, particularly in infants, produce jaundice. It is an important cause of jaundice in the newborn when plasma bilirubin levels may be very high. In adults, haemolytic jaundice is usually mild (2–3 mg/100 ml) because of the very high excretory capacity of the adult liver.

2. **Defective transport into the liver cell.**—This is seen in the inborn error, *Gilbert's disease* (p. 277).

3. **Disturbance of conjugation.**—This is a contributory factor in *neonatal jaundice*, especially in premature babies where the glucuronyl transferase enzyme system is immature. Congenital deficiency of this enzyme is seen in the *Crigler–Najjar* syndrome when jaundice may be severe. Novobiocin can produce jaundice at this stage, as can destruction of liver cells, such as in hepatitis.

4. **Disturbances of excretion of conjugated bilirubin.**—This is the largest group and is characterized by a rise in conjugated as well as

TABLE XVII

CAUSES OF JAUNDICE

Fraction of bilirubin elevated	Basic abnormality	Existing classifications		
Unconjugated	1. Excessive formation of bilirubin	Pre-hepatic	Haemolytic	*Retention jaundice* (a) Haemolytic
	2. Impaired entry of bilirubin into the liver cell			(b) Non-haemolytic
	3. Impaired conjugation of bilirubin	Hepatic	Hepatogenous	
Both, mainly conjugated	4. Impaired excretion of conjugated bilirubin			*Regurgitation jaundice* (a) Parenchymal
		Post-hepatic	Obstructive	(b) Mechanical

unconiugated bilirubin. *Liver cell destruction* and *intra- and extrahepatic cholestasis* fall into this group, as does the congenital *Dubin–Johnson syndrome* (p. 277). Most of the chemical tests of "liver function" are used to distinguish different causes of jaundice in this category.

Comparison with existing aetiological classifications is shown in Table XVII.

BIOCHEMICAL TESTS IN LIVER DISEASE

Many tests of "liver function" exist. Discussion in this chapter is confined to those tests commonly performed and which the authors have found useful. Most suffer from two main disadvantages:

1. The liver, like the kidney, has considerable functional reserve and many tests only become positive when there is widespread involvement of the organ. In general, tests involving excretory function are the most sensitive.

2. Most tests, such as the plasma protein changes, are also affected by diseases other than those of the liver. For this reason it is usual to perform a "battery" of tests.

Basic Processes in Liver Disease

There is no test or combination of tests specific for any particular disease. Most laboratories perform several tests of "liver function" which indicate the nature of the pathological process, but not necessarily the cause of it. There are two main pathological changes seen in liver disorders and either or both may be present in a single disease. These are:

(*a*) Liver cell destruction.
(*b*) Cholestasis.

(*a*) **Liver cell destruction.**—This may vary from areas of focal necrosis to destruction of most of the liver leading to liver failure. Examples of the main causes are:

(i) *Hepatitis*, which is most commonly viral but may occur in the course of other diseases such as infectious mononucleosis, or with septicaemia.

(ii) The action of *toxins* on the liver, especially chlorinated hydrocarbons such as carbon tetrachloride. Phosphorus is a hepatotoxin. A number of the hydrazine drugs such as iproniazid (a monoamine oxidase inhibitor) produce liver damage and therefore are no longer in clinical use.

(iii) Liver cell destruction may occur secondarily to prolonged *biliary obstruction*.

(iv) Cellular destruction of known or unknown aetiology may be followed by *cirrhosis*, and the process may persist in the cirrhotic liver.

The consequences of liver cell destruction vary with the degree of damage. Clinically there may be no evidence of liver dysfunction and only certain tests may give positive results. There may be jaundice and failure of synthetic function or there may be fatal liver failure.

(b) **Cholestasis.**—Cholestasis is "the syndrome associated with failure of bile to reach the duodenum" (Sherlock). The causes may be divided into intrahepatic and extrahepatic. The first are not amenable to surgery, the second may be. Distinction between the two is therefore important.

(i) *Intrahepatic cholestasis.*—This is frequently associated with liver cell destruction. The main causes are:
Viral hepatitis (cholangiolytic hepatitis).
Certain drugs such as methyl testosterone, chlorpromazine.
Pregnancy. Idiopathic cholestasis may develop in late pregnancy in certain individuals, and may recur in subsequent pregnancies. These patients also tend to develop cholestasis with oral contraceptive therapy. The cholestasis is thought to be hormonal in origin.
Cholangitis.
Biliary cirrhosis.
Cirrhosis (some cases).
Infiltrations of the liver (e.g. Hodgkin's disease, malignancy).
Intrahepatic biliary atresia.

(ii) *Extrahepatic cholestasis.*—The main causes are:
Gall stone in the common bile duct.
Carcinoma of head of pancreas, ampulla of Vater or rarely bile duct.
Fibrosis of duct.
External pressure from tumour; glands.
Extrahepatic atresia of bile duct.

The *consequences* of cholestasis depend largely on its duration. Retention of bilirubin leads to jaundice. The high levels of cholesterol found in some cases, especially in biliary cirrhosis, can rarely cause xanthomatosis. In chronic cases with prolonged absence of bile salts from the gut absorption of fat and fat-soluble vitamins is impaired (p. 206).

Scope of Tests Used in Liver Disease

Tests used in the diagnosis and assessment of liver disease may be classified as follows:
(a) Tests involving bile pigment metabolism.
(b) Other tests of excretory function.
(c) Tests showing liver cell dysfunction.
(d) Tests showing liver cell damage.
(e) Tests indicating cholestasis.

Tests Involving Bile Pigment Metabolism

The physiology of bile pigments has been outlined on p. 264. The essential tests required to assess jaundice are estimation of plasma bilirubin (both fractions), qualitative tests for urinary bile products and visual inspection of the faeces for stercobilin.

1. Raised levels of *unconjugated bilirubin* only indicate excessive red cell destruction, defective entry of bilirubin into the liver cell or defective conjugation of bilirubin. The diagnosis is rarely a problem and the causes have been outlined on p. 266.

2. In most cases of jaundice *both fractions* are raised. In cholestasis conjugated bilirubin predominates.

3. *Bilirubin in the urine* means that there is an increase in circulating conjugated bilirubin and is always pathological.

4. *Urobilin(ogen)* in the urine may indicate:

(i) Excessive amounts of bile pigment reaching the bowel and being reabsorbed, for example, due to haemolysis.

(ii) Normal amounts of bile pigment with liver damage and failure to re-excrete urobilinogen (Fig. 25), for example, hepatitis.

(iii) A concentrated normal urine may give a faint positive reaction for urobilinogen.

In fresh urine urobilinogen is present, but with time urobilin develops. The significance of the finding remains unaltered. The usual test for urobilin (p. 284) converts any urobilinogen present into urobilin and so is probably the test of choice.

Quantitative estimation of urobilinogen in a timed collection of urine eliminates the variation due to urinary concentration. Excretion is, however, affected by other factors such as the pH of the urine, and the estimation is only rarely of value.

Complete absence of urobilinogen from the urine in a case of jaundice indicates complete cholestasis (no bilirubin reaches the bowel for conversion and reabsorption). Conversely the presence of urobilinogen is incompatible with the diagnosis of *complete* biliary obstruction.

5. Complete absence of bile pigments in the faeces produces pale stools and indicates cholestasis. There are, however, other causes of pale stools such as steatorrhea (p. 211).

Other Tests of Excretory Function

The most commonly used test in this group is the *bromsulphthalein (BSP) retention test*. The dye BSP is injected intravenously (dose 5 mg/kg body weight). Most is conjugated in the liver and excreted in the bile. A small amount escapes in the urine. After 45 minutes blood is withdrawn from the opposite arm (to avoid contamination from the injection site) and the amount of BSP still circulating is measured. Normally less than 3 per cent of the dose remains. Excretion depends not only on the integrity of the liver cell, but also on adequate circulation in the liver and patency of the biliary tract.

Increased retention of BSP is a sensitive index of hepatocellular dysfunction. False positive results occur where there is impaired circulation in the liver, for example, in congestive cardiac failure, or if biliary obstruction is present. The test is unnecessary if the patient is jaundiced and its main function is as a sensitive test of liver function when other tests are normal.

Tests Indicating Liver Cell Dysfunction

The most readily measured function of the liver is protein synthesis and this may be assessed by:

1. Measurement of plasma proteins (including cholinesterase) and flocculation tests.

2. Measurement of coagulation factors.

1. *Plasma protein changes and the flocculation tests.*—As outlined in Chapter X, the liver synthesizes most of the plasma proteins with the notable exception of γ globulin. Impaired function, such as occurs in viral hepatitis, results in a fall in plasma albumin and α globulin. If the impairment becomes chronic (for instance in cirrhosis) the lowered albumin is accompanied by a raised γ and β globulin (p. 236).

The flocculation tests are based on the fact that certain substances on being added to plasma, tend to precipitate (or precipitate with) γ globulin. Albumin opposes this action. If albumin levels are low and if globulin levels are raised precipitation occurs leading to turbidity or flocculation. This is seen in many cases of liver disease, but is also seen in other diseases associated with similar protein changes. One of the most sensitive of these tests for this purpose is the *thymol turbidity test*, which is positive in early hepatitis. The advantage over electrophoresis is partly one of convenience, but in early hepatitis the thymol test is often abnormal before electrophoretic changes become obvious. Thymol flocculation is an extension of the thymol turbidity test and may rarely be positive with a negative turbidity, and vice versa. The *cephalin-cholesterol* test is of the same sensitivity as the thymol turbidity test. Other flocculation tests, such as zinc or ammonium sulphate turbidity, detect changes in γ globulin even if the albumin level is normal (see p. 229).

In summary, the flocculation tests depend on changes in plasma proteins and so are *not specific for liver disease*. Positive results may be obtained with any cause of a raised γ globulin.

Plasma levels of the enzyme *cholinesterase* (p. 295) fall with liver damage, but this fall parallels that of albumin, which is easier to measure.

2. *Changes in coagulation factors.*—Many of the coagulation factors are synthesized by the hepatic parenchymal cells. Hepatocellular damage may give rise to a bleeding state, or laboratory tests of coagulation may be abnormal. Four factors, II (prothrombin), VII, IX and X are only synthesized in the liver in the presence of vitamin K. Their activities (with the exception of factor IX) are conveniently measured by the *one-stage prothrombin time.* Deficiencies may arise in two ways. In cholestasis the absorption of the fat-soluble vitamins, including vitamin K, is impaired (p. 212). In the presence of parenchymal damage synthesis is impaired despite an adequate supply of vitamin K. These two mechanisms offer a way of distinguishing cholestasis from cellular damage by the response in the former to parenteral vitamin K. Shortening of the prothrombin time after vitamin K administration suggests cholestasis whereas total lack of response indicates liver cell damage. As in many liver function tests there is considerable overlap of results.

In severe liver disease deficiencies of factors V and I (fibrinogen) may also be encountered.

Tests Indicating Liver Cell Damage

Damage to liver cells, with or without necrosis, causes the acute release of intracellular constituents into the blood stream. This is detected by measuring plasma enzymes. The value of these estimations is that they provide information of a different sort to the tests already discussed.

1. *Aminotransferases* (*transaminases*).—Raised levels of aminotransferases are seen with liver cell damage due to any cause, most commonly viral hepatitis (p. 273). Particularly high levels are seen in cases of hepatic necrosis due to toxins. Mildly raised levels occur in cholestasis and some cases of cirrhosis. Both aspartate (Asp.AT: SGOT) and alanine (Al.AT: SGPT) aminotransferases are affected. Because myocardial infarction causes an increase in aspartate aminotransferase it has come to be regarded as the "heart" enzyme and alanine aminotransferase as the "liver" enzyme (p. 287). As the differential diagnosis in liver disease rarely includes myocardial infarcation either aminotransferase may be used. In many cases the Asp.AT, although less specific, is more sensitive a test than the Al.AT for liver disease.

2. *Isocitrate dehydrogenase.*—The changes in isocitrate dehydrogenase parallel those of the aminotransferases. The enzyme is much more specific for liver disease (p. 293) than the aminotransferases, but its estimation offers no special advantage for the detection of liver cell damage. Levels in uncomplicated extrahepatic obstruction are often normal.

3. *Lactate dehydrogenase.*—A similar pattern is seen in levels of lactate dehydrogenase (LDH). This test is less sensitive than those already discussed and offers little extra advantage in the investigation of liver disease. The isoenzyme affected is the slow moving liver fraction and levels of SHBD (the fast moving fraction from heart muscle) are usually normal.

Tests Indicating Cholestasis

1. *Plasma alkaline phosphatase.*—As mentioned on p. 290, plasma alkaline phosphatase is derived from at least two sources—the osteoblasts and the sinusoidal lining of hepatic cells. In addition the cells lining bile canaliculi synthesize alkaline phosphatase. The latter fraction is normally excreted in the bile and, if there is biliary obstruction, is regurgitated into the blood stream, as is conjugated bilirubin. Raised alkaline phosphatase levels in jaundice generally indicate cholestasis, although moderately raised levels, as in hepatitis, may be a result of liver cell damage. The higher the level of alkaline phosphatase the greater the likelihood of extrahepatic cholestasis.

If obstruction involves one of the hepatic ducts or if it is due to localized lesions such as multiple secondary carcinomata, a characteristic picture develops. There is retention of both bilirubin and alkaline phosphatase. Bilirubin, unlike alkaline phosphatase, can be excreted by liver cells in the unaffected part of the biliary system, so plasma levels may be only minimally raised. In the absence of bone disease the finding of a raised alkaline phosphatase out of proportion to plasma bilirubin is suggestive of a space-occupying lesion(s) or obstruction of one of the radicles of the common bile duct.

2. *5'-nucleotidase.*—This enzyme (p. 291) is one of the fractions included in the measurement of total alkaline phosphatase. Raised levels occur only in hepatic disease and may be used as an alternative test for cholestasis. Alternatively, it may be reserved for distinguishing a raised alkaline phosphatase due to liver disease from that due to bone disease if there is clinical uncertainty.

3. *Other tests.*—(*a*) The enzyme *leucine aminopeptidase* has been used to assess cholestasis. Changes parallel those of the enzymes already discussed and it offers no special advantage over the tests already discussed.

(*b*) *Plasma cholesterol levels.* These rise with biliary obstruction (p. 260), but this estimation is rarely of diagnostic value in liver disease.

Biochemical Changes in Individual Liver Diseases and the Selection of Tests

1. **Viral hepatitis.**—The basic pathological abnormality in this condition is cell necrosis of varying severity. In some cases cholestasis is a dominant feature (cholestatic hepatitis).

Bilirubinuria is often the first biochemical evidence of the disease, and is present before the onset of clinically detectable jaundice in many cases. The patient may notice darkening of the urine. During the prodromal phase aminotransferase levels are raised, reach their peak at about the time jaundice is noticed, and remain elevated for about a further two weeks.

The plasma bilirubin level rises but rarely exceeds 20 mg/100 ml The jaundice is due both to cell destruction and cholestasis and the rise affects both fractions, predominantly the conjugated one. At this stage the urine contains *urobilin(ogen)* and bilirubin. The *thymol turbidity* test is usually positive and the *alkaline phosphatase* level is moderately increased. In severe hepatitis albumin levels are low. There is an element of cholestasis in most cases of hepatitis and this usually appears shortly after the onset of jaundice, when the stools become pale and urobilin-(ogen) disappears from the urine. It reappears as the liver recovers only to disappear finally with complete recovery. Bilirubin disappears from the urine before urobilinogen. This pattern of urinary biliary constituents is seen in many, but not all cases of viral hepatitis. In some, cholestasis occurs from the onset and the patient notices pale stools as the first feature.

In summary, the findings during the course of viral hepatitis are:

TABLE XVIII

	Prodromal phase	Jaundice (liver damage)	Cholestatic phase	Relief of cholestasis	Recovery phase
Urine					
Bilirubin	+	+	+	—	—
Urobilin (ogen)	—	+	—	+	—
Faecal colour	N	N	pale	N	N

Anicteric hepatitis is not uncommon and may be diagnosed by bilirubinuria and raised aminotransferase levels.

The *course* of hepatitis may be followed by plasma bilirubin estimations together with the changes in urine and faeces outlined in the table above, aminotransferase levels, thymol turbidity and plasma proteins. Persistently high aminotransferase levels, or a second rise indicate extension or relapse. A rising γ globulin concentration suggests the development of a chronic phase.

The last tests to return to normal after an attack of hepatitis are the thymol turbidity and urinary urobilin(ogen). The thymol turbidity may remain abnormal for up to a year after the attack.

The *severity and extent* of liver cell destruction are shown best by the plasma albumin level and prothrombin time, although the latter is also affected by bile salt deficiency (p. 272). Bilirubin levels are affected by both cholestasis and cell damage and the rise in aminotransferases reflects the rapidity rather than degree of destruction of liver cells.

Most cases of hepatitis recover, but a very small percentage die in liver failure and a small number develop cirrhosis.

2. **Biliary obstruction.**—In complete extrahepatic biliary obstruction *plasma bilirubin* levels rise progressively for several weeks, when the curve tends to flatten out. Levels may fluctuate slightly but always tend to increase and may reach values of 50 mg/100 ml or greater. The rise is predominantly in the conjugated fraction. The urine contains bilirubin but no urobilin(ogen) and the stools are pale.

Plasma alkaline phosphatase concentrations increase progressively as do those of cholesterol and phospholipids. The rise in β-lipoprotein may occasionally be seen as an increase in β-globulin on routine electrophoresis. With prolonged obstruction there may be secondary liver damage due to bile necrosis of liver cells or ascending cholangitis and tests of liver cell dysfunction and damage become positive.

Differential diagnosis of hepatitis and extrahepatic obstruction.—The distinction of cases of apparently cholestatic jaundice requiring surgery (extrahepatic obstruction) from those in whom surgery and anaesthesia may be detrimental (hepatitis with intrahepatic obstruction) is a recurring clinical problem. As outlined above not only does prolonged extrahepatic obstruction cause liver damage but cholestasis develops in many cases of hepatitis. *It is most important to perform the relevant tests as early as possible* if the primary process is to be diagnosed. This is second in importance only to an adequate clinical history and examination.

In both conditions the rise of plasma bilirubin is predominantly in the conjugated fraction. Points helpful in differential diagnosis are the following:

(*a*) High aminotransferase levels, a positive thymol turbidity, or both, early in the course of the disease are in favour of hepatitis. In extrahepatic obstruction the levels of these enzymes may be normal and are rarely more than moderately raised.

(*b*) Raised alkaline phosphatase or 5′-nucleotidase levels indicate the presence of cholestasis but not its cause. The higher the alkaline phosphatase the greater the likelihood of extrahepatic obstruction. The value of 30 K.A. units is often quoted as the borderline between hepatitis and extrahepatic obstruction, but this can be accepted as a very rough guide only. Higher levels are found in most cases of cholestatic hepatitis and it is these cases that present the most difficult diagnostic problem. Early evidence of cell damage is frequently the only distinguishing factor.

(c) In problem cases the *prednisolone test* (see Appendix, p. 283) has been used. An unequivocal fall of plasma bilirubin after prednisolone is strong evidence for hepatitis rather than extrahepatic obstruction. The mechanism of this lowering of plasma bilirubin is unknown.

3. **Cirrhosis.**—In cirrhosis during phases of active cellular destruction there is frequently jaundice with moderately raised aminotransferase levels. The *alkaline phosphatase* may be raised out of proportion to the *plasma bilirubin*; this finding probably reflects intrahepatic cholestasis due to disorganization of the liver architecture. *Urobilin(ogen)* is frequently present in the urine, with or without *bilirubin*. Many cases show the typical *plasma protein* changes (p. 236) of a low albumin and diffusely elevated γ globulin. If ascites is present there may be dilutional hyponatraemia (p. 47).

During quiescent periods, or in mild cases, the only detectable abnormality may be increased BSP retention.

4. **Hepatocellular failure.**—Most cases of hepatocellular failure occur during the course of severe hepatitis or decompensated cirrhosis, or following ingestion of liver toxins. Jaundice is usually present although fulminating cases may die before it develops. Any or all of the biochemical abnormalities of hepatitis may be found depending on the stage of the disease.

Other features which may be seen include:

(a) A low plasma urea. Normally ammonia from deamination of amino-acids is utilized in the synthesis of urea in the liver. Impairment of this process results in deficient urea production and accumulation of amino-acids in the blood with consequent overflow aminoacidura (p. 338).

(b) A prolonged prothrombin time.

(c) Rarely hypoglycaemia (p. 144).

5. **Hepatic infiltration.**—Hepatomegaly may be a result of infiltration of the liver by carcinoma or lymphoma or replacement by granulomata. Such lesions produce intrahepatic obstruction resulting in a raised alkaline phosphatase or 5'-nucleotidase and frequently some degree of cellular destruction with elevated aminotransferase levels. In many cases liver function is unimpaired and bilirubin levels are normal.

6. **Haemolytic jaundice.**—Increased erythrocyte destruction of any aetiology produces an increase in the amount of bilirubin arriving at the liver for conjugation and excretion. The reserve capacity of the adult liver is such that jaundice, if present, is mild (usually below 4 mg/ 100 ml). The rise in plasma bilirubin is confined almost entirely to the unconjugated fraction. The increased load of excreted bilirubin in the

bile, however, results in increased stercobilinogen production in the gut and, after this has been reabsorbed, an increased urinary urobilin(ogen). Bilirubin does not appear in the urine (acholuric jaundice). Other "liver function" tests are unaffected with the exception in some cases of raised aminotransferase and LDH levels, due not to liver damage but to red cell destruction (p. 294).

In neonates, however, the massive red cell destruction seen in haemolytic disease of the newborn, coupled with the immature hepatic conjugating mechanism, can produce elevations of unconjugated bilirubin of 25–30 mg/100 ml or greater. Such elevations are associated with the risk of developing *kernicterus* and may be reduced by exchange transfusion. In premature infants, too, the poorly developed conjugating mechanism may result in so-called "physiological" jaundice with markedly raised levels of unconjugated bilirubin, also necessitating exchange transfusion.

The effects of certain drugs on jaundice in the newborn is considered on p. 279.

Congenital Hyperbilirubinaemia

A group of disorders has been described in which there is defective handling of bilirubin, apparently of congenital origin. The three best defined entities will be described briefly.

1. **Gilbert's disease.**—In patients with this disease there is probably defective transport of bilirubin into the liver cell. Plasma levels of *unconjugated bilirubin* are mildly raised (1–2 mg/100 ml), and tend to fluctuate. The condition may be noted at any age. A common means of discovery is the failure of bilirubin levels to return to normal after an attack of hepatitis, or any mild illness which may be misdiagnosed as hepatitis. The only other abnormality detectable by routine tests is a slightly prolonged BSP retention. The condition is harmless but must be differentiated from haemolysis and from hepatitis.

2. **Crigler-Najjar syndrome.**—In contradistinction to the other two syndromes discussed the Crigler–Najjar syndrome is *not* harmless. It presents in the first few days of life as jaundice due to a rise in *unconjugated bilirubin* levels. They may often be high enough (20 mg/100 ml or higher) to cause kernicterus. The probable cause is a deficiency of glucuronyl transferase (p. 264). In infants who survive, the level of bilirubin tends to stabilize, suggesting the existence of alternative pathways of bilirubin excretion.

3. **Dubin-Johnson syndrome.**—This condition is characterized by mildly raised *conjugated bilirubin* levels that tend to fluctuate. There is defective excretion of conjugated bilirubin. Bilirubin is present in the

urine. Alkaline phosphatase levels are normal. There may be hepato-megaly and the liver is dark brown due to the presence of a pigment with the staining properties of lipofuscin in the cells. The condition is harm-less and the diagnosis may be confirmed by the characteristic staining in the liver biopsy.

There is overlap between these and related conditions.

DRUGS AND THE LIVER

Many drugs are capable of producing jaundice with or without liver damage and a drug history is an essential part of the investigation of a patient with jaundice. A detailed discussion of this problem is beyond the scope of this book and interested readers should consult the reference given at the end of the chapter on which this summary is based.

There are several mechanisms whereby drugs can produce jaundice.

1. Drug-induced *haemolysis* is usually not severe enough to cause jaundice. If it does the findings are those of haemolytic jaundice. The subject is beyond the scope of this book and is dealt with in textbooks of haematology.

2. Novobiocin interferes with bilirubin *conjugation*.

3. Direct *hepatotoxins* such as carbon tetrachloride, DDT and *Amanita* mushroom poisoning produce liver cell necrosis of varying severity. Ingestion is usually accidental or with suicidal intent.

Tetracyclines by intravenous injection, especially during pregnancy, have produced acute fatty liver and death from liver failure.

4. *Hepatitis-like reaction.*—Several drugs produce a clinical, bio-chemical and histopathological syndrome closely resembling viral hepatitis.

(*a*) Hydrazine derivatives, e.g. iproniazid, phenelzine and rarely isoniazid.

(*b*) Chlordiazepoxide (rare).

(*c*) Halothane anaesthetics rarely produce severe liver damage and death.

5. *Cholestatic reaction.*—Another group of drugs produces the pic-ture of cholestatic jaundice:

(*a*) 17-α-alkylated steroids such as methyl testosterone, norethand-rolone, norethisterone (components of certain oral contraceptives).

(*b*) Phenothiazines, such as chlorpromazine.

(*c*) Rarely thiouracil, chlorpropamide, phenylbutazone.

(*d*) Antibiotics such as erythromycin and oleandomycin.

(*e*) Para-aminosalicylic acid (PAS) (rare).

(*f*) Cholestasis may occur as part of a generalized sensitivity reaction (e.g. to penicillin).

Neonatal jaundice and drugs.—In neonates, particularly if premature, the glucuronyl transferase system for bilirubin is immature (p. 264) and jaundice due to a rise in unconjugated bilirubin levels is common. This phase lasts two to three days in full term infants and five to six days in premature infants. The course and severity of unconjugated hyperbilirubinaemia may be influenced by drugs in three ways:—

(*a*) Several drugs displace bilirubin from plasma albumin and increase the risk of kernicterus. These include salicylates and sulphonamides.

(*b*) Novobiocin inhibits the glucuronyl transferase system and aggravates unconjugated hyperbilirubinaemia.

(*c*) Any drug producing haemolysis aggravates the condition.

BILE AND GALL STONES

BILE ACIDS AND BILE SALTS

Four bile acids are produced in man. Two of these, *cholic acid* and *chenodeoxycholic acid*, are synthesized in the liver from cholesterol and are referred to as *primary bile acids*. These are excreted in the bile into the gut where bacterial action converts them to *secondary bile acids*, *deoxycholic acid* and *lithocholic acid*, respectively. In human bile the bile acids are in the form of sodium salts, all conjugated with the amino-acids glycine or taurine (*bile salts*). Some of the secondary bile salts are absorbed and re-excreted by the liver (enterohepatic circulation of bile salts, p. 206). Bile therefore contains a mixture of primary and secondary bile salts.

The importance of the bile salts lies in their possession of both polar and non-polar chemical groups and their ability to coalesce into *micelles*. In these micelles the non-polar groups are orientated in the centre of the molecule and form a small pool of lipid solvent, while the polar (water-soluble) groups are on the outside.

Micelle formation is important not only for the absorption of dietary fat (p. 206), but for maintaining cholesterol in solution in bile (see below).

FORMATION OF BILE

About 1 to 2 litres of bile is produced in the liver daily. This *hepatic bile* contains bilirubin, bile salts, phospholipids and cholesterol as well as electrolytes in similar concentrations to those in plasma. Small amounts of protein are also present. In the gall bladder there is active reabsorption of sodium, chloride and bicarbonate, together with an isosmotic amount of water. The end result is *gall bladder bile* which is ten times more concentrated than hepatic bile and in which sodium is the major cation and bile salts the major anion. The concentration of other non-absorbable molecules, conjugated bilirubin, cholesterol and phospholipids also increases.

GALL STONES

Although most gall stones contain all constituents of bile, several types differing in the main constituent are recognized. Unlike renal calculi only about 10 per cent of gall stones contain sufficient calcium to be radio-opaque.

1. *Cholesterol gall stones* may be single or multiple and are not usually radio-opaque. They are yellowish and the cut surface has a crystalline appearance.

2. *Pigment gall stones* consist largely of bile pigments with organic material and variable amounts of calcium. They are small multiple stones, dark green or black and are hard. Rarely they are radio-opaque.

3. *Mixed gall stones*, the commonest form, are, as the name suggests, composed of a mixture of cholesterol, bile pigments, protein and calcium. They are multiple and appear as faceted dark brown stones with a hard shell and softer centre. They may be radio-opaque.

CAUSES OF GALL STONE FORMATION

Pigment stones are seen in *chronic haemolytic states* such as hereditary spherocytosis where there is an increase in bilirubin formation and excretion. In all other forms of gall stones, however, the aetiology is uncertain. The role of infection as a precipitating factor in gall stone formation is at present controversial.

Current theories are based on the demonstration of differences between bile in which gall stones have formed and normal bile. Such pathological bile has a greater concentration of cholesterol and a lower concentration of bile salts than normal. As mentioned above bile salts are required to maintain cholesterol in solution. In addition, the salts of cholic acid (with three OH groups) form more stable micelles than do those of chenodeoxycholic acid and deoxycholic acid (with two OH groups). Stone-forming bile has been shown to have a higher proportion of the dihydroxy bile salts than normal. This combination of bile salts deficient in quantity and quality would favour the precipitation of cholesterol. The cause of such alterations is not clear. It may be due to primary hepatic or gall bladder dysfunction or it may be the result of reduced enterohepatic circulation of bile salts due to biliary stasis or obstruction. It has been suggested that inflammation of the gall bladder wall leads to greater absorption of the more water-soluble bile salts (those with more OH groups).

Routine chemical analysis of gall stones is of little value.

CONSEQUENCES OF GALL STONES

Gall stones may remain silent for an indefinite length of time and be discovered only at laparotomy for an unrelated condition or on X-ray of the abdomen. They may, however, lead to several clinical consequences:

1. Acute cholecystitis, due to obstruction of the cystic duct by a gall stone with chemical irritation of the gall bladder mucosa by trapped bile and secondary bacterial infection.

2. Chronic cholecystitis.

3. Common bile duct obstruction, if a stone lodges in the bile duct. This may present as biliary colic, obstructive jaundice or acute pancreatitis if the pancreatic duct is also occluded.

4. Extremely rarely, carcinoma of the gall bladder occurs.

SUMMARY

LIVER DISEASE

1. The liver has a central role in many metabolic processes.

2. Bilirubin derived from haemoglobin is conjugated in the liver and excreted in bile. Conversion to stercobilinogen (faecal urobilinogen) takes place in the bowel. Some reabsorbed faecal urobilinogen is excreted in the urine.

3. Bilirubin metabolism may be assessed by plasma levels of total and conjugated bilirubin, by qualitative tests for bilirubin and urobilin(ogen) in the urine and by visual inspection of the stool.

4. Jaundice is due to a raised plasma bilirubin. No satisfactory classification exists other than separating jaundice due to a raised unconjugated bilirubin only from that in which both fractions are raised. The majority of cases of jaundice fall into the latter group.

5. The two basic processes in liver disease are liver cell destruction and cholestasis. Tests help to distinguish the underlying process, but not necessarily its cause.

6. Tests of liver function may be classified as:

    (a) Tests involving bile pigment metabolism.
    (b) Other tests of excretory function.
    (c) Tests showing liver cell dysfunction.
    (d) Tests showing liver cell damage.
    (e) Tests indicating cholestasis.

7. The selection of tests is governed by the particular problem. The main indications are:—

(*a*) Differential diagnosis of jaundice.
(*b*) Assessment of the severity and progress of liver disease.
(*c*) Detection of liver disease.

8. A group of congenital conditions exist, characterized by hyperbilirubinaemia. Most are relatively harmless, but the Crigler–Najjar syndrome may lead to kernicterus.

9. Drugs may produce jaundice in several ways and a drug history is important in the assessment of the jaundiced patient. In the neonate, drugs may increase the risk of kernicterus.

BILE AND GALL STONES

Bile secreted by the liver is concentrated in the gall bladder before passing into the gut. Cholesterol in bile is held in solution by bile salt micelles. A change in either the concentration or type of bile salts may lead to defective micelle formation and permit precipitation of cholesterol with gall stone formation.

FURTHER READING

SHERLOCK, SHEILA (1968). *Diseases of the Liver and Biliary System*, 4th edit. Oxford: Blackwell Scientific Publications.

APPENDIX TO CHAPTER XII

1. Bromsulphthalein (BSP) Retention Test

The test is preferably performed on the fasted patient to avoid turbidity of the plasma from recent fat ingestion.

(a) BSP solution is injected *slowly* intravenously. The recommended dose is 5 mg/kg body weight.

(b) 45 minutes after the injection blood is taken from a vein on the opposite arm to avoid contamination from the injection site.

The residual dye is estimated in the plasma by comparison with a standard solution. As different batches of BSP may vary, it is important to retain some of the solution injected for use as a standard. Normally less than 3 per cent of the dye is retained at 45 minutes. *Interpretation* is considered on p. 271.

Notes.—(a) Severe systematic reactions very rarely occur. *Local tissue necrosis* however is seen if the solution is injected outside the vein or if extravasation occurs.

(b) The test should not be performed immediately after cholecystography when falsely impaired retention has been described, presumably due to competition for excretion mechanisms.

(c) Urinary loss of BSP can normally be discounted. In patients with marked proteinuria, however, it may be significant and urine should be collected over the period of the test to assess the extent of the loss. As BSP is purple in alkaline solution it is advisable to reassure the patient that the urine may become coloured temporarily.

(d) If necessary the test may be repeated after 24 hours but it is then advisable to take a pre-injection sample of blood to exclude residual dye.

2. Prednisolone Test (p. 276)

This test may be used for the differential diagnosis of jaundice.

Plasma bilirubin is estimated before and after administering 30 mg prednisolone daily for 5 days. A fall of concentration of more than 40 per cent strongly suggests hepatitis rather than extra-hepatic obstruction. Lesser falls are equivocal.

3. Rapid Tests for Urinary Bile Constituents

(a) **Bilirubin.**—Urine containing bilirubin is usually dark yellow or brown. Chemical confirmation is best obtained by using Ictotest tablets (Ames). The test is performed according to the manufacturer's instructions and is of equal sensitivity to the earlier Fouchet's test, that is, it detects about 0·1 mg/100 ml of bilirubin.

(b) **Urobilinogen.**—There is no "tablet" test for urobilin or urobilinogen.

1. Mix about 2 ml of *fresh* urine with an equal volume of Ehrlich's reagent and allow to stand for 5–10 minutes.

2. Add 4 ml of saturated sodium acetate solution and mix.

A red colour denotes the presence of urobilinogen. Distinction from porphobilinogen (p. 327) is made by shaking the coloured solution with *n*-butanol. The colour due to urobilinogen is extracted into butanol (upper layer) whereas that of porphobilinogen is not.

(c) **Urobilin.**—This test is preferable to the above if the urine is not fresh, as urobilinogen is converted to urobilin on standing.

1. Mix 5 ml of urine with 2 drops of alcoholic iodine solution (converts urobilinogen to urobilin).

2. Add 5 ml of zinc acetate suspension, mix and allow to settle.

3. A greenish fluorescence in the supernatant is due to a zinc-urobilin complex. This is best seen in darkened surroundings by shining the light from a pencil torch through the fluid.

The interpretation of these tests is discussed on p. 270.

Chapter XIII

PLASMA ENZYMES IN DIAGNOSIS

GENERAL

ESTIMATION of plasma enzymes can be a sensitive method of diagnosing disease, but the changes are often non-specific. Enzymes are predominantly intracellular constituents and are released after damage to, or death of, cells. The main clinical use of these tests is in detection of such damage. Before considering the significance of enzyme changes in disease, a few general points will be discussed.

1. **Expression of results.**—The total amount of enzymes (as protein) in the blood is less than 100 mg/100 ml. Results are not expressed as concentrations, but as *activities* as measured in the laboratory. With the development of clinical enzymology many methods of estimation were introduced, each with its own units (for example, Reitman-Frankel units, King-Armstrong units, spectrophotometric units). In an attempt to achieve standardization international units were introduced, but even now results differ with variations in methodology. Enzyme activities must be interpreted in relation to the normal range of the issuing laboratory, and "normal ranges" will not be given.

In addition, a standardized nomenclature has been introduced which differs in certain respects from the earlier, more familiar names. This nomenclature will be used in this chapter.

2. **Normal levels of activity** are the result of several factors. The enzymes are derived from cells due to leakage or natural breakdown and are excreted or catabolized. The measured activity is also influenced by activators and inhibitors in plasma. *Raised levels* may be the result of increased production of enzyme or destruction of the producing cells or of deficient excretion or catabolism. Changes in activators or inhibitors are not thought to play a major role in clinical situations.

3. **Isoenzymes.**—A single enzyme activity may be due to closely related but slightly different molecular forms of the enzyme. These different forms (isoenzymes) can be identified by physical or chemical means and assume clinical significance when isoenzymes have different tissues of origin: for instance, different lactate dehydrogenase isoenzymes are found in heart and liver.

Non-specific Causes of Raised Enzyme Levels

Before attributing enzyme changes to a specific disease process, it is advisable to consider more generalized causes.

Physiological

(a) *Newborn.*—The levels of certain enzymes, e.g. aspartate amino-transferase, are moderately raised in the neonatal period.

(b) *Childhood.*—Alkaline phosphatase levels are high until after puberty.

(c) *Pregnancy.*—In the last trimester, levels of alkaline phosphatase and leucine aminopeptidase are raised. During and immediately after labour, moderate rises are noted in several enzymes, e.g. amino-transferases.

Trauma and Shock

Following major surgical procedures or after extensive trauma, levels of lactate dehydrogenase, aspartate aminotransferase and creatine phosphokinase may be raised. This increase is rarely sufficient to cause diagnostic confusion except after thoracic and cardiac surgery. If circulatory failure is present, due to cardiac failure or shock, increases in several enzymes may be noted, possibly due to decreased catabolism. The liver is the major, but probably not the only, source of the raised enzyme levels in shock.

These non-specific changes are most apparent in persons with pre-existing liver disease.

When raised levels (especially of lactate dehydrogenase) with no apparent cause are noted, the possibility of *malignancy* should be considered. *Infectious mononucleosis* and *haemolysis* are often associated with increases in aminotransferases and other enzymes.

Minor rises in aspartate aminotransferase are common as a non-specific finding in a variety of illnesses, some of which may be minor.

CAUSES OF ALTERED PLASMA ENZYME LEVELS

In this section the following abbreviations will be used:

Aspartate aminotransferase	Asp.AT
Alanine aminotransferase	Al.AT
Lactate dehydrogenase	LDH
Creatine phosphokinase	CPK
Alkaline phosphatase	Alk.phos.
Acid phosphatase	Acid phos.
5′-nucleotidase	5′-NT
Isocitrate dehydrogenase	ICD

AMINOTRANSFERASES (TRANSAMINASES)

The aminotransferases are enzymes that are involved in the transfer of an amino group from an amino-acid to an α-oxo acid. They are widely distributed in the body.

Aspartate Aminotransferase

Aspartate aminotransferase catalyzes the reversible transfer of an amino group from glutamate to oxaloacetate to form aspartate. It was formerly known as serum glutamate oxaloacetate transaminase (SGOT). It is widely distributed, with high concentrations in the heart, liver, skeletal muscle, kidney and erythrocytes, and destruction of any of these tissues may cause raised levels.

Causes of Increased Asp.AT

(a) Physiological—newborn (approximately $1\frac{1}{2}$ times adult "normal").

(b) Markedly raised levels (10–100 times normal).
  1. Myocardial infarction (p. 293).
  2. Viral hepatitis (p. 273).
  3. Toxic liver necrosis (p. 276).

(c) Moderately raised levels.
  1. Cirrhosis (up to twice normal).
  2. Cholestatic jaundice (up to 10 times normal).
  3. Malignant infiltrations in the liver.
  4. Skeletal muscle disease (p. 296).
  5. After trauma or surgery (especially cardiac surgery).
  6. Severe haemolytic anaemia.
  7. Infectious mononucleosis (liver involvement).

(d) Artefactually raised levels are seen in a haemolyzed specimen.

Alanine Aminotransferase

Alanine aminotransferase catalyzes the reversible transfer of an amino group from glutamate to pyruvate to form alanine and was formerly known as SGPT. It is present in high concentration in the liver and to a lesser extent in skeletal muscle, kidney and heart.

Causes of Raised Al.AT

(a) Markedly raised levels:
  1. Viral hepatitis (p. 273).
  2. Toxic liver necrosis (p. 272).

(b) Moderately raised levels:
1. Cirrhosis (p. 276).
2. Cholestatic jaundice (p. 273).
3. Liver congestion secondary to cardiac failure.
4. Infectious mononucleosis (liver involvement).
5. Extensive trauma and muscle disease (much less than Asp.AT).

LACTATE DEHYDROGENASE (LDH)

LDH catalyzes the reversible interconversion of lactate and pyruvate. It is widely distributed with high concentrations in the heart, skeletal muscle, liver, kidney, brain and erythrocytes.

Causes of Raised LDH Levels

(a) Marked increase (more than five times normal):
1. Myocardial infarction (p. 293).
2. Haematological disorders.

In blood diseases such as pernicious anaemia and leukaemias, very high values (up to 20 times normal) may be found. Lesser increases occur in other states of abnormal erythropoiesis, such as thalassaemia and myelofibrosis.

(b) Moderate increase:
1. Viral hepatitis.
2. Malignancy anywhere in the body.
3. Skeletal muscle disease.
4. Pulmonary embolism.
5. Infectious mononucleosis.
6. Acute haemolysis.
7. Cerebral infarction $\left.\right\}$ occasionally.
8. Renal disease

(c) Artefactually raised levels are found in haemolyzed specimens.

Isoenzymes of LDH

Five isoenzymes are commonly recognized by electrophoresis and are referred to as LD_{1-5}. LD_1 is the fastest moving fraction on electrophoresis and is the form found in heart muscle and erythrocytes, blast cells and kidney. LD_5 occurs predominantly in the liver. (In the American literature the nomenclature is reversed; LD_5 refers to the heart enzyme and LD_1 to the liver). LDH isoenzyme electrophoresis may not be generally available, but the heart isoenzyme may be measured by two further characteristics. It is relatively heat-stable and it is active against the substrate hydroxybutyrate. This latter property is measured as *hydroxybutyrate dehydrogenase* (HBD). Heat-stable LDH or HBD levels are raised in myocardial infarction, megaloblastic anaemias, acute leukaemias, and severe active renal damage (such as rejection of transplants) and much less so in liver disease. In many laboratories HBD is measured in place of LDH.

CREATINE PHOSPHOKINASE (CPK)

CPK is found in heart muscle, brain and skeletal muscle.

Causes of Raised CPK Levels

(*a*) Physiological:
1. Newborn—slightly raised.
2. Parturition—for a few days.

(*b*) Marked increase:
1. Myocardial infarction (p. 293).
2. Progressive muscular dystrophy (p. 296).

(*c*) Moderate increase:
1. Muscle injury.
2. After surgery (for about a week).
3. Severe physical exertion.
4. Hypothyroidism (thyroxine apparently influences the catabolism of the enzyme).

Estimations are not affected by haemolysis, but the enzyme is unstable and the test should be done as soon as possible after the specimen is taken.

AMYLASE

Amylase is the enzyme concerned with the breakdown of dietary starch and glycogen to maltose. It is present in pancreatic juice and saliva as well as in liver, Fallopian tubes and muscle. Amylase activity in normal plasma is most probably of hepatic origin. The enzyme is excreted in the urine.

The main use of amylase estimations is in the diagnosis of acute pancreatitis (p. 215), when levels may be very high. Moderately raised levels are seen in a number of conditions and are not diagnostic (p. 215).

Causes of Raised Plasma Amylase Levels

(*a*) Marked increase (5–10 times normal):
1. Acute pancreatitis.
2. Severe uraemia.

(*b*) Moderate increase:

  1. Other acute abdominal disorders:
    (i) Perforated peptic ulcer.
    (ii) Acute cholecystitis.
    (iii) Intestinal obstruction.
    (iv) Abdominal trauma.
    (v) Ruptured ectopic pregnancy.

  2. Salivary gland disorders:
    (i) Mumps—not usually required for diagnosis except in mumps encephalitis when it may be raised without obvious salivary gland enlargement.
    (ii) Salivary calculi.
    (iii) After sialography.

  3. Morphine administration (spasm of sphincter of Oddi).
  4. Severe uraemia (may be markedly raised).
  5. Myocardial infarction (occasionally).
  6. Acute alcoholic intoxication (transient).
  7. Macroamylasaemia—a rare condition, apparently symptomless, characterized by an abnormally large amylase molecule that cannot be excreted by the kidneys.

Low levels of plasma amylase may be found in infants up to one year and in some cases of hepatitis. They are of no diagnostic importance.

Alkaline Phosphatase

Alkaline phosphatases are a group of enzymes which hydrolyze phosphates at an alkaline pH. The activity measured by routine methods includes that of several isoenzymes. They are found in bone, liver, kidney, intestinal wall, lactating mammary gland and placenta. In bone the enzyme is found in *osteoblasts* (not osteoclasts) and is probably important for normal bone formation.

The generally accepted theory for the raised levels of alkaline phosphatase in biliary obstruction was, until recently, that the enzyme originating from bone was normally excreted in the bile and when this pathway was blocked it accumulated in the blood. Recent developments have shown this to be untrue and, because of the importance in interpretation of results, this facet will be considered in some detail.

Isoenzyme studies have shown that the alkaline phosphatase appearing in bile is different from that circulating in the blood, and is in fact derived from the lining cells of bile ducts. The enzyme in blood (from whatever source) is a protein molecule, too large to be excreted through hepatic cells and is catabolized as a protein. The source of the raised alkaline phosphatase in liver disease is two-fold. One isoenzyme is derived from the hepatic cells themselves and is released with cell destruction, the other is the biliary form described above. In biliary obstruction this isoenzyme is regurgitated into the blood stream together with conjugated bilirubin.

In adults, the normal levels of alkaline phosphatase are derived largely from the liver. In children there is an additional contribution from bone and this accounts for the higher levels of total activity found at this age. In both there is a variable contribution from the intestine. Pregnancy raises the "normal" values because of the production of heat-stable alkaline phosphatase by the placenta.

Isoenzyme separation by electrophoresis is not routinely available, but the liver and bile isoenzymes can be readily assessed by estimation of the *5'-nucleotidase activity.*

5'-NT activity closely parallels liver alk.phos., and appears to have a similar origin. Bone disease does not produce elevation of 5'-NT. Leucine aminopeptidase is an enzyme that closely follows 5'-NT. Its estimation has no special advantage.

Causes of Raised Plasma Alk.Phos.

(*a*) Physiological:
1. Children—until about the age of puberty (up to 2–2½ times adult normal).
2. Pregnancy—in the last trimester, values may be in the upper normal range or mildly increased.

(*b*) Bone disease (raised alk.phos.; normal 5'-NT):
1. Osteomalacia and rickets (p. 180).
2. Primary hyperparathyroidism with bone disease (p. 181).
3. Paget's disease of bone (may be very high).
4. Secondary carcinoma in bone.
5. Some cases of osteogenic sarcoma.

(*c*) Liver disease (raised alk.phos. *and* 5'-NT):
1. Cholestasis (p. 273).
2. Hepatitis (p. 273).
3. Cirrhosis of the liver (sometimes).
4. Space-occupying lesions—tumours, granulomata, infiltrations.

Low Levels of Plasma Alk.Phos.

1. Arrested bone growth:
   Achondroplasia.
   Cretinism.
   Vitamin C deficiency.
2. Hypophosphatasia.

ACID PHOSPHATASE

Acid phosphatase is found in the prostate, liver, red cells, platelets and bone. The main use of the estimation is in the diagnosis of prostatic carcinoma, and the level is usually little, if at all, affected in liver and bone disease. Many methods have been devised to measure the prostatic fraction only in plasma. There is no entirely satisfactory routine technique, but one of the best is based on the fact that the prostatic fraction is inhibited by 1-tartrate ("tartrate labile").

Normally acid phosphatase in prostatic secretion drains via the prostatic ducts and very little appears in the blood. In prostatic carcinoma *that has extended beyond the capsule of the prostate* this drainage is not available and plasma acid phosphatase levels rise. False negative results may obtain when the tumour is too undifferentiated to secrete acid phosphatase at all.

An important point to remember in assessing possible prostatic malignancy is to take blood before doing a rectal examination. Following rectal examination, passage of a catheter, or even in a constipated patient, the tartrate labile acid phosphatase may rise and values above normal may persist for up to a week. In any case in which a marginal rise is found estimations should be repeated on more than one occasion.

Causes of Raised Acid Phosphatase

(*a*) Tartrate labile:

1. Prostatic carcinoma with extension beyond the capsule.
2. Following rectal examination.
3. Acute retention of urine.
4. Passage of a catheter.

(*b*) Total:

1. Paget's disease and some cases of metastatic malignant disease (only if the alk.phos. levels are very high, and therefore of no diagnostic significance).
2. Gaucher's disease (probably from Gaucher cells).
3. Occasionally in thrombocythaemias.

ALDOLASE

Estimation of aldolase, another widely distributed enzyme, is used mainly in the diagnosis of muscle disorders (p. 296) and liver disease, in which it follows the same pattern as the aminotransferases. Raised levels are also found after myocardial infarction, extensive muscle trauma, haemolysis and generalized malignancy.

ISOCITRATE DEHYDROGENASE

Isocitrate dehydrogenase is yet another widely distributed enzyme. Its main diagnostic use is as an index of liver cell damage in which it follows the changes in the aminotransferases. Despite high concentrations in heart muscle, the level in myocardial infarction is normal. Other causes of moderately raised levels include placental infarction, megaloblastic anaemia and infectious mononucleosis.

ENZYME PATTERNS IN DISEASE

MYOCARDIAL INFARCTION

The enzyme estimations of greatest value in the diagnosis of myocardial infarction are CPK, Asp.AT and LDH (or HBD). The choice of estimation depends on the time interval after the suspected infarction. A guide to the sequence of changes is given below:

TABLE XIX

| Enzyme | Time after infarction | | Duration of rise (days) |
	Starts to rise (hours)	Peak elevation (hours)	
CPK	3	24	2–3
Asp.AT	6–8	24–48	4–6
LDH (SHBD)	12–24	48–72	7–12

Enzyme elevations are present in about 95 per cent of cases of myocardial infarction. Asp.AT and LDH may reach very high levels. The height of the rise is a rough index of the extent of damage and as such is of some value in prognosis. It is, however, only one of many factors. A second rise in enzyme levels after return to normal indicates extension of the infarction. Levels in angina are usually normal, any rise probably being indicative of some myocardial necrosis. If a patient is first seen after the total LDH has returned to normal, diagnosis may still be possible on the basis of a raised heart isoenzyme as detected by SHBD estimation or isoenzyme electrophoresis.

Some confusion may arise if the patient presents with cardiac failure and secondary liver involvement, with raised aminotransferase and LDH levels. Evaluation of the two processes is assisted by HBD (minimal rise if only the liver is involved) and the rise in alanine aminotransferase accompanying that in aspartate transaminase. Pulmonary embolism with right-sided cardiac failure usually produces this "liver pattern".

LIVER DISEASE

Enzyme changes in liver disease are discussed in context on p. 269. Only a summary is appended here.

1. Rises of aspartate aminotransferase, alanine aminotransferase, isocitrate dehydrogenase and, to a lesser extent, lactate dehydrogenase are indices of liver cell damage.

(a) Levels are raised in the prodromal phase of viral hepatitis and reach their maximum soon after the onset of jaundice, thereafter to return to normal. The magnitude of the increase reflects the extent of the process, but is not necessarily of prognostic significance.

(b) Very high levels occur with toxic hepatic necrosis (p. 272).

(c) In early extrahepatic cholestasis enzyme increases are minimal, but if obstruction persists cell damage with consequent rise in enzyme levels occurs.

(d) Levels in cirrhosis may be moderately raised, but only if the process is active.

2. Alkaline phosphatase and 5'-nucleotidase are useful mainly as indicators of cholestasis.

(a) Intrahepatic cholestasis, for example, in hepatitis, is associated with moderately (2–3 times normal) raised levels. Biliary cirrhosis produces very high levels.

(b) Extrahepatic cholestasis may cause very high enzyme levels.

(c) Space-occupying lesions in the liver may produce raised alk.phos. and 5'-NT as the only abnormality.

3. Cholinesterase levels are decreased with liver cell dysfunction. This estimation parallels plasma albumin as a guide to prognosis.

ENZYMES IN MALIGNANCY

1. Tartrate labile acid phosphatase in prostatic carcinoma (p. 292) is the only truly specific enzyme for malignancy.

2. Malignancy anywhere in the body may be associated with a non-specific increase in LDH and occasionally aminotransferases.

3. For follow-up of treated cases of malignancy, alkaline phosphatase estimations are of value. Raised levels may indicate secondaries in bone (normal 5'-NT) or liver (raised 5'-NT) (see p. 291). Liver secondaries may, in addition, produce increases in transaminases or LDH.

HAEMATOLOGICAL DISORDERS

The extreme elevation of LDH and HBD in megaloblastic anaemia and leukaemia has been mentioned (p. 288). Similar elevations may be seen in other conditions of abnormal erythropoiesis. Typically there is much less change in the level of aminotransferases than in that of LDH and SHBD. Severe haemolysis produces changes in aminotransferases and LDH.

CHOLINESTERASE AND SUCCINYLCHOLINE SENSITIVITY

There are two cholinesterases, one found predominantly in erythrocytes and nervous tissue (acetyl cholinesterase) and the other in plasma. This latter enzyme, cholinesterase ("pseudocholinesterase") is synthesized chiefly in the liver and is the one routinely measured.

Cholinesterase has been used as a test of liver function (p. 271). Low levels also result from poisoning by anticholinesterases such as the organophosphates. Inherited deficiencies are discussed below.

Causes of Decreased Cholinesterase

1. Hepatic parenchymal disease:
    (a) Hepatitis.
    (b) Cirrhosis.
2. Anticholinesterases (organophosphates).
3. Inherited deficiency.
4. Myocardial infarction.

Causes of Increased Cholinesterase

1. Recovery from liver damage.
2. Nephrotic syndrome.

Succinylcholine Sensitivity

The muscle relaxant succinylcholine is broken down by cholinesterase and this limits its period of action. In certain individuals, succinylcholine administration is followed by a prolonged period of apnoea. These persons have been found to have a deficiency in cholinesterase. Not only is there deficiency, but the enzyme present is qualitatively different from the normal (that is, it is an isoenzyme). This difference can be assessed by the "dibucaine number". Normal cholinesterase is 80 per cent inhibited by dibucaine (dibucaine number—80) while in persons homozygous for the defective gene the dibucaine number is about 20. Heterozygotes have intermediate dibucaine numbers and less severe clinical manifestations. A different abnormality exists, characterized by sensitivity to fluoride (fluoride number) and combinations of these give a spectrum of cholinesterase abnormalities with varying degrees of sensitivity to succinylcholine. Discovery of a patient with this abnormality requires investigation of the whole family and issuing of appropriate warning cards to all affected individuals.

CHEMICAL PATHOLOGY OF MUSCLE DISEASE

The muscular dystrophies are a group of genetically determined degenerative disorders of muscle. The biochemical abnormalities may be divided into two groups, the non-specific findings due to a decreased muscle mass in the established case and the more specific enzyme abnormalities of value in diagnosis.

Non-Specific Findings

1. With active destruction of muscle aminoaciduria may occur. This is of little use in diagnosis.

2. **Abnormalities of creatine and creatinine.**—The maintenance of muscle in a relaxed state is dependent on the presence of ATP. The immediate source of the high energy phosphate bonds for ATP is creatine phosphate.

Creatine is synthesized in the liver and carried in the blood stream to be taken up by the muscle under the influence of the enzyme CPK (p. 289) to form creatine phosphate. Any creatine not so taken up is excreted in the urine. Normally, in men, little if any creatine is present in urine, but in women and children with smaller muscle mass it is present.

During muscular contraction a certain proportion of the creatine phosphate is irreversibly degraded to creatinine which is excreted in the urine. The daily creatinine excretion is proportional to muscle mass and is greater in men than in women.

The normal state of affairs, then, is that men excrete little creatine and about 2 g/day of creatinine in the urine while in women and children excretion of creatine is higher and of creatinine lower (about 1·5 g/day).

If creatine uptake by muscle is impaired, either by low levels of muscle CPK as in muscular dystrophy, or because of decrease in muscle bulk from any cause, *creatinuria* occurs. Conversely, because of reduced muscle bulk and therefore activity, *less* creatinine is formed and excreted. This pattern of raised urinary creatine and lowered urinary creatinine may be seen in muscle atrophy of any origin.

This test is crude. Urinary creatine levels are so low that estimation is not very accurate. The test has now been replaced by enzyme methods.

Enzyme Abnormalities

Specific diagnostic changes may be detected by enzyme estimations. In muscular dystrophy, probably because of increased leakage of enzymes from the damaged cells, plasma levels of muscle enzymes are increased. The relevant enzymes are CPK, aldolase and the aminotransferases. Of these, CPK is the most valuable, followed by aldolase. Points to consider in interpretation are:

1. Levels are highest (up to 10 times normal or more) in the early stages of the disease. Later, when much of the muscle has wasted, they are lower and may even be normal.

2. Levels are higher on activity immediately after rest (build up of muscle CPK) than after prolonged activity.

3. In detecting affected newborns, it must be remembered that levels at this age are higher than in adults.

Carriers of the Duchenne type muscular dystrophy can often be detected by raised CPK levels.

Neurogenic muscular atrophy is not associated with enzyme changes.

SUMMARY

1. Enzyme activities in cells are high and natural decay and leakage produce secondary activity, usually low, in plasma.

2. The main use of plasma enzyme estimations is the detection of raised levels due to cell damage.

3. Few enzymes are specific for any one tissue but isoenzyme studies may increase specificity. In general, patterns of enzyme changes together with clinical findings are used for interpretation.

4. Non-specific causes of raised plasma enzyme activity include peripheral circulatory insufficiency, trauma, malignancy and surgery.

5. Enzyme estimations are of value in:

(*a*) Myocardial infarction—asp. aminotransferase, CPK, LDH and isoenzymes (p. 293).

(*b*) Liver disease—aminotransferases, ICD, alk.phos., and 5'-NT (p. 294).

(*c*) Bone disease—alk.phos. (p. 291).

(*d*) Prostatic carcinoma—tartrate-labile acid phos. (p. 292).

(*e*) Acute pancreatitis—amylase (p. 289).

(*f*) Muscle disorders—CPK, aldolase (p. 296).

APPENDIX TO CHAPTER XIII

1. Normal values for enzyme estimations must be obtained from the issuing laboratory. Minor differences in technique may lead to very different results.

2. The laboratory should also be consulted about the type of specimen required. In general, serum is preferable to plasma as anticoagulants may affect the result.

3. Haemolysis should be avoided particularly where enzymes found in erythrocytes (aminotransferases, LDH) are being measured.

4. Certain enzymes are unstable and the specimen should be sent to the laboratory without delay, e.g. CPK; acid phos.

FURTHER READING

WILKINSON, J. H. (1962). *An Introduction to Diagnostic Enzymology.* London: Edward Arnold.

Chapter XIV

DISORDERS OF PURINE AND URIC ACID METABOLISM

HYPERURICAEMIA AND GOUT

HYPERURICAEMIA may be asymptomatic, or give rise to the clinical syndrome of gout. In either case it should be treated; the relative insolubility of urate means that there is the danger of precipitation in all tissues. If this takes place in the kidney renal damage can result (compare the danger of hypercalcaemia, p. 178). Hyperuricaemia may be due to a primary lesion of purine metabolism, or be secondary to a variety of other conditions. The primary syndrome has a familial incidence.

Plasma urate is in the form of the monosodium salt. Uric acid is less soluble than its sodium salts.

NORMAL URATE METABOLISM

Urate is the end product of purine metabolism in man. In most other mammals it is further broken down to the soluble compound, allantoin, and it is the poor solubility of urates which makes man prone to clinical gout and renal damage by urate. The purines, adenine and guanine, are constituents of both types of *nucleic acid* (DNA and RNA). The purines used by the body for nucleic acid synthesis may be derived from the breakdown of ingested nucleic acid (mainly in proteins which are rich in cells), or may be synthesized in the body from small molecules *de novo*.

Synthesis of Purines

The synthetic pathway of purines is complex, and involves the incorporation of many small molecules into the relatively complex purine ring. The upper part of Fig. 26 summarizes some of the more important steps in this synthesis. Cytotoxic drugs such as 6-mercaptopurine and folic acid antagonists inhibit various stages in this pathway, so preventing DNA formation and cell growth.

The following stages in Fig. 26 should be especially noted.

Step (a) is the first one in purine synthesis. It involves condensation of phosphate with phosphoribose to form phosphoribosyl pyrophosphate (PRPP).

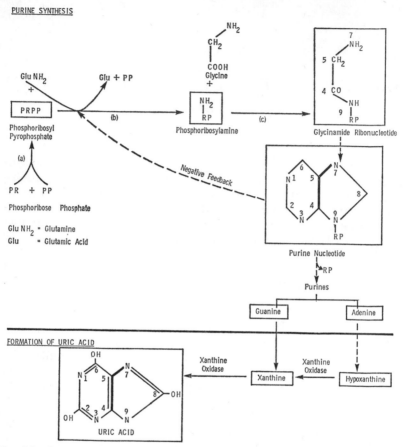

FIG. 26.—Summary of purine synthesis and breakdown to show steps of clinical importance. (See text for explanation of small letters.)

In Step (b) the amino group of glutamine is incorporated into the ribose phosphate molecule and phosphate is released. This is the *rate limiting* or controlling step in urate synthesis. It is subject to feedback inhibition from increased levels of purine nucleotides: thus the rate of synthesis is slowed when its products increase. This step may be at fault in primary gout.

Step (c) shows how the *glycine* molecule is added to phosphoribosyl-amine. Labelled glycine can be used to study the rate of purine synthesis. The atoms in the glycine have been numbered in the diagram to correspond with those of the purine and uric acid molecules, and the heavy lines further indicate the final position of the amino-acid in these molecules. By use of labelled glycine it has been shown that purine synthesis is increased in primary gout.

After many complex steps purine ribonucleotides (purine ribose phosphates) are formed and, as has already been stated, the level of these controls Step (b). Ribose phosphate is split off, thereby releasing the purines.

Fate of Purines

Purines arising from *de novo* synthesis, those derived from the diet, and those liberated by endogenous breakdown of nucleic acids may follow one of two pathways:

1. They may be synthesized into new nucleic acid.
2. They may be oxidized to uric acid.

Formation of uric acid from purines.—As shown in the lower part of Fig. 26, some of the adenine is oxidized to hypoxanthine and hypoxanthine is further oxidized by the liver enzyme, *xanthine oxidase*, to xanthine. Guanine can also form xanthine. Xanthine, in turn, is oxidized by xanthine oxidase to form uric acid. Thus the formation of uric acid from purines depends on xanthine oxidase activity, a fact of importance in the treatment of gout.

Excretion of uric acid.—75 per cent of the urate leaving the body is excreted in the urine and 25 per cent passes into the intestine, where it is broken down by intestinal bacteria (*uricolysis*). The urate filtered at the renal glomerulus is probably completely reabsorbed in the tubules and the urinary uric acid is derived from active tubular secretion: urinary excretion may be enhanced by various drugs used in the treatment of gout.

Renal excretion of urate is inhibited by such acids as lactic acid and keto acids.

CAUSES OF HYPERURICAEMIA

Figure 27 summarizes the factors which may contribute to hyperuricaemia. These are:

1. Increased rate of formation of uric acid.
   Increased synthesis of purines (a).
   Increased intake of purines (b).
   Increased turnover of nucleic acids (c).
2. Reduced rate of excretion of uric acid (f).

Steps (b), (c) and (f) are causes of secondary gout. Increased synthesis is probably the basic fault in primary gout.

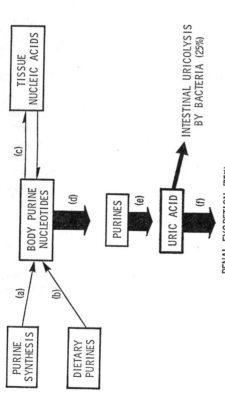

FIG. 27.—Origin and fate of uric acid in normal subjects.

Causes of Hyperuricaemia

Pathway (a) Increased in Primary Hyperuricaemia

Pathway (b) Affected by diet

Pathway (c) Increased in malignancy, infection, cytotoxic therapy, psoriasis etc.

Pathway (f) Decreased in renal failure, thiazide diuretic therapy, some cases of primary hyperuricaemia and acidosis

Treatment of Hyperuricaemia

Pathway (e) Reduced by Xanthine Oxidase inhibitors (eg. Allopurinol)

Pathway (f) Increased by Uricosuric Drugs (eg. Benemid)

DANGERS OF HYPERURICAEMIA

The solubility of urate in plasma is probably exceeded at levels over about 6 mg/100 ml. Precipitation in tissues may then be favoured by a variety of local factors of which the most important are probably tissue pH and trauma. Crystallization in *joints*, especially those of the foot, produces the classical picture of gout, first described by Hippocrates in 460 B.C. It is thought that local inflammation due to urate precipitation produces an increase in leucocytes in the area, and that lactic acid production by these lowers the pH locally: this reduces the solubility of urate and sets up a vicious circle in which further precipitation occurs. It should be noted that in attacks of acute gouty arthritis local factors are of more importance than the plasma urate levels; the latter may even be normal during the attack.

Precipitation can also occur in other tissues, and the subcutaneous collections of urate, which are especially common in the ear and in the olecranon and patellar bursae and tendons are called *gouty tophi*.

Gouty attacks are extremely painful and unpleasant and may lead to permanent joint deformity. Tophi are disfiguring but harmless. The lethal effect of hyperuricaemia is due to precipitation of urate in the kidney, leading to *renal failure*. For this reason it has been recommended that all cases with plasma uric acid levels consistently above 9 mg/100 ml should be treated.

PRIMARY HYPERURICAEMIA AND GOUT

Familial Incidence

In A.D. 150 Galen said that gout was due to "debauchery, intemperance and an hereditary trait". "Intemperance", as we shall see, may aggravate the condition. The striking familial incidence of hyperuricaemia confirms that there is probably "an hereditary trait", but in this respect we know little more than Galen did, since the mode of inheritance (like that of diabetes mellitus) is still obscure.

Sex and Age Incidence

Gout and hyperuricaemia are very rare in children, and rare in women of child-bearing age. The difference in incidence in males and females is not due to a sex-linked inheritance, because it can be transmitted by males. Plasma uric acid levels are low in children and rise in both sexes at puberty, more so in males than females. Women become more prone to hyperuricaemia and gout in the post-menopausal period (compare plasma cholesterol and iron levels).

Precipitating Factors

The classical image of the gouty subject is the red-faced, good living, hard drinking Squire depicted in novels and paintings of the 18th century. Galen mentioned "debauchery and intemperance" as causes of gout. Two factors probably account for the high incidence of clinical gout in this type of subject.

1. Alcohol has been shown to decrease renal excretion of uric acid. This may be because it is partly metabolized to lactic acid, which inhibits urate excretion.

2. A high protein diet contains a high proportion of purines.

Neither of these factors are likely to precipitate gout in a normal person, but may do so in a subject with a gouty trait.

Biochemical Lesion of Primary Hyperuricaemia

Use of labelled glycine has shown that *purine synthesis is increased* in primary hyperuricaemia. There may be overactivity of the enzyme controlling the formation of phosphoribosylamine (Fig. 26). This could be due to failure of normal feedback suppression by nucleotides.

Reduced renal secretion of urate has also been demonstrated in some cases of primary hyperuricaemia.

Principles of Treatment of Hyperuricaemia

Treatment may be based on:

Reducing purine intake (Step (b) Fig. 27).—This is not very effective by itself.

Increasing renal excretion of uric acid with *uricosuric drugs*, such as probenecid and salicylates in large doses (Step (f) Fig. 27). These are very effective if renal function is normal, but are useless in the presence of renal failure.

Reducing uric acid production by drugs which inhibit xanthine oxidase (Step (e) Fig. 27), such as *allopurinol* (hydroxypyrazolopyrimidine). This compound is structurally similar to hypoxanthine and acts as a competitive inhibitor of the enzyme.

Colchicine, which has an anti-inflammatory effect in acute gouty arthritis, does not affect uric acid metabolism.

Juvenile Hyperuricaemia (Lesch-Nyhan Syndrome)

This is a very rare inborn error, probably carried on an X-linked recessive gene, in which severe hyperuricaemia has been reported to occur in young male children. The syndrome is associated with mental deficiency, a tendency to self-mutilation, aggressive behaviour, athetosis and spastic paraplegia.

SECONDARY HYPERURICAEMIA

High plasma uric acid levels may be the result of a variety of conditions.

1. Increased turnover of nucleic acids ((c) in Fig. 27).
   (a) Rapidly growing malignancy, especially leukaemias and polycythaemia rubra vera. Treatment of malignant tumours.
   (b) Psoriasis.
   (c) Increased tissue breakdown in
     Starvation
     Tissue damage.
2. Reduced excretion of uric acid (Step (f) in Fig. 27).
   (a) Glomerular failure.
   (b) Thiazide diuretics.

Increased turnover of nucleic acids in malignancy can cause hyperuricaemia. *Treatment* of large tumours by radiotherapy or cytoxic drugs can cause massive release of urates and has been known to cause acute renal failure due to tubular blockage by crystalline urate. During such treatment renal excretion of dissolved urate should be encouraged by a high (preferably alkaline) fluid intake and uricosuric drugs. If renal function is poor allopurinol should be used, and fluids should not be forced.

Starvation and tissue damage.—In starvation and with tissue damage endogenous tissue breakdown is increased. Increased amounts of uric acid are produced. In both these conditions acidosis is probably present (due to ketosis in starvation, and due to tissue catabolism in both) and these acids probably inhibit renal excretion of urate aggravating the hyperuricaemia. Levels may reach 15 mg/100 ml, or more, in complete starvation.

Glomerular failure causes retention of uric acid as well as retention of other waste products of metabolism. When estimating plasma uric acid, urea should always be estimated on the same specimen to exclude renal failure as a cause of hyperuricaemia. It has already been mentioned that hyperuricaemia may *cause* renal failure and, in the presence of uraemia, it may be difficult to know which is cause and which is effect. As a rough guide the plasma uric acid would be expected to be about 10–12 mg/100 ml at a urea level of about 300 mg/100 ml; if it is much higher than this hyperuricaemia should be suspected as the primary cause of the renal failure. Clinical gout is rare in secondary hyperuricaemia due to renal failure.

Increased intestinal secretion and bacterial uricolysis have been claimed to occur in renal failure and may account for the fact that, although plasma urea and uric acid levels rise in parallel, the rise in uric acid is less on a molar basis than that of urea.

Hyperuricaemia, and even clinical gout, is a rare complication of therapy with *thiazide diuretics*. These inhibit renal excretion of uric acid.

PSEUDOGOUT

Pseudogout, while not a disorder of purine metabolism, produces a similar clinical picture to gout. Calcium pyrophosphate precipitates in joint cavities and calcification of the cartilages is seen radiologically. The crystals may be identified under a polarizing microscope. The plasma urate is normal.

HYPOURICAEMIA

Hypouricaemia is rare, except as a result of treatment of hyperuricaemia. It is an unimportant finding in the *Fanconi syndrome* (p. 12) when there is decreased tubular reabsorption of urate.

Xanthinuria is a very rare inborn error in which there is a deficiency of liver xanthine oxidase. Purine breakdown stops at the xanthine-hypoxanthine stage. Plasma and urinary uric acid levels are very low. The increased urinary excretion of xanthine may lead to the formation of xanthine stones (the reason why this does not happen during therapy with xanthine oxidase inhibitors is not clear). The mode of inheritance is probably autosomal recessive.

SUMMARY

1. Urate is the end product of purine metabolism.

2. Hyperuricaemia may be the result of:
   Increased nucleic acid turnover (malignancy, tissue damage, starvation).
   Increased synthesis of purines (primary gout).
   Reduced rate of renal excretion of uric acid (glomerular failure, thiazide diuretics).

3. Hyperuricaemia may be aggravated by:
   High purine diets.
   Acidosis and a high alcohol intake.

4. Primary hyperuricaemia and gout have a familial incidence and are rare in women of child-bearing age.

5. Because hyperuricaemia may cause renal damage it should be treated, even if asymptomatic.

6. Hypouricaemia is rare and usually unimportant. It occurs in the very rare inborn error, xanthinuria.

Chapter XV

DISORDERS OF IRON METABOLISM

In man the circulating iron-containing pigment, haemoglobin, carries oxygen from the lungs to metabolizing tissues, and in muscle myoglobin increases the local supply of oxygen. The ability to carry oxygen depends, among other factors, on the presence of ferrous iron in the haem molecule; iron deficiency is associated with deficient haem synthesis, and the symptoms of anaemia are due to tissue anoxia. Certain enzymes necessary for electron transfer reactions (and therefore, among other things, for oxidative phosphorylation) and the cytochromes also contain iron: it is doubtful if clinical iron deficiency, unless very severe, affects these.

NORMAL IRON METABOLISM

DISTRIBUTION OF IRON IN THE BODY

Figure 28 represents diagrammatically the distribution of iron in the body. The total body iron is about 4 g.

1. About 70 per cent of the total iron is circulating in erythrocyte *haemoglobin.*

2. About 25 per cent of the body iron is *stored* in the reticuloendothelial system, largely in the liver and spleen. This storage iron is complexed with protein to form *ferritin* and *haemosiderin*; haemosiderin may be aggregated ferritin and its granules, unlike those of ferritin, are visible under the light microscope.

A relatively small amount of this storage iron is found in the reticuloendothelial cells of the *bone marrow*, where it acts as a reserve supply for erythropoiesis.

Storage iron, unlike haem iron, can be stained with potassium ferrocyanide (Prussian Blue reaction).

3. *Only about 4 mg. (0·1 per cent) of the total body iron is circulating in the plasma,* bound to protein. This is the fraction measured in *plasma iron* estimations.

4. The remainder of the body iron is incorporated in myoglobin, cytochromes and iron-containing enzymes.

Iron can only cross cell membranes in the ferrous form: it is in this reduced state in both oxyhaemoglobin and "reduced" haemoglobin. In ferritin and haemosiderin, and when bound to transferrin, it is in the ferric state.

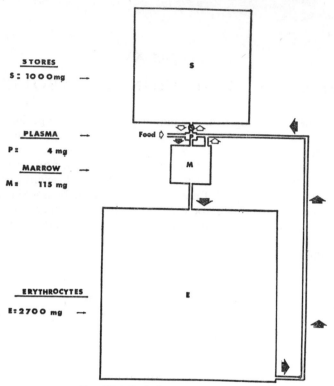

Fig. 28.—Body iron compartments.

The *control* of iron distribution in the body is poorly understood. Plasma iron concentrations can vary by 100 per cent or more for purely physiological reasons, and are also affected by a variety of pathological factors other than the amount of iron in the body. These variations in plasma iron are probably due to redistribution between stores and plasma.

IRON BALANCE

As shown in Fig. 28 iron, once in the body, is virtually in a closed system.

Iron Excretion

There is no control of iron excretion and loss from the body probably depends on the iron content of desquamated cells. Negligible amounts appear in the urine, and most of the loss is probably into the intestinal tract and from the skin. The total daily loss by these routes is about 1 mg.

In women the monthly menstrual loss of iron is about 16 mg and averages 0·5–1 mg a day over the month above the basal 1 mg daily. During pregnancy the mean extra daily loss to the foetus and placenta is about 1·5 mg.

It should be noted for comparison that a male blood donor losing a pint of blood every 4 months averages an extra loss of 2 mg daily above the basal loss of 1 mg (Table XX).

Iron Absorption

The control of body content of iron depends upon control of absorption.

Iron is absorbed by an active process in the upper small intestine. It can cross cell membranes, including those of intestinal cells, only in the ferrous form. Absorption of iron is inhibited by pancreatic juice (p. 209). Within the intestinal cell some of the iron is combined with the protein, apoferritin, to form ferritin: this, like ferritin elsewhere, is a storage compound. Its function, if any, in the process of iron absorption is not well understood: formerly it was thought to control this by "blocking" further absorption when it was saturated with iron ("mucosal block"), but this theory has been abandoned. Any remaining iron stays in the cell as ferritin and is lost into the intestinal tract when the cell dies.

Absorption normally amounts to about 1 mg of iron a day and just replaces loss. The percentage absorption of dietary iron depends to some extent on the food with which it is taken, but is usually about 10 per cent.

Iron absorption appears to be influenced by oxygen tension, by haemoglobin levels, by marrow erythropoietic activity, or by all three: the state of iron stores may also affect it. From the clinical point of view it is important to note that *iron absorption is increased by anaemia, whether or not this is due to iron deficiency*.

If an adequate diet is taken most normal women probably absorb slightly more iron than men to replace their greater losses.

IRON TRANSPORT IN PLASMA

Iron is carried in the plasma in the ferric form, attached to the specific binding protein, *transferrin* (siderophilin), and is at a concentration of about 100 μg/100 ml. The protein is normally capable of binding about 300 μg/100 ml of iron, and is therefore about a third saturated. Transferrin bound iron is carried to stores and to bone marrow: in stores it is laid down as ferritin and haemosiderin, and in the marrow some passes directly from transferrin into the developing erythrocyte to form haemoglobin.

TABLE XX

COMPARISON OF IRON LOSSES

	Source of loss	Extra loss	Daily extra loss	Daily total loss
Men and non-menstruating women	Desquamation	—	—	1 mg
Menstruating women	Desquamation + menstruation	16 mg/month	0·5 mg	1·5 mg
Pregnancy	Desquamation + loss to foetus and in placenta	380 mg/9 months	1·5 mg	2·5 mg
Male blood donors	Desquamation + 1 pint blood	250 mg/4 months	2·0 mg	3·0 mg

Little, if any, of the iron in the body is free. In intestinal cells and stores it is bound to protein in ferritin and haemosiderin, in the plasma it is bound to transferrin, and in the erythrocyte it is incorporated in haemoglobin. Free iron is toxic.

FACTORS AFFECTING PLASMA IRON LEVELS

Plasma iron estimation is frequently requested, but is rarely of clinical value, and results are often misinterpreted. As we have seen, plasma iron, like plasma potassium, represents a very small proportion of the total body content, and for this reason alone is likely to be a poor index of it: but, while plasma potassium levels normally are relatively constant, those of plasma iron are much less so and can vary greatly under physiological conditions.

Physiological Factors Affecting Plasma Iron Levels

The causes of physiological changes in plasma iron concentrations are not well understood, but they are very rapid, and almost certainly represent shifts between plasma and stores. The following factors are known to affect levels and some may cause changes of 100 per cent or more.

1. Sex and Age Differences

Plasma iron levels are higher in men than in women, like those of haemoglobin and the erythrocyte count. This difference is probably hormonal in origin. It is first evident at puberty, before significant menstrual iron loss has occurred, and disappears at the menopause. Androgens tend to increase plasma iron concentration and oestrogens to lower it.

2. Cyclical Variations

(a) **Diurnal (circadian) rhythm.**—Plasma iron is higher in the morning than in the evening. If subjects are kept awake at night this difference may be less marked.

(b) **Monthly variations in women.**—Plasma iron may reach very low levels just before or during the menstrual period. This reduction is probably due to hormonal factors rather than to blood loss.

3. Random Variations

Very large day to day variations (occasionally as much as threefold) occur in plasma iron, and these usually overshadow cyclical changes. They may sometimes be associated with physical or mental stress, but more usually a cause cannot be found.

4. Effect of Pregnancy and Oral Contraceptives

In women taking oral contraceptives the plasma iron rises to levels similar to those found in men. A similar rise occurs in the first few weeks of pregnancy: if iron deficiency develops in late pregnancy this effect may be masked.

PATHOLOGICAL FACTORS AFFECTING PLASMA IRON LEVELS

1. Iron deficiency and iron overload usually cause low and high plasma iron levels respectively.

Iron deficiency is associated with a hypochromic microcytic anaemia, and with reduced amounts of stainable marrow iron.

Iron overload is associated with increased amounts of stainable iron in marrow films and liver biopsy.

2. Many illnesses including *infection (acute or chronic, mild or severe)*, *uraemia, malignancy and autoimmune diseases such as rheumatoid arthritis* cause hypoferraemia. Many of these chronic conditions are associated with normocytic, normochromic anaemia. Iron stores are normal or even increased, and the anaemia does not respond to iron therapy.

3. In conditions in which the *marrow cannot utilize iron*, either because it is hypoplastic, or because some other factor necessary for erythropoiesis (such as vitamin B_{12} or folate) is absent, plasma iron levels are often high. Blood and marrow films may show a typical picture: in the case of, for instance, pyridoxine responsive anaemia and in thalassaemia, this may be similar to that of iron deficiency (sideroblastic anaemia), but iron stores are increased, and this can be shown on the marrow film.

4. In *haemolytic anaemia* the iron from the haemoglobin of broken down erythrocytes is released into the plasma and reticulo-endothelial system. Plasma iron may be high during the haemolytic episode and is usually normal in quiescent periods. Marrow iron stores are increased.

5. In *acute liver disease* disruption of cells may release ferritin iron into the blood stream and cause a transient rise of serum iron. In *cirrhosis* plasma iron levels may also be high, possibly because of increased iron absorption associated with a high iron intake.

TRANSFERRIN AND TOTAL IRON BINDING CAPACITY (TIBC)

It will be seen that plasma iron levels by themselves give no useful information about the state of iron stores. In the rare situations in which doubt remains about this after haematological investigations have been carried out, diagnostic precision may be improved by measuring the iron binding capacity of the plasma at the same time as the plasma iron. It is a waste of time and money to estimate only plasma iron.

Transferrin is usually measured indirectly by measuring the iron binding capacity of the plasma. An excess of inorganic iron is mixed with the plasma and any which is not bound to transferrin is removed, usually with a resin. The remaining iron is estimated on the plasma sample and the result expressed as a total iron binding capacity (TIBC) in μg of iron/100 ml of plasma.

Physiological Changes in TIBC

The TIBC is less labile than the plasma iron. However, it rises rapidly in subjects on *oral contraceptives*, and this point should be remembered when interpreting results in women. It also increases after about the 28th week of *pregnancy*, even in those women with normal iron stores.

Pathological Changes in TIBC

1. The *TIBC rises in iron deficiency* and *falls in iron overload*.
2. The *TIBC falls* in chronic infection, malignancy and the *other pathological conditions associated with a low plasma iron concentration* other than iron deficiency. This includes the nephrotic syndrome, in which the protein is lost in the urine.
3. The TIBC is unchanged in acute infection.

Thus the low plasma iron of iron deficiency is associated with a high TIBC. That of anaemia not due to iron deficiency is associated with a low TIBC.

PERCENTAGE SATURATION OF TIBC

The statement that the TIBC is normally a third saturated with iron is a very approximate one: physiological variations of plasma iron levels are rarely associated with much change in TIBC and the saturation of the protein varies widely; the percentage saturation is, of course, the

$$\frac{\text{Plasma Iron } (\mu g/100 \text{ ml}) \times 100}{\text{TIBC } (\mu g/100 \text{ ml})}$$

It has been claimed that percentage saturation is a better index of iron stores than plasma iron concentration alone, and that if it is below 16 per cent iron deficiency is present. The first part of the statement is obviously true, because the low plasma iron of iron deficiency is accompanied by a high TIBC; this will result in a lower percentage saturation than with the same level of plasma iron in other conditions. However,

TABLE XXI

CHANGES IN SERUM IRON (Fe) AND TOTAL IRON BINDING CAPACITY (TIBC)

	Fe	TIBC	% Saturation	Marrow stores
Low Iron Levels				
Iron deficiency	↓	↑	↓↓	↓ or absent
Chronic illnesses (e.g. infection and malignancy)	↓	↓	Variable	Normal or ↑
Acute illnesses (e.g. infection)	↓	Normal	↓	Normal
Premenstrual	↓	Normal	↓	Normal
High Iron Levels				
Iron overload	↑	↓	↑↑	↑
Oral contraceptives and late pregnancy	↑ (to male level)	↑	Normal	Normal
Early pregnancy	↑ (to male level)	Normal	↑	Normal
Hepatic cirrhosis	↑	↓	↑ to ↑↑	↑
Failure of marrow utilization and haemolysis	↑	Normal or ↓	↑	↑

saturation as low as 16 per cent can be found, for instance premenstrually and in acute infections, with no change in TIBC or in iron stores. It is probably more useful to take account of the results of both plasma iron and TIBC rather than to calculate the percentage saturation.

The findings in various conditions which may affect plasma iron levels and TIBC are summarized in Table XXI.

INVESTIGATION OF ANAEMIA

Anaemia may be due to iron deficiency, or to a variety of other conditions. The subject of the diagnosis of anaemia is covered more fully in textbooks of haematology. However, so that we may see the value of plasma iron estimations in perspective, it is worth considering the order in which anaemia may be usefully investigated.

1. The clinical impression of anaemia should be confirmed by haemoglobin estimation. Iron deficiency can, however, exist with haemoglobin levels within the "normal" range.

2. A blood film should be examined, or absolute values estimated. Iron deficiency anaemia is hypochromic and microcytic in type, and hypochromia may be evident before the haemoglobin level has fallen below the accepted normal range. Normocytic, normochromic anaemia is non-specific and usually associated with other disease: it is not due to iron deficiency. Typical appearances of other anaemias may be seen on the blood film.

In most cases of anaemia, consideration of these findings with the clinical picture will give the cause. Sideroblastic anaemias, although rare, are most likely to confuse the picture, since they too are hypochromic, but are not due to iron deficiency.

3. A marrow film may be required to confirm the diagnosis (for example, of megaloblastic anaemia). If such a film is available staining with potassium ferrocyanide will give by far the best index of the state of iron stores, if this information is still required.

If marrow puncture is not felt to be justified, and *in the rare cases* in which diagnosis is not yet clear, biochemical investigations may occasionally help.

4. Plasma iron *and* TIBC should be estimated. Plasma iron estimation alone is uninformative.

"IRON DEFICIENCY WITHOUT ANAEMIA"

It has been claimed that the symptoms of iron deficiency can occur when haemoglobin levels are within the "normal" range. Iron deficiency can certainly exist under these conditions, and in most, if not all, such cases the diagnosis may be made on the appearances of the blood film: haemoglobin levels will rise after a short course of oral iron. A low plasma iron level is a poor index of such iron deficiency and subjective, symptomatic response to treatment is extremely difficult to assess in an individual subject. Careful trials have shown statistically significant symptomatic relief (associated with a rise of haemoglobin concentration) only in a group of cases in which depleted marrow iron stores could be demonstrated before the trial started. In subjects with low serum iron levels and vague symptoms, with normal marrow stores, symptomatic improvement occurred as frequently (and in some groups more frequently) when a placebo was given as when iron was administered.

IRON THERAPY

Because the body does not control iron excretion, and because body content is controlled by absorption, *parenteral iron therapy* may easily lead to iron overload. Repeated blood transfusions carry the same danger, as a pint of blood contains 250 mg of iron. In anaemias other than that of true iron deficiency, stores are normal or even increased, and parenteral iron should not be given unless the diagnosis of iron deficiency is beyond doubt: even when this is so the oral is preferable to the parenteral route. Repeated blood transfusion may be necessary to correct severe anaemia in, for instance, chronic renal disease, but, in such cases, the danger of overload should be remembered and blood should not be given indiscriminately.

Anaemia increases the rate of iron absorption even in the presence of increased iron stores. Treatment of, for instance, chronic haemolytic anaemia with *oral iron supplements* may cause iron overload; it does not improve the anaemia, which is due to the rate of breakdown of erythrocytes exceeding the rate of production, and not to deficiency of iron. The released iron stays in the body. In other non-iron deficient anaemias the danger is similar.

Although iron absorption is controlled to some extent, this control is inefficient, even in the absence of anaemia. Iron overload has been reported in a non-anaemic woman who continued to take oral iron (against medical advice) over a matter of years.

Iron therapy is potentially dangerous and should be prescribed with care.

IRON OVERLOAD

As emphasized on p. 308, the excretion of iron from the body is limited. Iron absorbed from the gastro-intestinal tract, or administered parenterally, in excess of daily loss accumulates in body stores. If such "positive balance" is maintained over long periods, iron stores may exceed 20 g (about five times the normal amount).

Iron overload may occur under the following circumstances:
1. Due to increased absorption from the intestinal tract

   (*a*) Normal iron intake
   Idiopathic haemochromatosis
   Rarely in alcoholic cirrhosis,   } Exaggerated by excess
   sideroblastic or chronic   iron intake.
   haemolytic anaemias

   (*b*) High iron intake
   Bantu siderosis
   Excessive oral iron therapy in the absence of iron deficiency
   over long periods of time.
2. Increased parenteral administration of iron.
   Transfusion siderosis.
   Prolonged parenteral administration in the absence of iron
   deficiency.
3. Deficiency of plasma binding protein (transferrin). (Very rare.)

The effect of the accumulated iron depends on the distribution in the body. This in turn is influenced partly by the route of entry. Two main patterns are seen at post-mortem examination or in biopsy specimens.

(a) **Parenchymal iron overload** is typified by idiopathic haemochromatosis. Iron accumulates in the parenchymal cells of the liver, pancreas, heart and other organs. There is usually associated functional disturbance or tissue damage.

(b) **Reticulo-endothelial iron overload** is seen after excessive *parenteral administration of iron* or *multiple blood transfusions*. The iron accumulates in the reticulo-endothelial cells of the liver, spleen and bone marrow. There are few harmful effects other than a possible interference with haem synthesis, but under certain circumstances (p. 320), the pattern of distribution may change to that of the parenchymal type.

Two terms in common usage require definition. *Haemochromatosis* implies iron overload, usually parenchymal, with associated, presumably consequent, tissue damage. *Haemosiderosis* refers to iron overload, usually reticulo-endothelial, without such damage.

IDIOPATHIC HAEMOCHROMATOSIS

Idiopathic haemochromatosis is a genetically determined disease in which increased intestinal absorption of iron over many years produces large iron stores of parenchymal distribution. It manifests, usually in middle age, as cirrhosis with diabetes mellitus, hypogonadism and increased skin pigmentation. Because of the darkening of the skin, due to an increase in melanin rather than to iron deposition, the condition has been referred to as "bronzed diabetes", although the colour is more grey than bronze. Cardiac manifestations may be prominent, particularly in younger patients, many of whom die in cardiac failure. In about 10 per cent of cases hepato-cellular carcinoma develops.

The above concept of idiopathic haemochromatosis as a genetically determined disorder of iron absorption has been disputed by some workers. The main points of disagreement are the failure to demonstrate increased iron absorption in many cases, and the uncertain mode of inheritance. The difficulty in proving increased absorption is not surprising: the accumulation of 20 g of iron over a period of 30–40 years requires an increased absorption of less than 2 mg a day, not easily detectable by existing methods because of a wide normal range. In patients who present in the second or third decades, in whom the defect is presumably more severe, increased rate of absorption is demonstrable. A further point is the depressant effect on iron absorption of the massive body stores in the overt cases (p. 309). Increased absorption is demonstrable after removal of the excess in many cases.

The mode of inheritance is uncertain. Evidence for the genetic nature of the disease is found in the study of families of patients, in whom the role of such environmental factors as a high iron intake can be properly assessed. In addition, evidence of iron overload (see below) has been found in a significant proportion of close relatives of patients with idiopathic haemochromatosis.

Diagnosis of Idiopathic Haemochromatosis

1. **Plasma iron concentration and TIBC.**—The plasma iron concentration is almost invariably high, often above 200 μg/100 ml. This is associated with a reduced transferrin level (as shown by a lowered TIBC) and the percentage saturation is usually over 80 per cent, and often 100 per cent: in the presence of infection or malignancy, however, the plasma iron level and percentage saturation may be lower than expected; the TIBC remains low.

These findings may also be present in cases of cirrhosis of the liver due to other causes, and diagnosis may be very difficult.

2. **Liver biopsy.**—Histological examination of a liver biopsy will show large amounts of stainable iron, predominantly within the parenchymal cells. Assessment of iron stores requires careful interpretation as variations in staining technique may render iron visible at very different concentrations. Within a single laboratory with a standardized method, excessive iron should be readily recognized.

3. **Demonstration of increased iron stores.**—The final diagnosis of iron overload can only be made after proof of increased iron stores by a method other than liver histology.

(a) *Response to venesection.*—The lack of response of the patient to a therapeutic course of venesection offers the most convincing proof of increased iron stores, albeit retrospectively. Removal of a pint of blood (250 mg iron) repeated at short intervals produces a rapid fall in plasma iron, soon followed by iron deficiency anaemia, in a subject with normal iron stores. In patients with idiopathic haemochromatosis, however, 20 g or more of iron may be removed in this way before evidence of iron deficiency develops.

(b) *Use of chelating agents.*—An alternative method uses the chelating action of substances such as desferrioxamine, which bind iron and are subsequently excreted in the urine. Following administration of desferrioxamine, persons with increased iron stores excrete more iron in the urine than do normals.

4. **Other tests.**—(a) *Bone marrow aspiration* with staining for iron is not of great diagnostic value in this condition as this can only assess reticulo-endothelial stores.

(b) Examination of a *centrifuged urine specimen* for haemosiderin may indicate an excess of iron of renal tubular cell origin. If positive this test is of value although positive results also occur in paroxysmal nocturnal haemoglobinuria. A negative result does not exclude the diagnosis of idiopathic haemochromatosis.

Differential Diagnosis

The distinction between idiopathic haemochromatosis and alcoholic cirrhosis may present difficulty. In both conditions diabetes mellitus and hypogonadism may occur and although the incidence is higher in idiopathic haemochromatosis this does not help in the individual case. Examination of liver biopsy specimens may further confuse the issue. The liver in cases of alcoholic cirrhosis not infrequently shows increased stainable iron. Not only do some alcoholic drinks, notably wines, contain significant amounts of iron, but there is evidence that in cirrhosis there may be increased iron absorption due either to a direct effect of alcohol or associated pancreatic insufficiency (p. 309).

The following points may aid in the separation of the two conditions:

1. The majority of patients with cirrhosis do not have increased iron stores despite the histological appearance of the liver biopsy. Such patients become rapidly anaemic during repeated venesection.

2. The amount of stainable iron in the liver biopsy may not be sufficient to lead to suspicion of idiopathic haemochromatosis. When it is, it is situated predominantly in portal tracts. It may be possible to assess the relative severity of the cirrhosis and of the iron overload. Massive iron accumulation with less marked cirrhosis is in favour of idiopathic haemochromatosis and vice versa.

3. Functional impairment of the liver is frequently much less evident in idiopathic haemochromatosis than in alcoholic cirrhosis with apparently equivalent iron overload.

4. There may be evidence, either clinical or from a previous liver biopsy, that the cirrhosis preceded other features of iron overload. Rare cases of cirrhosis may have true iron overload and the distinction between the two conditions may be extremely difficult in the absence of such information. A family history or investigation of near relatives may help in diagnosis. The treatment of iron overload is the same in either case.

BANTU SIDEROSIS

A well-described form of alimentary iron overload is seen in the Bantu population of South Africa. Unlike idiopathic haemochromatosis where excessive iron is absorbed from a diet of normal iron content, the iron intake in cases of Bantu siderosis is grossly excessive. The main source of this iron is local beer, often brewed in iron containers: daily intakes of 80–100 mg (about 4 or 5 times normal) are not uncommon. At high oral intakes of iron control of absorption (the only means of controlling body iron, p. 309) is imperfect and daily absorption of 2–3 mg of iron leads to iron overload: over 30 per cent of Bantu males over the age of 40 have heavy deposition of iron in the liver.

In most cases the excess iron is confined to the reticulo-endothelial system and the liver (both portal tracts and parenchymal cells). In a small number of cases, usually those with the heaviest iron deposits and therefore presumably the highest intake of alcohol, cirrhosis develops. In such cases deposition in the parenchymal cells of other organs occurs and the clinical picture now closely resembles that of idiopathic haemochromatosis: it may be distinguished by the high concentrations of iron in the reticulo-endothelial system such as bone marrow and spleen (at autopsy).

Diagnostic approach is similar to that for idiopathic haemochromatosis. Liver biopsy shows the dual involvement and bone marrow aspiration demonstrates increased reticulo-endothelial stores.

OTHER CAUSES OF IRON OVERLOAD

Several types of anaemia may be associated with iron overload. In some, such as aplastic anaemia and the anaemia of chronic renal failure, the cause is multiple blood transfusions, and the iron accumulates in the reticulo-endothelial system. With massive overload (over 100 pints of blood), true haemochromatosis may develop with parenchymal overload.

In anaemias characterized by erythroid marrow hyperplasia (sideroblastic anaemias and haemolytic anaemia) there is increased absorption of iron from the intestine (p. 316). This may be aggravated by oral iron medication and in a few cases true haemochromatosis develops. It must be stressed again that prolonged iron therapy for anaemia other than that due to iron deficiency carries the risk of overload.

The very rare condition of congenital transferrin deficiency presents as a refractory anaemia and massive iron overload.

SUMMARY

1. No significant excretion of iron can occur from the body. Control of body stores is by control of absorption. For this reason parenteral iron therapy should be given with care.

2. Absorption of iron is increased by anaemia even in the absence of iron deficiency. For this reason oral iron therapy should not be given in anaemia other than that due to iron deficiency.

3. Plasma iron levels vary considerably under physiological circumstances.

4. Plasma iron levels fall in many cases of anaemia not due to iron deficiency.

5. For these two reasons (3 and 4) plasma iron levels alone are a very poor indication of body iron stores.

6. Iron is carried in the plasma bound to the protein transferrin. Transferrin is usually measured indirectly by measuring the total iron binding capacity (TIBC) of plasma.

7. The TIBC rises in iron deficiency and falls in iron overload.

8. The TIBC falls in many cases of anaemia associated with a low plasma iron, but not due to iron deficiency.

9. A low plasma iron concentration with a high TIBC is more suggestive of iron deficiency than a low plasma iron alone.

10. The quickest, cheapest and most informative tests for iron deficiency are simple haematological ones. These should be performed before requesting plasma iron estimation.

11. The factors governing the distribution of excessive iron are not fully understood. A feature common to all forms of parenchymal overload is a high percentage saturation of transferrin.

12. Iron overload may develop as a result of excessive absorption from a normal diet (idiopathic haemochromatosis) or from a high iron intake

(Bantu siderosis); or it may develop as a result of excessive parenteral iron administration. The distribution of the iron in the body differs in the various forms.

13. Iron overload can be demonstrated by the response to repeated venesection or by chelating agents. The diagnosis of idiopathic haemochromatosis can only be made if iron overload is present.

14. Virtually all cases of parenchymal iron overload show a high plasma iron concentration with a high percentage saturation of transferrin.

Chapter XVI

THE PORPHYRIAS

THE porphyrias are a group of diseases that have in common a disturbance of porphyrin metabolism. All types are uncommon in most parts of the world and several are extremely rare. Most are inherited diseases and the detection of a case must be followed by investigation of other members of the family. The peculiar importance of several of the commoner porphyrias is that, apart from presenting a diagnostic problem, the administration of certain drugs, notably barbiturates, can have serious or even fatal consequences.

In this chapter the porphyrias are dealt with in greater detail than is required for undergraduate examinations. We hope, however, that it may serve as a reference, particularly in areas of high incidence, when the diagnosis of porphyria is considered.

BIOSYNTHESIS AND CHEMISTRY

Porphyrins are formed during the biosynthesis of haem and related compounds such as cytochromes. They are tetrapyrroles and the general structure is shown diagrammatically in Fig. 29. Four pyrrole rings, linked by methene bridges, form the basic unit. Further chemical and biological differences are due to variation in the side chains. In addition the rings may vary in their relationship to one another, giving rise to four types of isomers. In nature only types I and III occur.

The most striking characteristic of the porphyrins is the fluorescence they exhibit on exposure to near ultra-violet light (maximal at a wavelength of about 400 nm). This property is used in their detection and measurement.

A knowledge of the outline of haem synthesis is helpful in understanding the abnormalities of porphyria. The main steps are outlined below and in Fig. 30.

1. The first colourless compound formed is δ-*aminolaevulinic acid* (ALA) by condensation of glycine and succinate, catalyzed by the enzyme *ALA-synthetase*. Normally this is a rate-limiting step controlled partly by the end product haem. The importance of ALA-synthetase in the pathogenesis of porphyria is further considered on p. 329.

2. Two molecules of ALA condense to form the colourless monopyrrole, *porphobilinogen* (PBG).

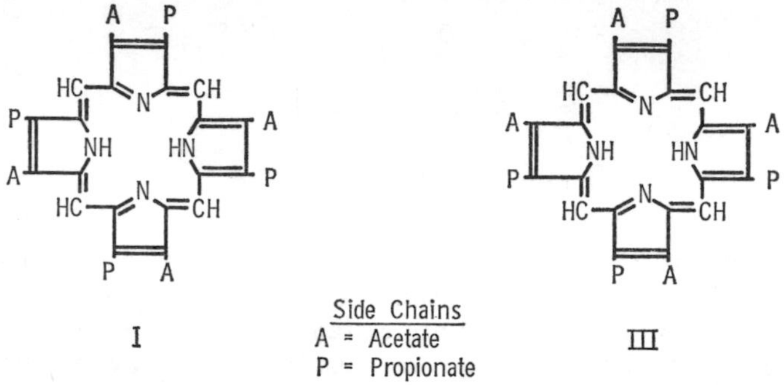

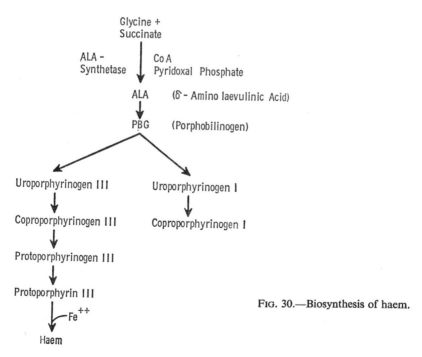

FIG. 29.—Uroporphyrin I and III (note the difference in side chains of the left hand ring).

3. Four molecules of PBG are combined to form uroporphyrinogen (tetrapyrrole). Both uroporphyrinogen I and III are formed.

4. Uroporphyrinogen III forms haem by the various steps shown in Fig. 30. Uroporphyrinogen I forms coproporphyrinogen I and is not converted further.

FIG. 30.—Biosynthesis of haem.

The porphyrinogens are colourless compounds that do not fluoresce under u.v. light but which may be oxidized spontaneously to the corresponding porphyrins, which, with the exception of protoporphyrin, are not in the direct line of haem synthesis.

All the above steps are controlled by enzymes.

The breakdown product of haem is bilirubin and this is discussed in Chapter XII. The liberated iron recirculates.

NORMAL PORPHYRIN METABOLISM

Synthesis of haem in the bone marrow, and related compounds in other tissues, is under fine control and normally very little porphyrin remains to be excreted.

1. *Urine* contains a small amount of porphyrin (mostly coproporphyrin I), insufficient to be detected by screening tests (see below).

One of the main factors influencing excretion of coproporphyrin is (as in the case of urobilinogen) urinary pH. Alkaline urine favours excretion.

Small amounts of ALA and PBG are also present.

2. *Faeces* contains a mixture of protoporphyrin and coproporphyrin, mostly from biliary excretion. These may be present in sufficient quantity to impart a slight fluorescence to extracts of faeces (see below).

SCREENING TESTS IN PORPHYRIA

Quantitative tests for porphyrins and porphyrin precursors are technically demanding and not generally available. There are, however, a number of screening tests used in most laboratories for the rapid diagnosis of porphyria (see Appendix, p. 332, for details). Such tests are not always adequate for the detection of latent cases.

1. Porphyrins in urine and faeces may be extracted into organic solvents where they are detected by the red fluorescence under u.v. light.

2. PBG may be detected by the reaction with Ehrlich's reagent.

There is no simple test for ALA.

DISORDERS OF PORPHYRIN METABOLISM

CLASSIFICATION OF THE PORPHYRIAS

The porphyrias are divided into two main groups. In one group the defect appears to be maximal in liver cells (hepatic porphyrias) while in the other it is apparently confined to the erythropoietic system (erythropoietic porphyrias). The latter group is very rare.

Hepatic

1. Acute intermittent porphyria.
2. Porphyria variegata.
3. Acquired cutaneous hepatic porphyria.
4. Hereditary coproporphyria.

Erythropoietic

1. Congenital erythropoietic porphyria.
2. Erythropoietic protoporphyria.

HEPATIC PORPHYRIAS

Acute Intermittent Porphyria (Swedish genetic porphyria: pyrrolloporphyria)

This is the commonest form of porphyria seen in the British Isles.

Acute intermittent porphyria is an inherited disease characterized, as the name implies, by intermittent acute attacks, with symptom-free intervening periods. The disease manifests more commonly in females than males and appears only after the onset of puberty. Main presenting features include:

1. *Abdominal* symptoms, especially colicky pain, vomiting and constipation. Differentiation from surgical causes of an "acute" abdomen requires recognition of the underlying porphyria.

2. *Neurological* manifestations may predominate and vary from peripheral neuritis to severe paralysis. Psychiatric disturbances are not uncommon.

Severe acute attacks are often accompanied by electrolyte disturbances, notably hyponatraemia. There is evidence that this may be due in part to inappropriate secretion of ADH (p. 379).

The cause of the acute attack is not always obvious, although the greater incidence in women, and the absence of symptoms before puberty, indicates a hormonal influence. There are however a number of drugs that can precipitate an acute attack and which must be avoided by the patient. Important ones are *barbiturates, oestrogens (including oral contraceptives), sulphonamides* and *griseofulvin*. A particular risk to the porphyric patient is the use of thiopentone during laparotomy for the supposed "acute abdomen". Severe neurological lesions may result.

The disease is transmitted as a Mendelian dominant.

Biochemical abnormalities and diagnosis.—The essential biochemical disturbance in acute intermittent porphyria is excessive production of the precursors ALA and PBG, and diagnosis requires demonstration of this.

1. The *urine* is usually of normal colour when first passed, and contains greatly increased amounts of *ALA* (no screening test) and *PBG* which gives a strong positive test in the acute phase. Non-enzymatic conversion of PBG to porphyrin in the urine specimen leads to gradual darkening of the urine to a red-brown or deep-red "port wine" colour. Tests for excess porphyrins will therefore also be positive at this stage.

2. Faecal porphyrin levels may be slightly increased during the acute phase.

Although screening tests for PBG in the urine may remain positive after the acute attack, detection of latent cases often requires quantitative estimation of ALA and PBG.

Porphyria Variegata (South African genetic porphyria: Protocoproporphyria)

This is relatively common in South Africa.

Porphyria variegata has many features in common with acute intermittent porphyria. It is also inherited as a dominant characteristic and manifests only after puberty. It is distinguished clinically by the occurrence of *skin lesions*. The main features are:

1. *Acute attacks* which occur more commonly in females. The attacks are similar to those of acute intermittent porphyria, namely abdominal or neurological symptoms, or both, and may be precipitated by the same drugs.

2. *Skin lesions* are seen more commonly in males and range in severity from annoying photosensitivity to blistering and scarring of the skin in exposed areas, notably the backs of the hands.

There is often increased skin pigmentation and, in women, facial hirsutism.

As in acute intermittent porphyria the main danger of the condition lies in administration of certain drugs. The authors have seen patients in these two groups rendered quadriplegic, with respiratory paralysis, by the use of barbiturates during anaesthesia for exploration of the "acute abdomen".

Biochemical abnormalities and diagnosis.—The major biochemical abnormality is the *excessive excretion of porphyrins in the faeces*. This is usually the only detectable laboratory abnormality in non-symptomatic cases. During an acute attack large amounts of *ALA*, *PBG* and *porphyrins* appear in the urine, but frequently disappear as the attack subsides. Raised *faecal porphyrin*, however, persists and diagnosis of latent cases is made on this feature.

Acquired Cutaneous Hepatic Porphyria (Porphyria Cutanea Tarda Symptomatica)

Unlike all other forms of porphyria this condition is acquired. It manifests with cutaneous lesions, again in sun-exposed areas, and ranging from photosensitivity to severe blistering and scarring. Hirsutism and hyperpigmentation are common. Acute attacks such as occur in the inherited hepatic porphyrias are not seen and the drugs precipitating these are harmless. Exacerbation of skin symptoms and mild abdominal pain may, however, be seen after chloroquine administration. This is thought to be due to release of accumulated porphyrins from the liver.

The condition has several aetiologies, amongst which are:

1. *Severe liver disease*, notably alcoholic cirrhosis. This form of porphyria is not uncommon among the Bantu of South Africa.

2. *Ingestion of toxins.* An outbreak of porphyria of this type occurred in Turkey in 1955 and was traced to wheat treated with hexachlorobenzene. The pigmentation and hirsutism earned for the unfortunate victims the title of "monkey children".

Biochemical abnormalities and diagnosis.—The major abnormality is a marked increase in the excretion of porphyrin in the *urine*, mostly *uroporphyrin*. Faecal porphyrin levels are normal or only slightly raised. ALA and PBG are not found.

Hereditary Coproporphyria

Hereditary coproporphyria is a recently described entity which resembles acute intermittent porphyria except that one case had mild photosensitivity. These patients may develop the acute attacks and are sensitive to similar drugs. The condition is apparently inherited as a Mendelian dominant.

The major biochemical abnormality is a marked increase in *faecal coproporphyrin* in both the acute and latent phases. During the acute attack *ALA, PBG* and *porphyrins* are present in the *urine*.

ERYTHROPOIETIC PORPHYRIAS

This group, although spectacular, is extremely rare and will only be described briefly.

Congenital Erythropoietic Porphyria

This type of porphyria has two unique characteristics. It has a recessive mode of inheritance and the abnormality in porphyrin metabolism involves type I isomers (all others involve type III).

The condition presents at, or shortly after, birth and manifests as extreme photosensitivity. Extensive blistering with secondary infection leads to mutilation of exposed areas. The teeth (and bones) may be red due to porphyrin and fluoresce in u.v. light. Hirsutism may be present and there is a haemolytic anaemia and splenomegaly. An interesting, if fanciful, theory is that these unfortunate individuals with hairy faces and shiny teeth who only ventured forth at night (to avoid the sun) gave rise to at least some of the werewolf legends.

The main biochemical abnormality is an excess of *porphyrins of type I in urine*, faeces and red cells. The carrier state is usually undetectable by chemical tests.

Erythropoietic Protoporphyria

This condition, of dominant inheritance, is characterized by increased photosensitivity from childhood onwards. Blistering, however, does not occur and there is no anaemia. It is possible that many mild cases go undetected.

The biochemical feature is an excess of protoporphyrin in faeces and red cells. The urine is usually normal.

Neither of these last two conditions are liable to the acute attacks of the hepatic porphyrias and there is no increased excretion of the porphyrin precursors, ALA and PBG.

THE NATURE OF THE PORPHYRIAS

The nature of the defect in the porphyrias has excited much speculation. An increased activity of ALA synthetase (first step, Fig. 30) has been demonstrated in liver biopsy specimens from patients with acute intermittent porphyria and porphyria variegata; partial failure of normal feed-back suppression of this rate-limiting step by haem (see p. 323) has been postulated as the primary lesion (compare primary hyperuricaemia, p. 304). It is interesting that some of the drugs known to precipitate attacks of acute intermittent porphyria have been shown to further increase ALA synthetase activity.

Skin manifestations are almost certainly due to excessive circulating porphyrin, particularly uroporphyrin, and they can be induced by injection of these compounds. In acute intermittent porphyria only porphyrin precursors accumulate and skin lesions are absent. The substance responsible for the acute attack is not known.

OTHER CAUSES OF EXCESSIVE PORPHYRIN EXCRETION

Porphyria is not the only cause of disordered porphyrin metabolism and it is for this reason that positive screening tests should be confirmed by quantitative analysis with identification of the porphyrin present. Three conditions need to be considered.

1. *Lead poisoning* causes defects at several stages of haem synthesis and eventually produces anaemia. The *urine* contains increased amounts of *ALA* (an early and sensitive test), sometimes PBG and *coproporphyrin*. This last is used as a screening test for lead poisoning. Certain of the symptoms of lead poisoning, such as abdominal pain, are similar

TABLE XXII

The Major Clinical and Biochemical Features of the Porphyrias

	Hepatic porphyrias							Erythropoietic porphyrias	
	Acute intermittent porphyria		Porphyria variegata		Hereditary coproporphyria		Acquired cutaneous hepatic porphyria	Congenital erythropoietic porphyria	Erythropoietic protoporphyria
	acute	latent	acute	latent	acute	latent			
Clinical Features									
1. Abdominal and neurological symptoms	+	−	++	−	+	−			
2. Skin lesions	−	−	+	+	rarely	−	+	+	+
Chemical Abnormalities									
1. Urine PBG and ALA	++	+	+++	−	+	−	−	−	−
2. Urine porphyrins	+	−	+++	+	+++	−	+	++	−
3. Faecal porphyrins	−	−	+++	+	+++	+	−	+	+
	Acute attacks precipitated by drugs (barbiturates, oestrogens, sulphonamides)							Erythrocyte porphyrins increased	

to those of the acute porphyric attack, and this may cause difficulty in differential diagnosis.

2. *Liver disease* may produce an increase in *urinary coproporphyrin*, possibly due to decreased biliary excretion. Occasionally there is mild photosensitivity (in acquired cutaneous hepatic porphyria (p. 327) there are more severe skin lesions due to uroporphyrin excess).

3. *Ulcerative lesions of the upper gastro-intestinal tract* may produce raised levels of *faecal porphyrin* by degradation of haemoglobin. If there is bleeding from the lower part of the tract the haemoglobin does not have time for conversion: this may help roughly to localize the site of bleeding.

SUMMARY

1. Porphyrins are by-products of haem synthesis. ALA and PBG are precursors.

2. Screening tests for porphyrins are based on the fluorescence excited by u.v. light.

3. The porphyrias are diseases associated with disturbed porphyrin metabolism. Most are inherited. The main clinical and biochemical features are outlined in Table XXII.

4. Acute attacks with abdominal or neurological symptoms are a feature of the congenital hepatic porphyrias. Such attacks are poten tially fatal and may be provoked by a number of drugs. The diagnosis of porphyria in the acute phase depends on the demonstration of ALA, PBG and porphyrins in the urine.

5. It is important to diagnose asymptomatic cases. Screening tests may be negative and quantitative estimations are required. Both urine and faeces should be examined.

6. Other causes of abnormalities in porphyrin excretion are lead poisoning, liver disease and upper gastro-intestinal bleeding.

7. The very rare erythropoietic porphyrias show excessive red cell porphyrin.

APPENDIX TO CHAPTER XVI

The screening tests for porphyria are usually carried out in the laboratory. In areas of high incidence, such as South Africa, however, simple side-room tests should be available.

The requirements are:

1. A near ultra-violet (Wood's) lamp.

2. An extracting solvent (equal parts of ether, glacial acetic acid and amyl alcohol).

3. Ehrlich's reagent (2 per cent *p*-dimethylaminobenzaldehyde in 5N HCl).

4. *n*-Butanol.

(a) Test for Porphobilinogen

(i) Equal parts of *fresh* urine and Ehrlich's reagent are mixed. If PBG is present a red colour develops.

(ii) If a red colour develops, 3 ml of *n*-butanol is added, the tube shaken and the phases allowed to separate. If the red colour does not enter the butanol (upper layer) it is PBG.

It is important to use *fresh* urine as PBG disappears on standing. A number of other substances, especially urobilinogen, may also give a red colour with Ehrlich's reagent. All such known substances are, however, extracted into the butanol layer.

(b) Test for Porphyrins

(i) **Urine.**—About 10 ml of urine is mixed with 2 ml of the porphyrin extracting solvent (item (2)) and the phases allowed to separate. A red fluorescence in the upper layer under u.v. light indicates the presence of porphyrin.

(ii) **Faeces.**—A pea-sized piece of faeces is mixed into 2 ml of the solvent. A red fluorescence under u.v. light denotes either porphyrin or chlorophyll (with a similar structure and derived from the diet). These may be distinguished by adding 1·5 N HCl which extracts porphyrin but not chlorophyll.

Chapter XVII

INBORN ERRORS OF METABOLISM

GENERAL DISCUSSION

THE chemical make-up of an individual is determined by the 20,000–40,000 gene pairs transmitted from generation to generation on the chromosomes. Random selection and recombination during meiosis, as well as occasional mutation, introduce individual variations. Such variations may at one extreme be incompatible with life or, at the other, produce biochemical differences detectable only by special techniques, if at all. In the latter category are the genetic variations of plasma proteins such as the transferrins or haptoglobins: such differences are useful in population and inheritance studies but do not necessarily impair function. Between the two extremes there are many variations that do produce functional abnormalities. It is to these variations that the term "inborn errors of metabolism" applies.

Because the sequence of bases making up the DNA strands in the genes codes, via RNA, for protein structure, it is not surprising that most, if not all, inherited biochemical abnormalities can be explained by defective synthesis of a single protein. This abnormality may occur in structural proteins, such as in the abnormal globins of the haemoglobinopathies, or in an enzyme, in which case chemically detectable metabolic consequences may result. The abnormality in the protein may be quantitative or qualitative: the haemoglobinopathies and cholinesterase variants fall, at least partly, into the latter group.

Deficiency of a single enzyme in a metabolic chain may produce its effects in several ways. Let us suppose that substance A is acted on by enzyme X to produce substance B, and that substance C is on an alternative pathway.

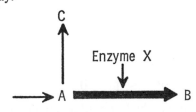

1. The effect may be due to deficiency of the products of the enzyme reaction, B. Examples of this are cortisol deficiency in congenital adrenal

hyperplasia (p. 104), and the hypoglycaemia of some forms of glycogen storage disease (p. 148).

2. The effect may be due to the accumulation of the substance acted on by the enzyme (A) (for instance galactose-1-phosphate in galacto-saemia, p. 343).

3. If a substance cannot be metabolized by the normal route because of an enzyme deficiency it may pass through an alternative pathway, and some product of the latter may produce effects (C). The virilization due to androgens in congenital adrenal hyperplasia falls into this group.

The effects of the last two types of abnormality will be aggravated if the whole metabolic pathway is controlled by feed-back from the final product. For instance, in congenital adrenal hyperplasia, cortisol deficiency stimulates steroid synthesis and the accumulation of andro-gens, with consequent virilization, is accentuated.

The clinical effects of some inborn errors are evident only in artificial situations. Patients with cholinesterase variants develop prolonged paralysis only if succinylcholine is administered during anaesthesia, and in some subjects with glucose-6-phosphate dehydrogenase defi-ciency haemolysis occurs only if they ingest drugs such as primaquine. Such cases appear "normal" without the intervention of modern therapeutics.

CLINICAL IMPORTANCE OF INBORN ERRORS OF METABOLISM

Therapy of most inborn errors of metabolism is disappointing. There is no way of replacing deficient enzymes, and management is usually based either on reducing the intake of the substance (or its precursor) which cannot be metabolized (for instance, the milk-free diet of galacto-saemia), or by replacing the missing end product of the pathway, such as cortisol in congenital adrenal hyperplasia. The recognition of many inborn errors of metabolism is of academic interest only, either because the abnormality produces no clinical effect, or because no effective treatment is available. However, there is a group of such diseases in which recognition in early infancy is vital, since *treatment may prevent irreversible clinical consequences or death.* Some of the most important of these are:

Phenylketonuria (p. 340).
Galactosaemia (p. 343).
Maple syrup urine disease (p. 340).

Examples of conditions which should be sought *in relatives of affected atients,* either because *further ill effects may be prevented,* or because a *recipitating factor should be avoided,* are:

Cholinesterase abnormalities (p. 295).
Glucose-6-phosphate dehydrogenase deficiency (p. 344).
Acute intermittent porphyria (p. 326) and porphyria variegata.
Haemochromatosis (p. 317).
Cystinuria (p. 338).
Wilson's disease (p. 345).

Other conditions can be *treated symptomatically*. Examples are:

Hereditary nephrogenic diabetes insipidus (p. 40).
Congenital disaccharidase deficiency (p. 217).

Some inborn errors of metabolism are completely, or almost completely, harmless. Their importance lies in the fact that they produce *effects which may lead to misdiagnosis* or which may alarm the patient. Examples of these are:

Renal glycosuria (p. 150).
Alkaptonuria (p. 343).
Gilbert's disease (p. 277).

Finally, the clinical effects of some inborn errors of metabolism may not appear until after reaching child-bearing age, and in these cases *genetic counselling* of relatives is desirable. An example of this type of disease may be:

Wilson's disease (p. 345).

It is important to consider the possibility of inborn errors in any case of "failure to thrive" in infancy, or in any bizarre chemical picture in childhood. Notice should be taken of any unusual smell or staining of the napkins, since conditions such as maple syrup urine disease have drawn attention to themselves by such features. In such cases consultation between clinical and laboratory staff may help to elucidate the cause.

PATTERNS OF INHERITANCE

Inheritance of any characteristic by an individual depends on transmittance of the gene coding for that characteristic from one or both of the parents.

1. Let us suppose that one parent (parent 1 in the example below) carries an "abnormal" gene (A). Each parent carries two genes for any characteristic, each of which combines with one of the two from the other parent. If N is a normal gene, the possible gene combinations in the offspring are shown in the square.

Parent 2
N   N

Parent 1 A	*AN*	*AN*
N	NN	NN

It will be seen that, on a *statistical basis,* half the offspring will carry one abnormal gene (AN): they are *heterozygotes* for this gene, like Parent 1. None will carry two abnormal genes (homozygotes).

2. Similarly, if both parents are heterozygous, a quarter of the offspring (in a large series) will be homozygous (AA) and half heterozygous.

Parent 2
A   N

Parent 1 A	*AA*	*AN*
N	*AN*	NN

3. If one parent is homozygous and the other "normal" all offspring would be heterozygotes.

Since most genes producing clinical abnormalities are rare, example 1 above has the highest statistical likelihood. With consanguineous marriages example 2 becomes more probable, since blood relatives are more likely to carry the same abnormal genes than two people mating at random.

The *consequences* of the carriage of the abnormal gene depend on the potency of the "abnormal" gene compared to that of the normal one.

A *dominant* gene produces the abnormality in heterozygotes and homozygotes alike. Thus, in example 1, Parent 1 and half the offspring would be affected, and in example 2, both parents and 75 per cent of the offspring would be affected. Some genes are incompletely dominant and may be passed on by an apparently unaffected subject (an example is porphyria variegata).

A *recessive* gene produces the abnormality only in homozygous individuals. Thus, in example 1, neither parents nor offspring would be affected, and in example 2 the parents would appear normal but 25 per cent of the offspring would be affected.

Although the *disease* may only appear in homozygotes (i.e. have a recessive mode of inheritance), chemical tests may detect lesser abnormalities in heterozygotes. In some diseases of "dominant" inheritance the homozygote is more severely affected than the heterozygote. The terms "dominant" and "recessive" are obviously relative ones.

Because, as has been pointed out above, many genes producing clinical effects are recessive in nature, it is obvious that clinical consequences are most likely as the result of consanguineous marriages.

Sex-linked Inheritance

The modes of inheritance so far discussed are known as *autosomal*. Some abnormal genes are carried only on the sex chromosomes; this is almost always the X chromosome. No Y linked disease is known.

X linked recessive inheritance.—Females carry two X chromosomes and males one X and one Y. In X linked recessive inheritance an abnormal X chromosome (Xa) is latent when combined with a normal X chromosome, but active when combined with a Y. If the mother carries Xa she will appear to be normal, but, statistically, half the sons would be affected (YXa). Half the daughters would be carriers (XXa), but all daughters would appear clinically normal.

```
                       Mother
                     Xa      X
        Father  X |  XXa    XX  |←Daughters
                Y |  YXa    YX  |←Sons
```

If the father is affected and the mother carries two normal genes, none of the sons will be affected, but all daughters will be carriers.

```
                       Mother
                      X       X
        Father  Xa |  XXa    XXa |←Daughters
                Y  |  XY     XY  |←Sons
```

Inherited disease manifesting only in male offspring, but carried by females, is typical of X linked recessive inheritance. The female is only clinically affected in the extremely rare circumstance when she is homozygous for the abnormal gene. This would require mating between an affected father and carrier mother.

Haemophilia is the classical example of X linked recessive inheritance.

X linked dominant inheritance.—In this type of inheritance both XXa and YXa (males and females) are affected. An example is familial hypophosphataemia (p. 187).

DISEASES DUE TO INBORN ERRORS OF METABOLISM

It is impossible and unnecessary in a book of this size to discuss all the known inborn errors of metabolism: many new ones are being described each year. Selection must be biased by what the authors feel to be important, and others might disagree. On p. 334 some of the more clinically important abnormalities have been listed, and in the Appendix a fuller (but by no means complete) list is included under systematic headings; this includes the mode of inheritance, where known. Many of these conditions have been mentioned briefly in the relevant chapters. A few remain, which the authors feel to be of relative importance.

AMINOACIDURIA

Amino-acids are normally filtered at the glomerulus, and reach the proximal renal tubule at concentrations equal to those in plasma: almost all are actively reabsorbed at this site. Aminoaciduria may therefore be of two types:

1. *Overflow aminoaciduria* in which, because of raised blood levels, amino-acids reach the proximal tubule at concentrations higher than the reabsorptive capacity of the cells.

2. *Renal aminoaciduria* in which plasma levels are low because of urinary loss due to defective tubular reabsorption.

Non-specific aminoaciduria, whether overflow or renal in type, is almost always due to an acquired lesion, such as failure of deamination of all amino-acids in acute or subacute hepatic necrosis with consequent raised plasma levels, or non-specific proximal tubular damage from any cause (p. 12). In the latter, known as the *Fanconi syndrome*, other substances also reabsorbed in the proximal tubule are lost in excessive amounts (phosphoglucoaminoaciduria): its occurrence in inborn errors of metabolism is much more commonly due to secondary tubular damage by the substance not metabolized normally (for instance, copper in Wilson's disease) than to a direct primary genetic defect. Acquired lesions will not be discussed further in this chapter.

Excessive excretion of a *specific pattern* of amino-acids, whether overflow or renal, is almost always due to a genetic defect.

RENAL AMINOACIDURIA DUE TO INHERITED ABNORMALITIES OF TRANSPORT MECHANISMS

Groups of chemically similar amino-acids are often reabsorbed in the renal tubule by a single mechanism. In several cases similar group-specific mechanisms are involved in intestinal absorption and defects involve both the renal tubule and intestinal mucosa. Inborn errors involving the following group pathways have been identified:

(*a*) The dibasic amino-acids (with two amino and one carboxyl group), cystine, ornithine, arginine and lysine (COAL is a useful mnemonic) (cystinuria).

(*b*) Many neutral amino-acids (with one amino and one carboxyl group) (Hartnup disease).

(*c*) The imino-acids, proline and hydroxyproline, probably shared with glycine (glycine iminoaciduria).

In this chapter we shall discuss cystinuria and Hartnup disease.

Cystinuria

Cystinuria is due to an inherited abnormality of tubular reabsorption the dibasic amino-acids, cystine, ornithine, arginine and lysine, resulting in excessive urinary excretion of these four amino-acids. A similar transport defect is present in the intestinal mucosa, but, although cystine absorption is diminished, failure of renal tubular re-absorption results in a high urinary excretion of the endogenously produced amino-acid.

Many cases of cystinuria are asymptomatic, Cystine is non-toxic, but is relatively insoluble and the danger is due to its precipitation in the renal tract. The solubility of cystine is such that only in homozygotes do urinary concentrations reach levels at which precipitation and stone formation may occur, although increased excretion can be demonstrated in heterozygotes.

The *diagnosis* of cystinuria is made by the demonstration of excessive urinary excretion of cystine and the other characteristic amino-acids. The demonstration of the latter is necessary to distinguish the stone-forming homozygote from heterozygous cystine-lysinurias and from cystinuria occurring as part of a generalized aminoaciduria.

The management of cystinuria is aimed at the prevention of calculi by a high fluid intake. The risk may be further reduced by administration of penicillamine, which results in the excretion of a more soluble product.

The relatively harmless condition described above must not be confused with *cystinosis*. This is a very rare inherited disorder of cystine metabolism characterized by accumulation of intracellular cystine in many tissues. In the kidney this produces tubular damage and consequently the Fanconi syndrome. The amino-aciduria is non-specific and of renal origin. Death occurs at an early age.

Hartnup Disease

Hartnup disease, named after the first-described patient, is a rare but interesting disorder in which there is a renal and intestinal transport defect involving neutral amino-acids.

As in cystinuria the defect is present in both the proximal renal tubule and the intestinal mucosa. Most, if not all, the clinical manifestations can be ascribed to the reduced intestinal absorption and increased urinary loss of tryptophane. The amino-acid is normally partly converted to nicotinamide, this source being especially important if the dietary intake of nicotinamide is marginal (p. 358). The clinical features of Hartnup disease are intermittent and resemble those of pellagra, namely:

1. A red, scaly rash on exposed areas of skin.
2. Reversible cerebellar ataxia.
3. Mental confusion of variable degree.

The thesis that nicotinamide deficiency is the cause of the clinical picture is supported by the response to administration of the vitamin and the fact that the features of the disease are frequently preceded by a period of dietary inadequacy.

In spite of the generalized defect of amino-acid absorption protein malnutrition is not seen: this may possibly be due to absorption of intact peptides by a different pathway.

An associated chemical feature is the excretion of excessive amounts of *indole* compounds in the urine. These originate in the gut from the action of bacteria on the unabsorbed tryptophane.

Hartnup disease has a recessive mode of inheritance.

Diagnosis is made by demonstrating the characteristic amino-acid pattern in the urine. Heterozygotes are not detectable by present techniques.

Overflow Aminoaciduria

Excessive excretion of specific amino-acids due to high blood levels occurs in a variety of inborn errors of amino-acid metabolism. Maple syrup urine disease will be described briefly here.

Maple Syrup Urine Disease

In maple syrup urine disease there is deficient decarboxylation of the three *branched-chain amino-acids,* leucine, isoleucine and valine. These accumulate in the blood and are excreted in the urine together with their corresponding oxoacids. The odour of the urine, which resembles that of maple syrup, gives the disease its name.

The disease presents in the first week of life and, if untreated, severe neurological lesions develop with death in a few weeks or months. If, on the other hand, the condition is recognized and a diet low in branched-chain amino-acids is given, normal development seems possible.

Diagnosis is made by demonstrating the excessive excretion of branched-chain amino-acids in blood and urine.

The condition has a recessive mode of inheritance.

Disorders of Aromatic Amino-Acid Metabolism

The main chemical reactions of this pathway are outlined in Fig. 31, together with the sites of known enzyme defects. It will be seen that *tyrosine,* normally produced in the body from phenylalanine, is the precursor of several important substances.

The inherited defects in thyroid synthesis are considered on p. 161.

Phenylketonuria

This condition, if untreated, leads to mental retardation. Extensive screening of newborns is carried out in many countries to detect early cases. The problems arising from such surveys are discussed later.

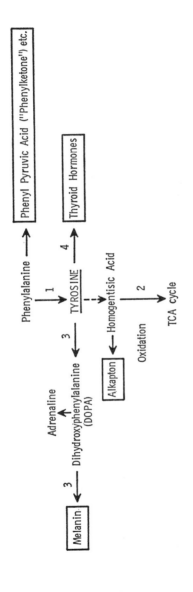

FIG. 31.—Some inborn errors of the aromatic amino-acid pathway.

Squares indicate some of the substances detectable in abnormal amounts in the diseases discussed

Enzyme Affected

1. Phenylalanine Hydroxylase (Phenylketonuria)

2. Homogentisic acid oxidase (Alkaptonuria)

3. Tyrosinase (Albinism)

4. Thyroid enzymes (Thyroid Dyshormonogenesis)

The clinical features of established phenylketonuria are:

1. Irritability, feeding problems, vomiting and fits in the first few weeks of life.

2. Mental retardation developing at 4–6 months with unusual psychomotor irritability.

3. Generalized eczema in many cases.

4. A tendency to reduced melanin formation. Many patients have a pale skin, fair hair and blue eyes.

The abnormality in phenylketonuria is a deficiency of the enzyme *phenylalanine hydroxylase*. Phenylalanine accumulates in the blood and is excreted in the urine together with its derivatives, such as phenylpyruvic acid: the disease acquires its name from the recognition of this (phenylketone) in the urine. The cerebral damage is thought to be due to the high circulating levels of phenylalanine or one of its metabolites.

Diagnosis.—1. The phenylalanine concentration may be measured in blood taken from a heel-prick. The technique is suitable for mass screening and tests are best performed in special centres. Phenylalanine may be estimated chemically, or, more often, by its effects on the growth of *B. subtilis* on special media (*Guthrie test*). The timing of the test is critical. If performed too early when the infant is on a low protein intake, phenylalanine levels may be low: however, early detection is important if treatment is to be successful. It is recommended that tests be performed 6–10 days after birth (just before the infant leaves hospital). A possible cause of false negative results by the Guthrie test is the presence of antibiotics in the blood sample.

2. Detection of phenylpyruvic acid in the urine with *ferric chloride or Phenistix* (Ames) is the classical method of detecting phenylketonuria. This test may only be positive after about six weeks when phenylalanine levels are very high. Since at this stage the infant has been discharged from hospital and possibly lost to the screening programme, measurement of blood phenylalanine levels is now the recommended procedure.

Since the introduction of screening tests it has become apparent that raised blood levels of phenylalanine occur in other conditions than phenylketonuria, particularly in premature babies, when it is possibly due to delayed maturation of enzyme systems. These cases may be distinguished by repeated blood testing and by estimation of blood tyrosine levels (not raised in phenylketonuria, but raised in many of the other cases). More puzzling is the discovery of a number of children with blood phenylalanine levels in the phenylketonuric range but without apparent mental retardation. The reason for this is unknown.

Management.—The aim of management is the reduction of blood phenylalanine levels and to this end a low phenylalanine diet is prescribed. Such treatment is difficult, expensive and tedious for the patient and parents, and requires careful biochemical monitoring of blood phenylalanine levels. Tyrosine must be included in the diet as it is the precursor of many important metabolites (Fig. 31).

Alkaptonuria

An inherited (probably recessive) deficiency of *homogentisic acid oxidase* results in alkaptonuria. Homogentisic acid accumulates in blood, tissues and urine. Oxidation and polymerization of this substance produces the pigment "alkapton", in much the same way as polymerization of DOPA (see Fig. 31) produces melanin. Deposition of alkapton in cartilages, with consequent darkening, is called *ochronosis*: this may cause arthritis in later life and may be clinically visible as darkening of the ears. Conversion of homogentisic acid to "alkapton" is speeded up in alkaline conditions and the most obvious abnormality in alkaptonuria is passage of urine which is black, or which darkens as it becomes more alkaline on standing. The condition is often first noticed by the mother who is worried by the black nappies, which only become blacker when washed in alkaline soaps or detergents. The condition is compatible with a normal life span and treatment is unnecessary, but arthritis in middle and later life is common. Homogentisic acid is a reducing substance and reacts with Benedict's solution or Clinitest tablets.

Albinism

A deficiency of *tyrosinase* in melanocytes causes albinism. Several forms, generalized and localized, are recognized. Generalized albinism is inherited as a recessive character. The patient lacks pigment in skin, hair and iris (the eyes appear pink) and the condition is especially striking in negroes. Acute photosensitivity occurs because of pigment lack in the skin and iris.

DISORDERS OF CARBOHYDRATE METABOLISM

Many of the inborn errors of carbohydrate metabolism have been discussed in Chapter VI. Only galactosaemia will be discussed here.

Galactosaemia

Galactosaemia results from the inability to convert galactose to glucose-1-phosphate. The normal pathway is shown in a simplified form in Fig. 32 and the site of the "block" is indicated. Deficiency of the enzyme *galactose-1-phosphate uridyl transferase* results in accumulation of galactose-1-phosphate intracellularly. This accumulation may be the cause of many of the clinical manifestations.

The condition becomes apparent only after milk has been added to the infant's diet. The main features are:

1. Vomiting and diarrhoea with failure to thrive.
2. Hepatomegaly leading to jaundice and cirrhosis.
3. Cataract formation.
4. Mental retardation.
5. Renal tubular damage (Fanconi syndrome).
6. Hypoglycaemia.

Blood galactose levels are raised and galactose in the urine is a cause of a positive reaction with Benedict's solution or Clinitest tablets. This feature is dependent on ingestion of galactose and may be absent if the subject is not receiving milk. Tubular damage may result in generalized aminoaciduria.

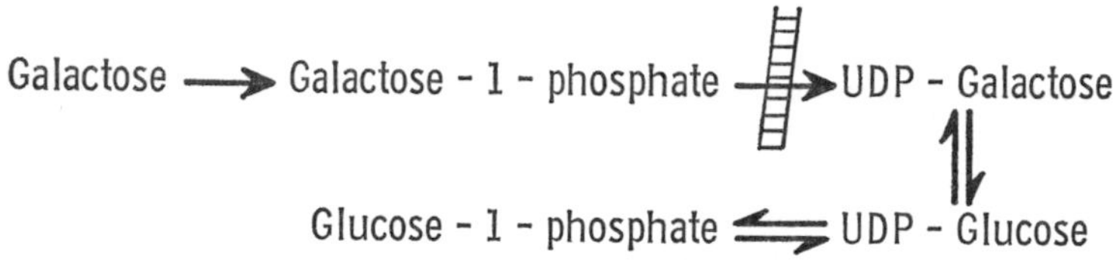

Galactose ⟶ Galactose - 1 - phosphate ⟶ UDP - Galactose

Glucose - 1 - phosphate ⇄ UDP - Glucose

FIG. 32.—Site of enzyme defect in galactosaemia.

The *diagnosis* is made by identifying the urinary sugar as galactose by paper chromatography and by demonstrating a deficiency of galactose-1-phosphate uridyl transferase in the erythrocytes. The latter test should be done on cord blood in all newborn infants with affected siblings.

Treatment is removal of milk and milk products from the diet. As with many diseases due to inborn errors, the condition frequently improves as the child grows older. This may be due to the development of an alternative metabolic pathway. Galactosaemia is inherited as a recessive. It is less common than phenylketonuria.

DISORDERS OF ERYTHROCYTE METABOLISM

Haemolytic Conditions

The erythrocyte derives its energy requirements solely from glycolysis. A number of inherited enzyme defects of the glycolytic pathway, such as that of *pyruvate kinase*, that manifest as haemolytic anaemia (congenital non-spherocytic haemolytic anaemia) has been described.

Another form of haemolytic anaemia is seen with deficiency of *glucose-6-phosphate dehydrogenase* (*G-6-PD*). This is the first enzyme in the hexose monophosphate shunt (p. 127) and is required for the formation of NADPH. This, in turn, is probably essential for the maintenance of an intact red cell membrane. Numerous variants of G-6-PD deficiency have been described. In many cases haemolysis is precipitated by drugs, notably certain antimalarial drugs, such as primaquine, sulphonamides and vitamin K analogues.

For further details of this interesting group of enzyme defects the reader is referred to haematology textbooks.

Methaemoglobinaemia.—The iron in both reduced and oxyhaemoglobin is normally in the ferrous form; carriage of oxygen involves its trapping in the haemoglobin molecule, not oxidation of iron. If the iron is converted to the ferric form oxygen carrying power is diminished.

Maintenance of 99 per cent of haemoglobin iron in the divalent form, despite its continuous auto-oxidation, depends on two pathways: both are enzymatic, the enzymes being *methaemoglobin reductases* (diaphorases). Methaemoglobin reductase I requires NADH as coenzyme, and normally this is by far the most important pathway. NADPH is required for the action of methaemoglobin reductase II, and this pathway is activated by reducing agents such as methylene blue and ascorbic acid.

Most cases of methaemoglobinaemia are acquired. Rare cases are associated with an inherited defect of *methaemoglobin reductase* I and administration of methylene blue or ascorbic acid, by activating the reductase II, can temporarily relieve the condition. A second type of methaemoglobinaemia is really a haemoglobinopathy and is due to an abnormality in the globin of haemoglobin; it is not affected by reducing agents. In either case the patient presents with cyanosis of an atypical hue, and withdrawn blood does not turn bright red if oxygen is bubbled through it.

For further details students should consult textbooks of haematology.

INHERITED DEFICIENCIES OF CARRIER PROTEINS

Many hormones and trace metals are carried in the blood stream bound to albumin or to a specific carrier protein. Deficiencies of transferrin (p. 317) and of thyroxine-binding globulin (p. 168) have been mentioned. Caeruloplasmin deficiency is seen in Wilson's disease.

Wilson's Disease (Hepatolenticular Degeneration)

Wilson's disease is an inherited condition characterized by excessive deposition of copper in the basal ganglia of the brain, liver, renal tubules and the eye. These accumulations produce:

1. Neurological symptoms due to basal ganglia degeneration.
2. Liver damage leading to cirrhosis.
3. Renal tubular damage with any or all of the biochemical features of this condition, including aminoaciduria (Fanconi syndrome).
4. Kayser–Fleischer ring at the edge of the cornea due to copper deposition in Descemet's membrane.

Like haemochromatosis this disease does not usually present clinically in childhood, but the condition should always be sought in "idiopathic" cirrhosis in children. Cirrhosis may be present without the neurological abnormalities. Some cases only develop clinical symptoms in early adult life, often after childbearing, and for this reason genetic counselling of relatives is necessary.

The basic defect in Wilson's disease is unknown. Most cases show a reduced concentration of the copper-binding protein *caeruloplasmin* in the plasma. This may possibly allow increased passage of free copper into the tissues. However, cases occur with normal levels of apparently normal caeruloplasmin, and in most patients there is poor correlation between the levels of the protein and the severity of the disease. A low concentration of caeruloplasmin remains, however, one of the diagnostic features of the disease. Other biochemical abnormalities noted in Wilson's disease include low plasma copper levels and increased urinary copper excretion, as well as those produced by the cirrhosis and renal tubular damage. Copper concentrations in liver biopsy specimens are high.

The clinical condition has a recessive mode of inheritance but heterozygotes may also have reduced caeruloplasmin levels. Distinction between presymptomatic homozygotes and heterozygotes is important as the former require treatment.

In some cases a liver biopsy may be necessary for the diagnosis. In assessing caeruloplasmin concentration it is important to remember that *low levels* may also occur in the nephrotic syndrome due to non-specific protein loss and during the first few months of life. *Raised levels* are seen with active liver disease (this may account for some "normal" levels in patients with Wilson's disease), in the last trimester of pregnancy and in persons taking oral contraceptives.

Treatment with agents chelating copper, such as penicillamine, is aimed at reducing tissue copper concentration.

SUMMARY

1. Inborn errors of metabolism are diseases due to inherited defects of protein synthesis. Most of those presenting with clinical symptoms are due to abnormalities of enzyme synthesis.

2. Inborn errors of metabolism may produce no clinical effects, may only produce them under certain circumstances (for example, cholinesterase variants) or, at the other extreme, may produce severe disease. Some are incompatible with life.

3. Recognition of some inherited abnormalities is of academic interest only. Diagnosis is important if the condition is serious but treatable, if

precipitating factors can be avoided or if confusion with other diseases is possible.

4. Inheritance may be autosomal or sex-linked, dominant or recessive. In diseases producing severe clinical effects inheritance is most commonly autosomal recessive, and they are most common in the offspring of consanguineous marriages.

5. In many cases in which the clinical disease is inherited in a recessive manner, lesser degrees of the abnormality can be detected by chemical testing.

6. Some inborn errors of metabolism not mentioned elsewhere in the book are discussed in this chapter.

FURTHER READING

CARTER, C. O. (1969). *An ABC of Medical Genetics.* Reprinted from *The Lancet,* May 17th to June 29th.

STANBURY, J. B., WYNGAARDEN, J. B., and FREDRICKSON, D. S., Eds. (1966). *The Metabolic Basis of Inherited Disease,* 2nd edit. New York: McGraw-Hill Book Co.

APPENDIX TO CHAPTER XVII

The following list of inborn errors of metabolism is far from complete. It is meant for reference only, and the student should not attempt to learn it. Most of the abnormalities have been discussed in this book, and a page reference is given. Where it is known the mode of inheritance is given, unless the heading applies to a group of diseases of different modes in inheritance.

D = Autosomal Dominant
R = Autosomal Recessive
X linked D = X linked Dominant
X linked R = X linked Recessive

	Inheritance	Page
I. DISORDERS OF CELLULAR TRANSPORT
Most of these are recognized as renal tubular transport defects, and in some defective intestinal transport can also be demonstrated.		
Generalized Proximal Tubular Transport
Phosphoglucoaminoaciduria	?	338
Amino-Acids
Dibasic amino-acids—Cystinuria	R	338
Neutral amino-acids—Hartnup disease	R	339
Glucose
Renal glycosuria	D	150
Water (Failure to Respond to ADH)
Hereditary nephrogenic diabetes insipidus	X linked R	40
Sodium (Failure to Respond to Aldosterone)
Pseudo-Addison's disease	?	42
Potassium (all cells)
Familial periodic paralysis	D	49
Calcium (Failure to Respond to PTH)
Pseudohypoparathyroidism	X linked D	184
Phosphate
Familial hypophosphataemia	X linked D	187
Hydrogen Ion
Renal tubular acidosis	D	72
Bilirubin (Liver Cells)
Congenital hyperbilirubinaemias	—	277

	Inheritance	Page
II. DISORDERS OF AMINO-ACID METABOLISM		
Aromatic Amino-Acids		
Phenylketonuria	R	340
Alkaptonuria	R	343
Albinism	R	343
Thyroid dyshormonogenesis	All R	161
Sulphur Amino-Acids		
Cystinosis	R	339
Branched Chain Amino-Acids		
Maple syrup urine disease	R	340
III. DISORDERS OF CARBOHYDRATE METABOLISM		
Glycogen storage diseases	R	148
Galactosaemia	R	343
Hereditary fructose intolerance	R	145
Essential pentosuria	R	150
Essential fructosuria	R	150
Diabetes mellitus	?	133
IV. ABNORMALITIES OF PLASMA PROTEINS		
Immunoglobulin deficiencies	—	245
Lipoprotein abnormalities	All R	259
Carrier protein abnormalities		
Transferrin	?R	317
Thyroxine binding globulin deficiency	X linked	168
Wilson's disease	R	345
Cholinesterase variants	R	295
V. ERYTHROCYTE ABNORMALITIES		
Haemoglobinopathies (see haematology texts)		—
Glucose-6-phosphate dehydrogenase deficiency	X linked	344
Methaemoglobinaemia		
Methaemoglobin reductase 1 deficiency	R	345
VI. DISORDERS OF PORPHYRIN AND IRON METABOLISM		
Porphyrias	—	323
Haemochromatosis	?	317
VII. DISORDERS OF STEROID METABOLISM		
Congenital adrenal hyperplasias	All R	104
VIII. DISORDERS OF PURINE METABOLISM		
Primary gout	?	303
Xanthinuria	? R	306
Lesch-Nyhan syndrome	? X linked R	304

	Inheritance	Page
IX. DISORDERS OF DIGESTION		
Disaccharidase deficiencies	R	217
Cystic fibrosis of the pancreas	R	211
X. DISORDERS OF OXALATE METABOLISM		
Primary hyperoxaluria	? R	20

Chapter XVIII

VITAMINS

VITAMINS, like protein, carbohydrate and fat, are organic compounds which are essential dietary constituents (the name "vitamines" originally meant amines necessary for life): unlike most other constituents they are required only in very small quantities. They must be taken in the diet because the body either cannot synthesize them at all or, under normal circumstances, not in sufficient amounts for its requirements: vitamin D, for instance, can be synthesized in the skin under the influence of ultraviolet light, but in temperate climates the amount of sunlight is insufficient to provide the required amount, while in hot countries the inhabitants tend to avoid the sun.

A normal mixed diet contains adequate quantities of vitamins and deficiencies are rarely seen in affluent populations except in those with intestinal malabsorption, in those on unsupplemented artificial diets, or in food faddists. Vitamin supplementation of a normal diet is unnecessary. Some vitamins (notably A and D) produce toxic effects if taken in excess.

The biochemical function of many vitamins is now understood, but it is not always easy to relate this knowledge to the clinical picture seen in deficiency states.

CLASSIFICATION OF VITAMINS

In 1913 McCollum and Davis first showed that two growth factors are required for normal health, one being fat soluble and the other water soluble. Since then each of these two groups has been shown to consist of many compounds, but classification can still be made on the basis of this solubility. The distinction is important clinically, because steatorrhoea is associated with deficiency of fat soluble vitamins, but with relatively little clinical evidence of lack of most water soluble vitamins (the exception being vitamin B_{12} and folate, p. 214).

FAT SOLUBLE VITAMINS

The fat soluble vitamins are:

A
D
K
(E)

Each of these has more than one active chemical form, but variations in structure are very slight, and in the following discussion we will refer to each vitamin as a single substance.

VITAMIN A

Source of Vitamin A

Precursors of vitamin A (the carotenes) are found in the yellow and green parts of plants and are especially abundant in carrots: for this reason this vegetable has the reputation of improving night vision, but it is doubtful if it has any effect on a subject eating a normal diet. The vitamin is formed by hydrolysis of the β carotene molecule, each of these producing a possible total of two molecules of vitamin A. In the body this hydrolysis occurs in the intestinal mucosa, but the yield of vitamin is much below the theoretical one, especially in children in whom a source of the vitamin itself is essential. The vitamin is stored in animal tissues, particularly in the liver, and these are the only source of pre-formed vitamin A.

Stability of Vitamin A

Vitamin A is rapidly destroyed by ultraviolet light and should be ept in dark containers.

Function of Vitamin A

1. Vitamin A is essential for normal *mucopolysaccharide synthesis* and deficiency causes drying up of mucus secreting epithelium.

2. The *retinal pigment*, rhodopsin (visual purple), is necessary for vision in dim light (scotopic vision). Rhodopsin consists of a protein (opsin) combined with vitamin A. In bright light rhodopsin is broken down. It is partly regenerated in the dark, but, because this regeneration is not complete, vitamin A is needed to maintain the levels in the retina. The complete cycle is complex. Vitamin A deficiency is associated with poor vision in dim light, especially if the eye has recently been exposed to bright light.

Clinical Effects of Vitamin A Deficiency

The clinical effects of vitamin A deficiency are:
"Night blindness".
Drying and metaplasia of ectodermal tissues.
Xerosis conjunctivae and xerophthalmia. Keratomalacia.
?Follicular hyperkeratosis.
"Night blindness".—In vitamin A deficiency the rate of light adaptation can be shown to be reduced, although it is uncommon for the patient to complain of this.

Xerosis conjunctivae and xerophthalmia.—The conjunctivae and cornea become dry and wrinkled with squamous metaplasia of the epithelium and keratinization of the tissue, resulting from deficiency of mucus secretion. *Bitot's spots*, seen in more advanced cases, are elevated white patches found in the conjunctivae and composed of keratin debris. If deficiency continues keratomalacia occurs with ulceration and infection and consequent scarring of the cornea, causing blindness. Keratomalacia is an important cause of blindness in the world as a whole.

Squamous metaplasia occurs in other epithelial tissues. Skin secretion is diminished, and hyperkeratosis of hair follicles may be seen (*follicular hyperkeratosis*): these dry horny papules, varying in size from a pinhead to quarter-inch diameter, are seen mainly on the extensor surfaces of the thighs and forearms. It is not certain if follicular hyperkeratosis is directly due to vitamin A deficiency.

Squamous metaplasia of the bronchial epithelium has also been reported and may be associated with a tendency to chest infection.

Causes of Vitamin A Deficiency

Hepatic stores of vitamin A are so large that clinical signs only develop after a year or more of dietary deficiency.

Deficiency is very rare in affluent communities. In steatorrhoea overt clinical evidence is rarely seen, but blood levels have been shown to be low. By contrast, deficiency is relatively common in underdeveloped countries, especially in children, and is a common cause of blindness.

Laboratory Diagnosis of Vitamin A Deficiency

This depends on the demonstration of low blood vitamin A levels.

Treatment of Vitamin A Deficiency

In treatment of xerophthalmia doses of 50,000 to 75,000 international units of vitamin A in fish liver oil should be given. Response to treatment of "night blindness" and of early retinal and corneal changes is very rapid. Once corneal scarring has occurred blindness is irreversible.

Hypervitaminosis A

Vitamin A in large doses is toxic. Acute intoxication has been reported in Arctic regions as a result of eating polar bear liver, which has a very high vitamin A content, but a more common cause is overdosage with vitamin preparations: the symptoms of acute poisoning are nausea and vomiting, abdominal pain, drowsiness and headache. In chronic hypervitaminosis A there is fatigue, insomnia and bone pains, and loss of hair with desquamation and pigmentation of the skin.

VITAMIN D (CALCIFEROL)

Source of Vitamin D

Vitamin D, like vitamin A, is stored in animal liver and fish liver oils are rich in this factor.

There are various chemical forms of vitamin D, all of which are derived from sterols by opening of the B ring. In the skin 7-dehydro-cholesterol can be converted by ultraviolet light to vitamin D_3 (Fig. 33), and artificial ultraviolet irradiation of ergosterol (found in yeast and green plants) produces ergocalciferol, which does not occur naturally, but which is biologically active and is used therapeutically.

Function of Vitamin D and Clinical Effects of Deficiency

Vitamin D is necessary for normal calcium metabolism and deficiency causes rickets in children and osteomalacia in adults. The subject is discussed more fully in Chapter VIII.

Causes of Vitamin D Deficiency

Liver stores of vitamin D are usually adequate for several months' needs and clinical deficiency is slow to develop. The commonest cause in affluent communities is steatorrhoea, and rickets is now rare in Britain, except in recent immigrants.

The *treatment* of vitamin D deficiency has been discussed on p. 194.

Hypervitaminosis D

Overdosage with vitamin D causes hypercalcaemia, with all its attendant dangers (p. 178). In chronic overdosage, because of increased liver stores, this may persist for several weeks after the therapy is stopped.

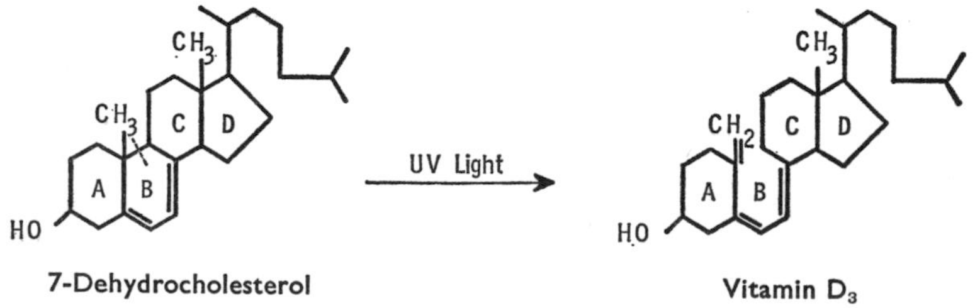

7-Dehydrocholesterol   Vitamin D_3

FIG. 33.—Formation of vitamin D in the skin.

Vitamin K

Vitamin K cannot be synthesized by man but, like many of the B vitamins, it can be manufactured by the bacterial flora of the colon: unlike them it can probably be absorbed from this site and dietary deficiency is therefore not seen. In steatorrhoea the vitamin, whether taken in the diet or produced by bacteria, cannot be normally absorbed and deficiency may occur (p. 212).

Vitamin K is necessary for prothrombin synthesis in the liver and deficiency is accompanied by a bleeding tendency with a prolonged prothrombin time. If these findings are due to deficiency of the vitamin they are cured by parenteral administration (p. 212).

Vitamin E (Tocopherols)

Vitamin E is a fat soluble vitamin. In experimental animals deficiency has been reported to cause foetal death and sterility in both sexes, and also to be related to muscular dystrophy. Deficiency has not been shown to produce clinical effects in man, and therapeutic trials for various conditions have produced disappointing results.

WATER SOLUBLE VITAMINS

The water soluble vitamins are:
The B Complex
Thiamine (Aneurine: B_1)
Riboflavin (B_2)
Nicotinamide (Pellagra Preventive (PP) factor: niacin)
Pyridoxine (B_6)
(Biotin and Pantothenic acid)
Folic Acid (Pteroylglutamic acid)
Vitamin B_{12} (Cyanocobalamin)
Ascorbic Acid (Vitamin C)

The B Complex

This group of food factors were originally lumped together in the B group (with the exception of vitamin B_{12} and folate, which were later discoveries). The biochemical function of most of them is now well understood, and they mostly act as coenzymes. It is not easy to relate the clinical findings to the underlying biochemical lesion.

Many of these vitamins are synthesized by colonic bacteria. Opinions vary as to the importance of this source in man, but since the absorption of water soluble vitamins from the large intestine is poor, most of it is probably unavailable. However, clinical deficiency is rare, especially in affluent communities. When deficiency does occur it is usually multiple, involving most of the B group and protein: for this reason it may be difficult to decide which signs and symptoms are specific for an individual vitamin and which are part of a general malnutrition syndrome.

THIAMINE

Source of Thiamine and Cause of Deficiency

Thiamine cannot be synthesized by animals: it is found in most dietary components, and wheat germ, oatmeal and yeast are particularly rich in the vitamin. Adequate amounts are present in a normal diet, but the deficiency syndrome is still prevalent in rice eating areas: polished rice has the husk removed and this is the only source of thiamine in this food. In other areas thiamine deficiency occurs most commonly in alcoholics.

Function of Thiamine

Thiamine is a component of thiamine pyrophosphate, which is an essential coenzyme for *decarboxylation of α-oxoacids* (cocarboxylase): one of these important reactions is the conversion of pyruvate to acetyl coenzyme A (acetyl CoA). In thiamine deficiency pyruvate cannot be metabolized and accumulates in the blood. Blood pyruvate levels have been used as a measure of deficiency.

Clinical Effects of Thiamine Deficiency

Deficiency of thiamine causes the syndrome known as *beri-beri*, which includes anorexia and emaciation, neurological lesions (motor and sensory polyneuropathy, Wernicke's encephalopathy), and cardiac arrhythmias. In the so-called "wet" form of the disease there is oedema, sometimes with cardiac failure. Some of these findings may be due to associated protein deficiency rather than that of thiamine.

Beri-beri can be aggravated by a high carbohydrate diet, possibly because this leads to an increased rate of glycolysis and therefore of pyruvate production.

Treatment of Thiamine Deficiency

True beri-beri responds to 5–10 mg thiamine daily, although occasionally higher dosages may be required. In cases where multiple deficiency is suspected a mixture of the vitamins in the "B Complex" should be given.

RIBOFLAVIN

Source of Riboflavin

Riboflavin is found in large amounts in yeasts and germinating plants such as peas and beans.

Function of Riboflavin

There are about 15 flavoproteins, mostly enzymes incorporating riboflavin in the form of flavin mononucleotide (FMN) and flavin adenine dinucleotide (FAD). FMN and FAD are reversible *electron carriers* in biological oxidation systems and are in turn oxidized by cytochromes.

Clinical Effects of Riboflavin Deficiency

Ariboflavinosis causes a rough scaly skin, especially on the face, cheilosis (red, swollen, cracked lips), angular stomatitis and similar lesions at the mucocutaneous junctions of anus and vagina, and a swollen tender, red tongue, which is described as magenta coloured. Congestion of conjunctival blood vessels may be visible clinically on microscopic examination of the eye with a slit lamp.

NICOTINAMIDE

Source of Nicotinamide

Nicotinamide can be formed in the body from nicotinic acid. Both substances are plentiful in animal and plant foods. Some nicotinic acid can also be synthesized in the mammalian body from tryptophane. Probably both dietary and endogenous sources are necessary to provide sufficient nicotinamide for normal metabolism.

Function of Nicotinamide

Nicotinamide is the active constituent of the important coenzymes in *oxidation-reduction reactions*, nicotinamide adenine dinucleotide (NAD), and its phosphate (NADP). Reduced NAD and NADP are, in turn, re-oxidized by flavoproteins, and the functions of riboflavin and nicotinamide are closely linked. NAD and NADP are essential, amongst other things, for glycolysis and oxidative phosphorylation.

Clinical Effects of Nicotinamide Deficiency

Nicotinamide deficiency produces a clinical syndrome often remembered by the mnemonic "three Ds"—diarrhoea, dermatitis and dementia. The dermatitis is a sunburn-like erythema, especially marked in areas exposed to the sun, and later leading to pigmentation and thickening of the dermis. The "dementia" takes the form of irritability, depression and anorexia, with loss of weight. As in riboflavin deficiency, there may be glossitis and stomatitis. Many of the symptoms of the multi-deficiency disease *pellagra* may be due to nicotinamide deficiency, and nicotinic acid has been called "pellagra preventive factor" (P.P. Factor).

Causes of Nicotinamide Deficiency

Dietary deficiency of nicotinamide, like that of the other B vitamins, is rare in affluent communities.

Hartnup disease is due to a rare inborn error of renal, intestinal and other cellular transport mechanisms for the monoamino monocarboxylic acids, including tryptophane (p. 339). Subjects with the disease may present with a pellagra-type rash, which can be cured by nicotinamide therapy of 40–200 mg daily. Probably, if the supply of tryptophane for synthesis in the body is reduced, dietary nicotinic acid is insufficient to supply the body's needs over long periods of time: under these circumstances only slight reduction of intake may precipitate pellagra. A similar clinical picture has been reported in the *carcinoid syndrome*, when tryptophane is diverted to the synthesis of large amounts of 5-hydroxytryptamine (p. 371).

PYRIDOXINE

Source of Pyridoxine and Cause of Deficiency

Pyridoxine is widely distributed in food and dietary deficiency is very rare. The antituberculous drug *isoniazid* (isonicotinic hydrazide) has been reported to produce the picture of pyridoxine deficiency, probably by competition with it in metabolic pathways.

Function of Pyridoxine

Pyridoxal phosphate is a coenzyme for the *aminotransferases* (transaminases), and for *decarboxylation of amino-acids*.

Clinical Effects of Pyridoxine Deficiency

Deficiency may produce roughening of the skin. A pyridoxine-responsive anaemia can occur (p. 312).

BIOTIN AND PANTOTHENIC ACID

Lack of these two vitamins of the B group probably almost never produces clinical deficiency syndromes.

Biotin is present in eggs, but large amounts of raw egg white in experimental diets have caused loss of hair and dermatitis thought to be due to biotin deficiency. Probably the protein avidin, present in the egg white, combines with biotin and prevents its absorption. Biotin is a coenzyme in carboxylation reactions.

Pantothenic acid is a component of coenzyme A (CoA), which is essential for fat and carbohydrate metabolism. It is very widely distributed in foodstuffs.

ROLE OF B VITAMINS IN FORMATION OF ACETYL CoA

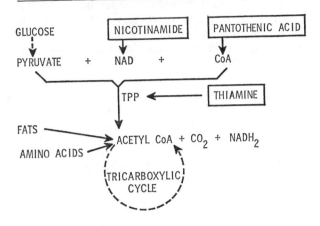

ROLE OF B VITAMINS IN ELECTRON TRANSFER

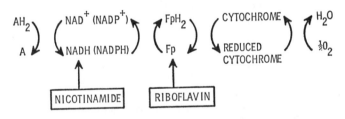

A = SUBSTRATE (E.G. PYRUVATE) Fp = FLAVOPROTEIN

AH_2 = REDUCED SUBSTRATE (E.G. LACTATE)

B VITAMINS IN ☐

FIG. 34.—Some biochemical interrelationships of B vitamins.

Figure 34 summarizes some of the biochemical interrelationships of the B vitamins discussed so far. Note that, as a general rule, deficiency of this group results in lesions of skin, mucous membranes and the nervous system.

FOLIC ACID AND VITAMIN B_{12}

These two vitamins are included in the B group and are essential for the normal maturation of the erythrocyte; deficiency of either causes *megaloblastic anaemia*. Their effects are so closely interrelated that they are usually discussed together. A fuller discussion of diagnosis and treatment will be found in haematology textbooks.

Folate is present in green vegetables and some meats. It is easily destroyed in cooking and *dietary deficiency* may rarely occur. It is absorbed throughout the small intestine and in contrast to most of the other B vitamins (except B_{12}) clinical deficiency occurs relatively commonly in intestinal *malabsorption syndromes*. During *pregnancy* and lactation low blood folate levels are common and may be associated with megaloblastic anaemia. The active form of the vitamin is tetrahydrofolic acid, and this is essential for transfer of "one carbon" units: it is particularly important in *purine and pyrimidine* (and therefore DNA and RNA) synthesis. Competitive *folic acid antagonists* such as aminopterin have been used as cytotoxic drugs in the treatment of malignancy because they inhibit DNA synthesis.

Vitamin B_{12} is usually known as cyanocobalamin. When the cyanide group is replaced by adenine nucleotide this vitamin, like folate, has coenzyme activity in nucleic acid synthesis, and this conversion takes place in the body. Its biochemical functions are less clearly understood than those of folate, but it is probably required for normal metabolism of that vitamin. It is absorbed mainly in the terminal ileum and in *malabsorption syndromes* affecting this region deficiency can occur: it also occurs in the *blind loop syndrome* because of bacterial competition for the vitamin.

Absorption of the vitamin depends on its combination with intrinsic factor, secreted by the stomach, and in true *pernicious anaemia* malabsorption of B_{12} is the result of absence of this factor.

Dietary deficiency of vitamin B_{12} is very rare.

Deficiency of vitamin B_{12}, like that of folic acid, causes megaloblastic anaemia: unlike that of folate it can result in *sub-acute combined degeneration* of the cord. Although the megaloblastic anaemia of B_{12} deficiency can be reversed by folate, this therapy should never be given in pernicious anaemia because it does not improve the neurological lesions and may even aggravate them.

Table XXIII summarizes the synonyms of the B vitamins, their known biochemical actions, and the clinical syndromes associated with deficiency.

ASCORBIC ACID

Source of Ascorbic Acid

Ascorbic acid is found in fruit and vegetables and is especially plentiful in citrus fruits. It cannot be synthesized by man and other primates, nor by guinea-pigs.

TABLE XXIII
The "B Complex" Vitamins

Name	Synonyms	Biochemical function	Clinical deficiency syndrome
Thiamine	Aneurin Vitamin B_1	Cocarboxylase (as thiamine pyro-phosphate)	Beri-beri (Neuropathy) Wernicke's Encephalo-pathy
Riboflavin	Vitamin B_2	In flavoproteins (electron carriers) (as FAD and FMN)	Ariboflavinosis (affecting skin and eyes)
Nicotinamide	P.P. factor Niacin	In NAD and NADP (electron carriers)	Pellagra (dermatitis, diarrhoea, dementia)
Pyridoxine	Adermin Vitamin B_6	Coenzyme in decarboxy-lation and deamination (as phosphate)	Pyridoxine responsive anaemia ? Dermatitis
Biotin		Carboxylation co-enzyme	Probably unimportant clinically
Pantothenic acid		In Coenzyme A	
Folic acid	Pteroyl glutamic acid	Metabolism of purines and pyrimidines	Megaloblastic anaemia
Vitamin B_{12} group	Cobalamins	Coenzyme in synthesis of nucleic acid	Megaloblastic anaemia Subacute combined degeneration of the cord

Functions of Ascorbic Acid

Ascorbic acid can be reversibly oxidized in biological systems to de-hydroascorbic acid and, although its functions in man are not well worked out, it probably acts as a hydrogen carrier. It seems to be required for normal collagen formation.

Causes of Ascorbic Acid Deficiency

Deficiency of ascorbic acid causes scurvy and was commonly seen on the long sea voyages of exploration in the 16th, 17th and 18th centuries. Although Hawkins, as early as 1593, realized that oranges and lemons could cure the disease, and although in 1601 Sir James Lancaster introduced the regular use of oranges and lemons in the ships of the East India Company, a good description of scurvy can be found in Anson's account of his voyage around the world in 1740–44 (*Anson's Voyage Round the World*, edited by S. W. C. Pack in Penguin Books, Chapter 10); this demonstrates the importance of reading the literature.

Dehydroascorbic acid is easily oxidized further and irreversibly in the presence of oxygen, thus losing its biological activity; this reaction is catalysed by heat. Scurvy was at one time fairly common in bottle-fed infants, as the ascorbic acid was often destroyed in the preparation of the feeds. With our present knowledge of the aetiology of the disease, and with dietary supplementation, it is now rarely seen in this age group. It is most commonly seen in old people (especially men) living on their own on poor incomes, who do not eat fresh fruit and vegetables and who tend to cook in frying pans, where the combination of heat and the large area of food in contact with air irreversibly oxidizes the vitamin.

Clinical Effects of Ascorbic Acid Deficiency

Anson described "large discoloured spots", "putrid gums" and "lassitude" as characteristic of scurvy.

Many of the signs and symptoms of scurvy can be related to poor collagen formation.

1. Deficiency in *vascular walls* leads to a bleeding tendency with a positive Hess test, petechiae and ecchymoses ("large discoloured spots"), swollen, tender, spongy bleeding gums ("putrid gums") and, occasionally, haematuria and epistaxis. In infants subperiosteal bleeding and haemarthroses are extremely painful and may lead to permanent joint deformities.

2. There is *poor healing* of all wounds.

3. Deficiency of *bone matrix* causes osteoporosis and poor healing of fractures. In children bone formation ceases at the epidiaphyseal junctions, which look "frayed" radiologically.

4. There may be *anaemia*, possibly partly due to impairment of erythropoiesis. This anaemia may sometimes be cured by ascorbic acid alone. Bleeding aggravates the anaemia.

This florid form of the disease is rarely seen nowadays and the patient most commonly presents complaining that bruising occurs with only minor trauma.

All the signs and symptoms are dramatically cured by the administration of ascorbic acid.

Diagnosis of Scurvy

The laboratory diagnosis of scurvy can only be made *before* therapy has started. Once ascorbic acid has been given it is difficult to prove that deficiency was previously present.

The *ascorbic acid saturation test* is based on the fact that if the tissues are "saturated" with ascorbic acid any further vitamin administered will be lost in the urine (see Appendix, p. 364).

Ascorbic acid may be estimated in the blood, but levels vary widely in normal subjects. Leucocyte ascorbic acid is said to give a better indication of scurvy than that of plasma or whole blood. For practical purposes the saturation test is still probably the best one.

SUMMARY

1. Vitamins have important biochemical functions, most of which are now well understood. Unfortunately the relationship of these to clinical syndromes is not obvious.

2. The fat soluble vitamins, especially vitamin D, may be deficient in steatorrhoea. Both vitamin A and vitamin D are stored in the liver and deficiency takes some time to develop.

3. **Vitamin A** is necessary for the formation of visual purple and for normal mucopolysaccharide synthesis. Deficiency is associated with poor vision in dim light and with drying and metaplasia of epithelial surfaces, especially those of the conjunctiva and cornea.

4. **Vitamin D** is necessary for normal calcium metabolism and deficiency causes rickets in children and osteomalacia in adults.

5. Both vitamin A and vitamin D are toxic in excess.

6. **Vitamin K** is necessary for prothrombin formation and deficiency is associated with a bleeding tendency.

7. **Thiamine** deficiency causes beri-beri.

8. **Riboflavin** deficiency causes ariboflavinosis.

9. **Nicotinamide** can be manufactured from tryptophane in the body, but dietary deficiency causes a pellagra-like syndrome, which may also be seen in Hartnup disease, when tryptophane absorption is deficient.

10. **Pyridoxine** responsive anaemia may occur.

11. **Folic acid and vitamin B_{12}** deficiency produce megaloblastic anaemia, and deficiency of vitamin B_{12} can also cause sub-acute combined degeneration of the cord. Compared with the other B vitamins, deficiency of these is relatively common in malabsorption syndromes, and vitamin B_{12} deficiency can be a feature of the "blind-loop syndrome". Classical pernicious anaemia is due to intrinsic factor deficiency with consequent malabsorption of vitamin B_{12}.

12. **Ascorbic acid** deficiency causes scurvy.

FURTHER READING

MARKS, J. (1968). *The Vitamins in Health and Disease*. London: J. & A. Churchill.

APPENDIX TO CHAPTER XVIII

ASCORBIC ACID SATURATION TEST

One gram of ascorbic acid is administered orally at 8 a.m. The bladder is emptied and the urine discarded.

Any urine passed between 8 a.m. and 11 a.m. is put in a collection bottle. At 11 a.m. the bladder is again emptied and the urine added to the collection.

Because of the ease with which ascorbic acid can be destroyed the specimen must be sent to the laboratory immediately for estimation. If "saturation" is complete (see below) the test can be terminated; if it is not the procedure is repeated on the following day.

Interpretation

"Saturation" is said to be complete when 50 mg of the 1 g dose of ascorbic acid is excreted in the 3-hour urine collection.

In normal subjects "saturation" is complete on the first or second day of the test. In scurvy it takes much longer, but not usually more than a week.

Warning.—It should be noted that in malabsorption syndromes "saturation" may appear not to occur, even after several weeks. This is not diagnostic of scurvy, but is probably due to the fact that the absorption of the ascorbic acid is slower than usual and that it does not reach the kidneys in normal amounts during the 3 hours. Scurvy is very rare in such syndromes.

Chapter XIX

PREGNANCY
AND ORAL CONTRACEPTIVE THERAPY

ASSESSMENT OF FOETO-PLACENTAL FUNCTION

UNTIL recently an indication for induction of labour was clinical evidence of foetal distress. Tests have now been devised which, it is hoped, will give earlier warning of impending foetal death. These tests are still very unsatisfactory, but may be used as an adjunct to clinical impressions.

URINARY OESTRIOL

Production of Oestriol by the Foetus and Placenta

Soon after fertilization the ovum is implanted in the uterine wall: secretion of chorionic gonadotrophin by the developing placenta maintains the corpus luteum of the luteal phase and the continued secretion of oestrogen and progesterone from the corpus luteum prevents the onset of menstruation. Oestriol secretion at this stage is very low and it only rises very slowly during the first weeks of pregnancy.

Chorionic gonadotrophin secretion reaches a peak at about 13 weeks of pregnancy, and then falls. At this stage the foeto-placental unit takes over hormone production, and secretion of both oestrogen and progesterone rises rapidly.

The foetus and the placenta are now an integrated endocrine unit and both are required for the production of oestriol. The hormone passes into the maternal circulation and ultimately into the urine.

Value of Urinary Oestriol Estimation

The 24-hourly urinary oestriol secretion reflects both *placental and foetal function*. Accurate estimation of low concentrations of oestrogen fractions, including oestriol, is a lengthy procedure. Results of foeto-placental monitoring, if they are to be useful, are required on the same day as the completion of collection of the 24-hour urine specimen. Several rapid analytical methods for urinary oestriol estimation have been devised but, because of their relative insensitivity, they are only of value after about the 28th week of pregnancy, when oestriol excretion is high.

Urinary oestriol excretion continues to rise throughout the later weeks of pregnancy, but unfortunately the "normal range" of excretion at any particular stage is so wide that a single reading, unless very low, is of little diagnostic help: for instance, the range at 36 weeks is 10–33 mg/24 hours. A sudden drop of level in a series of estimations is of more ominous significance than a single low reading and may be of help in deciding whether to terminate pregnancy.

URINARY PREGNANEDIOL

Pregnanediol is a metabolite of progesterone, and the urinary excretion of the latter is a reflection of the level of circulating progesterone and therefore, in pregnancy, of the function of the *placenta*. Excretion of pregnanediol, like that of oestriol, rises rapidly after about the 13th week of pregnancy, and reaches levels measurable by rapid methods after about the 28th week. Since oestriol measures foetal as well as placental function its measurement during pregnancy has replaced that of pregnanediol.

HEAT-STABLE ALKALINE PHOSPHATASE

The placenta produces one of the alkaline phosphatase isoenzymes and the level of this rises in late pregnancy. This enzyme is stable at a temperature at which alkaline phosphatase from other sources is inactivated. Thus, if plasma is heated to the critical temperature and the enzyme assayed after cooling, the remaining activity may be used as a test of placental function. Like urinary oestriol excretion, the heat-stable alkaline phosphatase level has a very wide normal range. The value of this estimation is still being assessed. Like pregnanediol excretion, the level of heat-stable alkaline phosphatase reflects only *placental* and not foetal function.

METABOLIC EFFECTS OF PREGNANCY AND ORAL CONTRACEPTIVE THERAPY

The level of many plasma constituents is affected by steroid hormones: for example, the "normal" range of plasma uric acid and plasma iron differs in males and females after puberty. It is therefore not surprising to find that pregnancy affects plasma concentrations of many substances, because in this state there are very high circulating levels of oestrogens and progestogens. Oral contraceptive therapy is said to prevent ovulation by mimicking pregnancy, as the tablets contain synthetic oestrogens and "progestogens", and many of the metabolic changes seen during pregnancy are also found in some women taking the "pill". Most of these changes have been attributed to the oestrogen rather than the progestogen fraction, but it may be very difficult to be sure exactly which hormone is producing the change: sometimes it may be due to interaction between hormones. The mechanism of the changes is poorly understood, but steroids are known to affect protein synthesis.

EFFECT ON CARBOHYDRATE METABOLISM

It is well known that steroids affect carbohydrate metabolism. Cushing's syndrome is associated with diabetes and patients on large doses of corticosteroids may become diabetic. Cortisone has been given to subjects suspected of being "prediabetic" in spite of a normal glucose tolerance curve to uncover "latent diabetes" (p. 140).

During pregnancy many women develop a *diabetic type of glucose tolerance curve*, which usually reverts to normal after parturition. Similarly, some subjects taking oral contraceptive preparations develop a reversible "diabetes", very rarely, if ever, severe enough to be accompanied by a raised fasting blood sugar. There is no good evidence that such tablets cause true diabetes in normal subjects, but in those with latent diabetes the disease may be precipitated earlier than it would be in the normal course of events.

There may also be *renal glycosuria* both in pregnancy and in subjects taking oral contraceptives.

EFFECT ON SPECIFIC CARRIER PROTEINS AND ON SUBSTANCES BOUND TO THEM

The plasma level of many specific carrier proteins is increased in pregnant subjects and in those taking oral contraceptive preparations. If this fact is not recognized an erroneous diagnosis may be made. In most cases the rise in carrier protein is accompanied by a proportional increase of the substance bound to it, without any change in the unbound fraction. As the protein bound fraction is a transport form and because, in most cases, it is the free substance that is physiologically active, this rise in concentration is of no clinical importance.

Thyroxine Binding Globulin (TBG)

The level of TBG is increased both in pregnant subjects and in those taking oral contraceptive preparations. This causes a rise in *protein bound iodine* (PBI) and *total plasma thyroxine* (T_4) concentrations, with a fall in *resin uptake*. The true cause of the rise in PBI (or T_4) will be recognized if the resin uptake test is also performed (p. 168); if either is estimated alone the PBI (or T_4) may lead to a false diagnosis of thyrotoxicosis, and the resin uptake to one of myxoedema. Since the free thyroxine level is unaffected thyroid function is normal, a fact reflected in a normal neck uptake of iodine. The BMR is normal in subjects taking oral contraceptive preparations.

Cortisol Binding Globulin

The level of cortisol binding globulin and therefore of plasma cortisol increases as a result of pregnancy and of oral contraceptives. The free cortisol level, and therefore adrenal function, is normal, but if the fact is not recognized a false diagnosis of Cushing's syndrome may be made.

Transferrin

The plasma concentration of the iron binding protein, transferrin, also increases within a day or two of starting oral contraceptive preparations. This is reflected in a rise in total iron binding capacity (TIBC). The rise in pregnancy occurs after about the 20th week. *Plasma iron* concentrations also increase but, unlike the substances already discussed, the rise is probably independent of that of the binding protein.

Caeruloplasmin

The copper binding protein caeruloplasmin is increased in concentration in subjects taking oral contraceptives and in pregnancy. It also rises during oestrogen therapy. There is an associated rise in *plasma copper* levels, but this is unlikely to lead to misdiagnosis. The increase in this bluish protein may impart a green colour to the plasma.

Lipoproteins

The plasma level of some lipoproteins is increased in subjects taking oral contraceptive preparations and is associated with an increased plasma triglyceride, and sometimes cholesterol, concentration. In late pregnancy triglycerides are also increased but, compared with subjects taking oral contraceptives, there is a more marked rise in plasma cholesterol.

Other Proteins

The reduction of serum protein concentration in pregnancy has been thought to be due to dilution following fluid retention. Albumin and total protein levels have been reported to fall slightly during oral contraceptive therapy, but this change is unlikely to cause diagnostic confusion. It seems that only binding proteins are *increased* in these subjects.

PLASMA FOLATE LEVELS

Plasma folate levels have been reported to be reduced during oral contraceptive therapy. The relationship to the low folate levels and anaemia of pregnancy is not certain.

TABLE XXIV

SOME METABOLIC EFFECTS OF PREGNANCY AND ORAL CONTRACEPTIVE THERAPY
WHICH MAY CONFUSE DIAGNOSIS

Test		Comments
Hormone Levels:		
Adrenal hormones		
Plasma cortisol	Raised	Secondary to rise in binding protein. Adrenal function normal
Thyroid hormones		
PBI	Raised	Secondary to rise in binding protein.
Total plasma T$_4$		Thyroid function normal
Resin uptake	Lowered	
Pituitary hormone		
Urinary gonadotrophin	Lowered on oral contraceptives	Feed-back suppression
Carbohydrate metabolism		
Glucose tolerance test	"Diabetic"	Reversible abnormalities
"Renal threshold"	Reduced	
Iron metabolism		
TIBC	Raised on oral contraceptives and in late pregnancy	
Plasma iron	Relatively raised	

LIVER FUNCTION TESTS

Some subjects develop a cholestatic jaundice during pregnancy and the same people are prone to a similar syndrome when taking oral contraceptive preparations. Although changes in flocculation tests and in aminotransferase levels have been reported in subjects taking oral contraceptives this is probably an extremely rare complication in normal people. The present authors have not seen it in a series comprising several hundreds of subjects.

HORMONE SECRETION

The effect of oral contraceptives on cortisol binding globulin and therefore on plasma cortisol has already been mentioned. No effect has been demonstrated on 17-oxo and 17-hydroxysteroid excretion. *Gonadotrophin levels* are very low in subjects taking oral contraceptives because of feed-back suppression. These revert to normal when the tablets are stopped.

The changes which may occur during pregnancy and oral contraceptive therapy are summarized in Table XXIV.

SUMMARY

Assessment of Foeto-Placental Function

1. After the 28th week of pregnancy estimations of daily oestriol excretion, in conjunction with the clinical findings, may help in assessing placental function and the health of the foetus.

2. After the 28th week of pregnancy estimations of urinary pregnanediol excretion may also help in assessing placental function.

3. The placenta produces an alkaline phosphatase isoenzyme which is stable at relatively high temperatures. This has also been used to assess placental function.

Metabolic Effects of Pregnancy and Oral Contraceptive Therapy

Pregnancy and oral contraceptive therapy produce similar metabolic effects which, if not recognized, may lead to misdiagnosis. The more important of these are listed in Table XXIV.

Chapter XX

ENDOCRINE EFFECTS OF TUMOURS

Tumours of endocrine tissue, whether benign or malignant, often produce an excess of the hormone normally elaborated by that organ. Most of these syndromes (for instance, hyperparathyroidism due to a parathyroid adenoma) have been discussed in the relevant chapters. Two rare syndromes are associated with neoplasia of cells which, although normally producing hormones are, because of their scattered nature, less commonly thought of as endocrine organs. These are the carcinoid syndrome, due to an excessive production of 5-hydroxytryptamine by malignant tumours of argentaffin cells, and the syndrome which is due to oversecretion of the catecholamines, adrenaline (epinephrine) and noradrenaline (norepinephrine), by the cells of the sympathetic nervous system (phaeochromocytoma and neuroblastoma).

Many malignant tumours of non-endocrine origin, such as bronchial carcinoma, can elaborate hormones normally foreign to them. These interesting syndromes are more common than had previously been realized, and the second part of the chapter will be devoted to a brief discussion of such endocrine abnormalities.

THE CARCINOID SYNDROME

Normal Metabolism of 5-Hydroxytryptamine

Small numbers of *argentaffin cells* (that is, cells which will reduce, and therefore stain with silver salts) are normally found in tissues derived from embryonic gut. The commonest sites for these cells are the ileum and appendix, derived from embryonic midgut, but some are also found in such foregut derivatives as the pancreas and stomach, and in the rectum, which originates from the hindgut. They produce *5-hydroxytryptamine* (5HT: serotonin) from tryptophane, the intermediate product being *5-hydroxytryptophane* (5HTP). 5HT is deaminated and oxidized to *5-hydroxyindole acetic acid* (5HIAA) under the influence of monoamine oxidases (Fig. 35): the latter enzymes, as well as the aromatic amino-acid decarboxylase, are found in other tissues as well as in argentaffin cells. 5HIAA is normally the main urinary excretion product of argentaffin cells.

FIG. 35.—Metabolism of tryptophane.

Causes of the Carcinoid Syndrome

Malignant or benign tumours of argentaffin cells may manufacture an excess of 5HTP, 5HT and 5HIAA, the last usually being the major end product: rarely the neoplastic cells lack the aromatic amino-acid decarboxylase, in which case 5HTP is produced in excess and a smaller proportion of 5HT and 5HIAA is formed from this in other tissues.

The most usual site for these uncommon tumours is the ileum or appendix: neoplasms at the latter site rarely metastasize and may be histochemically different from the other small intestinal argentaffin tumours. Less commonly the neoplasm is bronchial, pancreatic or gastric in origin, any other site being extremely rare.

The carcinoid syndrome is usually associated with an excess of circulating 5HT. Ileal and appendiceal tumours do not produce the clinical syndrome until they have metastasized, usually to the liver, but primary tumours at other sites do cause symptoms. It is thought that at least some of the secretions of intestinal neoplasms are inactivated in the liver, whereas at other sites they are released in an active form into the systemic circulation.

Clinical Picture of the Carcinoid Syndrome

The clinical syndrome includes *flushing, diarrhoea* and *bronchospasm.* There may be *lesions of the heart,* typically *right sided,* except in the case of bronchial carcinoid. The diarrhoea may be so severe as to cause a malabsorption syndrome. The relationship of 5HT to the signs and symptoms is not clear; it can increase gut motility and therefore may contribute to the diarrhoea, but other substances secreted by the tumour probably cause the other symptoms. One of the possibilities is kallikrein, a proteolytic enzyme acting on a plasma protein to release bradykinin. Bradykinin has been shown to cause vasodilation and bronchial constriction. Histamine has also been suggested as a cause for the flushing, especially in tumours elaborating a preponderance of 5HTP.

Diagnosis of the Carcinoid Syndrome

In the carcinoid syndrome urinary 5HIAA secretion, estimated on a 24-hour specimen of urine, is usually greatly increased. An excretion of more than 25 mg in 24 hours is diagnostic, provided that walnuts and bananas are excluded from the diet for 24 hours before the collection is made.

In very rare cases, usually with bronchial or gastric tumours, the cells lack aromatic amino-acid decarboxylase. Urinary 5HIAA may not be obviously increased, and there is increased secretion of 5HTP. If there is a strong clinical suspicion of the carcinoid syndrome and the urinary 5HIAA excretion is normal, it may be more useful to estimate total 5-hydroxyindole excretion (which includes 5HTP, 5HT and 5HIAA). This is very rarely necessary in practice.

CATECHOLAMINE SECRETING TUMOURS

The adrenal medulla and the sympathetic ganglia consist of sympathetic nervous tissue: this is derived from the embryonic neural crest and is composed of two types of cells—the *chromaffin cells* and the *nerve cells*—both of which can elaborate the active catecholamines.

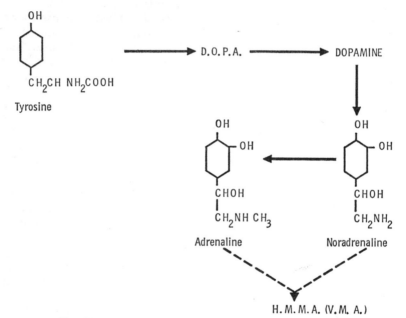

FIG. 36.—Synthesis and metabolism of the catecholamines.

Adrenaline (epinephrine) is almost exclusively a product of the adrenal medulla, while most noradrenaline (norepinephrine) is formed at sympathetic nerve endings.

METABOLISM OF THE CATECHOLAMINES

Adrenaline and noradrenaline are formed from tyrosine via dihydroxyphenylalanine (DOPA), and dihydroxyphenylethylamine (DOPamine). DOPA, DOPamine, adrenaline and noradrenaline are all catecholamines (dihydroxylated phenolic compounds). The most important breakdown product of adrenaline and noradrenaline is 4-hydroxy 3-methoxy-mandelic acid (HMMA; vanillylmandelic acid, VMA): this is excreted in the urine (Fig. 36).

ACTION OF THE CATECHOLAMINES

Both adrenaline and noradrenaline act on the cardiovascular system and, in excess, cause *hypertension* and *sweating*. Noradrenaline produces vasoconstriction and pallor, while adrenaline causes peripheral vaso-dilation and *tachycardia*.

Adrenaline increases the rate of glycogenolysis (p. 129) and may cause hyperglycaemia.

For a more detailed discussion of the action of these two hormones the student is referred to textbooks of pharmacology.

CATECHOLAMINE SECRETING TUMOURS

Tumours of the sympathetic nervous system, whether adrenal or extra-adrenal, can produce catecholamines. Tumours with this property are of two main types:

1. Tumours of chromaffin tissue. *Phaeochromocytoma.*
    In adrenal medulla 90 per cent.
    Extra-adrenal 10 per cent.
2. Tumours of nerve cells. *Neuroblastoma.*
    In adrenal medulla 40 per cent.
    Extra-adrenal 60 per cent.

Although both these types of neoplasm secrete catecholamines their age incidence and the clinical pictures are quite different.

Phaeochromocytoma occurs mainly in *adult* life and is usually benign. The symptoms and signs can be related to excessive secretion of cate-cholamines and include *paroxysmal hypertension* accompanied by *anxiety, sweating,* a throbbing headache and either facial pallor or flush-ing during the attack. The attack may also be accompanied by hyper-glycaemia and glycosuria. Occasionally hypertension may be persistent. This tumour accounts for only about half a per cent of all cases of hypertension, but if a young adult presents with high blood pressure for no obvious reason its presence should be sought, as the condition may be cured by surgery. Table XXV summarizes some relatively rare causes of hypertension which should be excluded in such patients before "essential" hypertension is diagnosed, and in which biochemical investigations aid the diagnosis.

A familial syndrome in which phaeochromocytoma, medullary car-cinoma of the thyroid and neurofibromatosis coexist has been described.

TABLE XXV
METABOLIC CAUSES OF HYPERTENSION

Investigations

Renal disease	Plasma urea or creatinine.
	Examination of urine for casts and protein.
	Clearance tests if necessary (p. 16).
Primary aldosteronism	Plasma potassium and bicarbonate (p. 45).
Phaeochromocytoma	Urinary HMMA (VMA).

Neuroblastoma is a very *malignant* tumour of sympathetic nervous tissue occurring in *children*. Secretion of catecholamines in these cases is often as high as, or higher than, that of a phaeochromocytoma, but the clinical syndrome described above is rare: the reason for this is not clear, but may be due to release of hormones into the blood stream in an inactive form. Some of the tumours secrete DOPamine in excess.

DIAGNOSIS OF CATECHOLAMINE SECRETING TUMOURS

Because HMMA (VMA) is the major catabolic product of catecholamines, chemical diagnosis of the tumours can usually be made by estimating its excretion in a 24-hour specimen of urine. An excretion of more than twice "normal" is diagnostic, provided that all vanilla products, bananas and coffee are excluded from the diet for 24 hours before the test. Slightly raised excretion may be found in cases of essential hypertension.

Rarely HMMA excretion is normal, but that of total catecholamines is increased. Estimation of the latter should be reserved for cases clinically highly suggestive of phaeochromocytoma, but with a normal excretion of HMMA.

If hypertension is paroxysmal, urine should be collected during the attack: this may be the only time at which increased excretion can be demonstrated.

HORMONAL EFFECTS OF TUMOURS OF NON-ENDOCRINE TISSUE

This section will best be understood after the student has read the chapters concerned with the hormones discussed.

Hormone secretion at sites other than that of the tissue normally producing it is known as "*ectopic*"; *inappropriate* secretion (p. 43) may or may not be ectopic in origin (see ADH), but ectopic secretion is always inappropriate since it is not under normal feed-back control.

Many tumours of non-endocrine tissue may secrete hormonal substances very similar to, and probably identical with, the natural hormone: some tumours are known to secrete two or more such hormones.

MECHANISM OF ECTOPIC HORMONE PRODUCTION

It is not yet certain why ectopic hormone secretion should occur, but although many theories have been propounded we feel that the one below is by far the most likely. For further discussion the interested student should consult the references at the end of the chapter.

DNA, through RNA formation, controls peptide and protein synthesis, the sequence of bases in the DNA molecule determining the structure of the peptide synthesized. All cells in the body are derived from one cell, the fertilized ovum. The DNA complement of this cell is determined by that of the unfertilized ovum and that of the sperm, and during the subsequent repeated cell division the DNA is replicated so that every daughter cell has a genetic complement identical with that of the fertilized ovum. Unless mutation were to occur during differentiation of tissues (and there is evidence that it does not), every cell in the body must have the potential to produce any protein coded for in the fertilized ovum.

It is thought that during functional cell differentiation (which, of course, proceeds at the same time as histological changes) various parts of the DNA molecule are consecutively "repressed" (stopped from functioning), and "derepressed": for instance in the early stages of blastula formation no RNA and therefore no protein is produced and DNA replication is dominant, while at other times different proteins are manufactured. In the fully differentiated cell much of the genetic information is probably repressed and only the peptides essential for cell metabolism and those concerned with the special function of the organ are made. If the cell undergoes neoplastic change the altered histological picture reflects altered chemical function, probably resulting from the changed pattern of repression of the DNA molecule. It is now easy to see how a cell could revert to synthesizing a peptide or protein which is foreign to it in its fully differentiated state.

If this were the correct explanation, the ectopic hormone should be chemically identical with that normally produced by endocrine tissue. Hormonal substances have been extracted from tumour tissue and although in no case has the complete structure been worked out, evidence based on biological activity and chemical and immunological properties is strongly suggestive that many of these are identical with the naturally occurring hormones. As might also be expected if the above theory were correct, tumours have been described secreting two or more peptide hormones.

It seems to us, then, that derepression is by far the most likely explanation for this interesting set of syndromes. However, this derepression cannot be non-specific because some hormones are secreted much more commonly by one type of tumour than another. This may reflect

a differing chemical background in different parts of the body.
The student should remember that this theory is not yet proven. We
hope we may have interested him in the subject and that he will be
stimulated to read further.

HORMONAL SYNDROMES

Many of these syndromes have been discussed in the relevant chap-
ters. The following may be due to hormone secretion by the tumour:
  Hypercalcaemia (Parathyroid Hormone)
  Hyponatraemia (Antidiuretic Hormone)
  Hypokalaemia (Adrenocorticotrophic Hormone)
  Polycythaemia (Erythropoietin)
  Hypoglycaemia ("Insulin-like substance")
  Gynaecomastia (Gonadotrophin)
  Zollinger-Ellison Syndrome (Gastrin)
  Hyperthyroidism (Thyrotropin)
  Carcinoid Syndrome (5HT and 5HTP)
It should be noted that all the hormones mentioned above are pep-
tides except 5HT and 5HTP: the syndrome associated with the latter
may be the result of overproduction of a single enzyme (see below).

None of these hormones produced at ectopic sites is under normal
feed-back control. Secretion therefore continues under conditions in
which it should be absent, and is inappropriate.

While absolute proof of hormone secretion depends on its isolation
from the tumour tissue, in many cases strong presumptive evidence
enables the clinician to diagnose the syndrome with a high degree of
probability.

Hypercalcaemia due to Parathyroid Hormone Secretion

Tumour types and incidence.—In our experience this is probably the
most common of these syndromes. Parathyroid hormone (PTH), or a
peptide very similar to it, has been extracted from a wide variety of
tumour types, and presumptive evidence for its secretion is available in
a great many cases.

Biochemical syndrome.—As discussed in Chapter VIII, inappropriate
PTH secretion, whether ectopic or parathyroid in origin, is associated
with high plasma calcium and low plasma phosphate concentrations,
unless accompanied by renal failure. If both these findings are present,
and especially if there is no obvious evidence of bony metastases, it is
probable that the hypercalcaemia is due to ectopic PTH secretion.

The hypercalcaemia of some cases of malignancy is said to be due to
lysis of bone by secondary deposits, with release of calcium and phosphate into the blood stream. As discussed on p. 186 the authors feel that

this is a very rare cause and that most cases (including many of those of myeloma) are due to ectopic PTH secretion. The student should keep an open mind and study the cases he meets, noticing particularly the level of phosphate in relation to that of plasma urea (p. 188).

The hypercalcaemia of malignancy, unlike that of primary hyper-parathyroidism, may often be suppressed by large doses of corticosteroids (p. 189).

With the development of improved therapy of malignant disease it is now important to control hypercalcaemia in these patients, who should probably have plasma calcium estimated at frequent intervals. Severe hypercalcaemia may prove lethal before therapy of the primary lesion can be started: if this abnormality is treated the patient may have several years of useful life to come. The treatment is discussed on p. 193.

Hyponatraemia Due to Inappropriate Antidiuretic Hormone (ADH) Secretion

Tumour types and incidence.—Ectopic ADH production is most commonly associated with the relatively rare oat-cell carcinoma of the bronchus, although the syndrome has been reported in a wide variety of tumours. Mild hyponatraemia may be overlooked in a severely ill patient, in whom such a finding is common; it is our experience that if further evidence is sought the syndrome is found to be relatively common.

Inappropriate ADH secretion can occur with various non-malignant syndromes, but in many of these cases the hormone is thought to originate in the hypothalamic-posterior pituitary region and therefore not to be ectopic in origin.

Biochemical and clinical syndrome.—ADH causes water retention. Water retention without sodium retention causes hyponatraemia, and therefore a reduction in plasma osmolarity (p. 44), which normally cuts off ADH production by feed-back control. If the low plasma osmolarity is to be corrected the urinary osmolarity must be even lower, so that the excess of water is excreted: this is the "appropriate" response. If, however, ADH is not under feed-back control, water retention continues in spite of low plasma osmolarity, and the urine passed is relatively concentrated. Thus the essential points in the diagnosis of inappropriate ADH secretion are:

1. A low plasma osmolarity.
2. In spite of this low plasma osmolarity, the urinary osmolarity is relatively high.

It should be noted that both findings are essential. A low plasma osmolarity occurs, for instance, in Addison's disease, but the urine is dilute. A high urinary osmolarity is present in dehydration but the plasma osmolarity is also high.

Continued expansion of the plasma volume reduces aldosterone secretion (p. 44), and the urine is of relatively high sodium concentration (note that plasma osmolarity can be attributed almost entirely to sodium salts: urinary osmolarity depends on a great many other ions). Retention of fluid dilutes other plasma constituents and these patients tend to have low plasma urea and protein concentrations.

The fall of plasma sodium concentration is usually gradual and allows time for equilibrium between cells and extracellular fluid: symptoms are therefore slight.

If the apparatus for measuring osmolarity (an osmometer) is not available a presumptive diagnosis can be made if the following findings are present:

1. A well hydrated, normotensive, relatively fit patient in spite of a low plasma sodium concentration.

2. A normal or low blood urea concentration.

3. A urine of relatively high sodium concentration and a relatively high specific gravity and urea concentration.

In the hyponatraemia of Addison's disease the patient is usually dehydrated, hypotensive and severely ill by the time there is a marked fall in plasma sodium concentration. The plasma urea concentration is usually raised. If the patient has been overloaded with fluid of low sodium concentration in the presence of a normal feed-back mechanism the urine, though containing sodium, will be of low specific gravity and urea concentration.

Treatment.—This consists of restriction of fluids.

Hypokalaemia Due to Adrenocorticotrophic Hormone (ACTH) Secretion

Tumour types and incidence.—Inappropriate ACTH secretion is probably rarer than the two syndromes already discussed. It occurs most commonly with the relatively rare oat-cell carcinoma of the bronchus, but has been described less frequently with a variety of other tumours, especially those of thymic and pancreatic origin.

Clinical and biochemical syndrome.—The ACTH stimulates secretion of all adrenal hormones except aldosterone (p. 91). In spite of this the picture of ectopic ACTH secretion is more like that of primary aldosteronism than of Cushing's syndrome: the patient usually presents with hypokalaemic alkalosis and hardly ever shows the Cushingoid clinical picture. The reason for this is not clear, but may be associated with the much higher level of hormones found in this condition than in true Cushing's syndrome.

Treatment.—This involves potassium replacement and treatment of the primary tumour. The prognosis is very poor.

Polycythaemia Due to Erythropoietin Secretion

The association of polycythaemia and renal carcinoma (hypernephroma) has been recognized for some years. It is now thought that the erythroid hyperplasia is often due to excessive production of an erythropoietin-like molecule by the tumour; erythropoietin stimulates marrow erythropoiesis. As this hormone is a normal product of the kidney this is not strictly an example of ectopic hormone secretion: however, the syndrome has been reported rarely in association with other tumours.

Hypoglycaemia Due to an "Insulin-Like" Hormone

Severe hypoglycaemia has been reported in association with many tumours: these are usually large neoplasms of retroperitoneal mesenchymal tissues resembling fibrosarcomata, or hepatic tumours. Various theories have been suggested for the aetiology of the hypoglycaemia, but there is evidence that at least some of the neoplasms produce a substance with insulin-like biological properties. This is said to be immunologically distinct from insulin, and is therefore unusual in the present context. In our experience the syndrome is very rare.

Gynaecomastia Due to Gonadotrophin Production

Various types of tumour, including carcinoma of the bronchus, breast and liver, have been reported to cause gynaecomastia and be associated with high circulating levels of chorionic gonadotrophin. In children with hepatoblastoma there is precocious puberty. Although this syndrome is rarely recognized it is possible that mild degrees of gynaecomastia are overlooked.

Zollinger-Ellison Syndrome Due to Gastrin Production

This is discussed on p. 219.

Hyperthyroidism Due to Thyrotrophin Production

Some tumours of trophoblastic cells (choriocarcinoma, hydatidiform mole and one case with a testicular teratoma) have been shown to elaborate a thyrotrophin-like substance. In spite of markedly raised plasma levels of hormone on bioassay (but not on immunoassay), clinical signs of thyrotoxicosis were rare: tachycardia was the commonest finding. Laboratory findings included unequivocally raised plasma protein bound iodine levels and the neck uptake of radio-iodine was also high.

Carcinoid Syndrome Due to 5-Hydroxytryptamine and 5-Hydroxytryptophane Production

All the syndromes so far discussed have been due to peptide hormones and, as we have seen, derepression of DNA could lead to their production. In the carcinoid syndrome, reported as a rare accompaniment of oat-cell carcinoma of the bronchus, there is usually excessive urinary excretion of 5HTP and 5HT, out of proportion to that of 5HIAA. How can we explain this overproduction of a non-peptide hormone?

It should be stressed that the following theory is speculative and is meant only as a working hypothesis.

The student should study Fig. 35, p. 372: the production of 5HTP from tryptophane requires only one enzyme, tryptophane-5-hydroxylase, while the decarboxylase and monoamine oxidase are normally found in non-argentaffin tissue. If derepression resulted in excessive production of this one enzyme there would be an excess of 5HTP. 5HT and 5HIAA could be produced in other tissues in relatively smaller amounts than are usual in the carcinoid syndrome. It would, of course, be more difficult to explain overproduction of a substance synthesized by a pathway requiring several enzymes.

SUMMARY

The Carcinoid Syndrome

1. Argentaffin cells manufacture 5-hydroxytryptamine (5HT) which is converted to 5-hydroxyindole acetic acid (5HIAA) and excreted in the urine.

2. Tumours of argentaffin tissue are usually found in the intestine, and these do not produce typical symptoms of the carcinoid syndrome until they have metastasized.

3. The carcinoid syndrome is usually associated with an increased secretion of 5HIAA in the urine.

Catecholamine Secreting Tumours

1. Tumours of sympathetic nervous tissue are associated with increased urinary excretion of the catecholamines, adrenaline and noradrenaline, and their breakdown product, hydroxymethoxymandelic acid (HMMA: VMA).

2. Phaeochromocytoma is a rare tumour, usually of adult life, occurring most commonly in the adrenal medulla. It is associated with hypertension and other symptoms of increased catecholamine secretion.

3. Neuroblastoma is a tumour of childhood, occurring in the adrenal medulla or in extra-adrenal sympathetic nervous tissue. Catecholamine secretion is increased, but symptoms are rarely referable to this.

Hormonal Effects of Tumours of Non-Endocrine Tissue

1. Many malignant tumours produce hormonal substances normally foreign to them, which may be identical with the hormones produced in endocrine glands.

2. The commonest of these is parathyroid hormone. Hypercalcaemia should be sought and treated in cases in which the malignancy is thought to be responsive to therapy.

FURTHER READING

BAYLISS, R. I. S. (1966). "Endocrine Disorders". In: *Progress in Clinical Medicine*, 5th edit., p. 86. Ed. by R. Daley and H. G. Miller. London: J. & A. Churchill.

Lancet (1967). Editorial: Hormones and Histones? **1,** 86.

ODELL, W. D. (1968). "Humoral Manifestations of Non-endocrine Neoplasms". In: *Textbook of Endocrinology*, 4th edit., Chap. 20, p. 1211. Ed. by R. H. Williams. Philadelphia: W. B. Saunders Co.

Chapter XXI

THE CEREBROSPINAL FLUID

CEREBROSPINAL fluid (CSF) is formed from plasma by the filtering and secretory activity of the choroid plexus, and is reabsorbed into the blood stream by the arachnoid villi. The mechanism of its production is not fully understood, but it seems in many ways to be, like the glomerular filtrate, an ultrafiltrate of plasma, since it contains very little protein, and the concentrations of electrolytes are mostly compatible with a Donnan effect due to the difference in protein content between CSF and plasma. Some active secretion of, for example, chloride may occur.

Circulation of CSF is very slow, allowing long contact with cerebral cells: their uptake of glucose may account for the relatively low concentration of this sugar in the CSF.

Concentrations of substances in the CSF should always be compared with those of plasma, as alterations in the latter are reflected in the CSF, even when cerebral metabolism is normal.

EXAMINATION OF THE CSF

Biochemical investigation of the CSF is usually of relatively little value compared with simple inspection and bacteriological and cytological examination of the fluid. Textbooks of bacteriology should be consulted for further details.

TAKING THE SAMPLE

CSF should be taken into sterile containers and sent for *bacteriological examination first*. Any remaining specimen can be used for relevant chemical investigations, but if the tests are performed in the opposite order bacteriological contamination may occur. If possible, a few millilitres of CSF should be taken into two or three separate containers (see below—Appearance of CSF).

Specimens for glucose estimation, like those for blood glucose, should be taken into a tube containing fluoride. This minimizes glycolysis, by any cells present, after the specimen has been taken.

APPEARANCE

Normal CSF is completely clear and colourless and should be compared with water: slight turbidity is most easily detected by this method.

Colour

Bright red blood may be due to:

1. A recent haemorrhage involving the subarachnoid space.
2. Damage to a blood vessel during puncture.

If CSF is taken into three tubes, these will be equally blood-stained in the first case and the later tubes progressively less so in the second.

Xanthochromia (yellow coloration).—This may be due to:

1. The presence of *altered haemoglobin* several days after a cerebral haemorrhage.
2. The presence of large amounts of *pus*. The cause will be obvious from the gross turbidity of the fluid, and from the presence of pus cells on microscopy.
3. The presence of *cerebral tumours* near the surface of the brain, impairing circulation of the CSF. Specimens from these cases have a very high protein content and tend to clot spontaneously after withdrawal due to the presence of fibrinogen. In Froin's syndrome due to blockage of the spinal canal there is also a reduced or absent Queckenstedt test (see textbooks of neurology).
4. *Jaundice* due to a rise in unconjugated bilirubin may impart a yellow colour to the CSF.

Turbidity

This is due to an *excess of white cells* (*pus*). Slight turbidity will, of course, occur after haemorrhage, but the cause of this will be apparent from the colour of the specimen.

Spontaneous Clotting

This occurs when there is an excess of fibrinogen in the specimen, usually associated with a high total protein content.

The following are the most frequently requested chemical estimations.

PROTEIN CONTENT

Normal CSF is mainly plasma ultrafiltrate and contains very little protein. The normal figures are usually quoted as 20–40 mg/100 ml. Quantitative estimation at this level is relatively inaccurate and little significance can be attached to concentrations up to 60 or 80 mg/100 ml.

Total Protein

CSF will have a high protein content under the following conditions:

1. In the presence of *blood* (due to haemoglobin and plasma proteins).

2. In the presence of *pus* (due to cell protein and exudation from inflamed surfaces).

These two causes will be obvious from inspection and microscopic examination of the specimen, and nothing further is to be gained by estimating protein.

3. In non-purulent inflammation of the cerebral tissues, when there is a moderate rise of protein concentration. It is when such conditions are suspected that the estimation is most useful:

Tuberculous meningitis
Syphilitic meningitis
Disseminated sclerosis
Encephalitis
Polyneuritis.

4. In Froin's syndrome due to blockage of the spinal canal, when stasis results in fluid reabsorption. There is xanthochromia and protein concentrations are very high (usually 500 mg/100 ml or more).

Tests for Abnormal Ratios of Proteins in the CSF

These tests are not useful in the presence of blood or pus. They may, however, detect abnormalities when the total protein is only equivocally increased.

In inflammatory conditions of the central nervous system there is often a disproportionate increase in γ globulin concentration compared with that of other protein fractions. This can be demonstrated by electrophoresis of CSF, but this is not a routine procedure. Excess of γ globulin may, however, be detected by tests similar in basis to the flocculation tests used on serum (p. 271). In the *Pandy* reaction turbidity is detected when the abnormal CSF is added to phenol and in the *Nonne-Apelt* reaction there is turbidity with ammonium sulphate.

The Lange colloidal gold reaction depends on precipitation of gold sol when the proportions of protein fractions are abnormal. Lange originally suggests serially diluting CSF with saline: precipitation varied from 0 (no precipitation) to 5 (complete precipitation). The differing protein concentration and pH in the consecutive tubes, resulting from serial dilution, affected precipitation and various patterns were said to be diagnostic of groups of pathological conditions. Thus, in the "paretic curve", said to be found in disseminated sclerosis and meningovascular syphilis, precipitation was high in the first tubes (with the highest proportion of CSF) and gradually lessened in the last tubes (with the highest proportion of saline), while in the "meningitic" curve of meningitis precipitation was maximal in the middle tubes. In practice, results are very variable, and no diagnostic reliance can be placed on the pattern: this may be because the precipitation is pH dependent, and the pH of water used can vary. It is probably better to use buffer solution instead of saline for the serial dilution: any precipitation will then be heaviest in the first tubes and the number of tubes involved is merely a reflection of the amount of γ globulin present. This test is probably of most value in cases of suspected *disseminated sclerosis* (*D.S.*), a condition in which a positive gold reaction occurs in about 50 per cent of cases, and in which this may be the only detectable abnormality in the CSF.

GLUCOSE CONTENT

Provided that CSF for glucose estimation has been mixed with fluoride a low glucose concentration occurs in:

1. Infection.
2. Hypoglycaemia.

1. CSF glucose is normally metabolized only by cerebral cells. If many leucocytes and bacteria are present these also utilize the sugar and abnormally low levels are obtained. If obvious pus is present the estimation of CSF glucose adds nothing to diagnostic precision. It is most useful when the CSF is clear and *tuberculous meningitis* is suspected.

2. CSF glucose concentration parallels that of blood. In the presence of hypoglycaemia (which may cause coma) CSF glucose levels may be low although there is no primary cerebral lesion. In case of doubt both blood and CSF concentrations should be measured.

In hyperglycaemia CSF glucose levels will be high.

CHLORIDE CONTENT

The chloride concentration in the CSF is higher than that in plasma by about 20 mEq/litre. This is mostly accounted for by the Donnan effect, the additional difference probably being due to secretion of the ion by the choroid plexus.

Changes in *CSF chloride concentration parallel those in plasma*. The level has been said to be lowered specifically in tuberculous meningitis, but there is evidence that this is merely a reflection of plasma chloride levels: tuberculous meningitis is of insidious onset and the patient often presents after some weeks of vomiting with chloride loss. CSF chloride estimation has no value as a diagnostic aid.

PROCEDURE FOR EXAMINATION OF CSF

CSF very cloudy.—Send for bacteriological examination. Chemical estimations unnecessary.

CSF heavily bloodstained in three consecutive specimens. Cerebral haemorrhage. Chemical estimation unnecessary.

CSF clear or only slightly turbid.—Send for bacteriological examination and for estimation of *glucose* and *protein* concentration. If there is any possibility that coma is due to hypoglycaemia send blood for glucose estimation at the same time. If D.S. or neurological syphilis is suspected the *Lange colloidal gold test* may be of value.

CSF xanthochromic and Queckenstedt sign reduced.—Send specimen for protein estimation. Examine under microscope for erythrocytes.

SUMMARY

1. Biochemical analysis of the CSF is less important than simple inspection and bacteriological examination.

2. Estimation of CSF protein concentration is most useful if non-purulent inflammation of cerebral tissues is suspected.

3. The Lange gold curve reflects an increase in CSF γ globulin, and is of most value when disseminated sclerosis or neurological syphilis are suspected.

4. Estimation of CSF glucose concentration is most useful in cases of suspected tuberculous meningitis.

5. CSF chloride estimation has no value as a diagnostic aid.

Chapter XXII

CHEMICAL PATHOLOGY AND
THE CLINICIAN

INTRODUCTION

THE study of chemical pathology is that of physiology and biochemistry applied to medical practice. In essence, like haematology, it is a clinical subject, and as such its study overlaps that of clinical medicine and surgery in particular. An understanding of the basis of chemical pathology, as we have seen, is essential for much diagnosis and treatment.

The medical student or the clinician need not know technical details of laboratory estimations, unless they are ones which he is likely to be called upon to perform himself. However, correct interpretation of laboratory results requires some understanding of both the acceptable analytical reproducibility and of physiological variations in normal individuals, and this subject will be discussed in the next chapter. It is also desirable that the clinician should be aware of the speed with which tests can be completed, and of laboratory organization in so far as it affects this; above all he should realize that the technique of collecting specimens can affect results drastically, and should co-operate with the laboratory in its attempt to produce rapid, accurate answers, quickly identifiable with the relevant patient. To this end he should understand the importance of accurately completed forms, correctly labelled specimens, taken at the right time by the right technique, and speedy delivery to the laboratory. In an emergency *therapy based on correctly estimated results from a wrongly labelled or collected specimen may be as lethal as faulty surgical technique*: moreover, even if the error is recognized, precious time could have been saved by a few minutes' thought and care in the first place. *An emergency situation warrants more, not less, than the usual accuracy in collection and identification of specimens.*

REQUEST FORMS

CLINICAL INFORMATION

Control of accuracy of results is largely the concern of the laboratory and most departments take stringent precautions to this end. However, when very large numbers of estimations are being handled it is impossible to be sure that every result is correct; fortunately the error rate is very low. The clinician can play his part by co-operating with the pathologist in minimizing the chance of error, not only by taking suitable specimens, but also by giving *relevant* clinical information. "Unlikely" results are checked in most laboratories and, for instance, if the blood urea concentration of a patient had fallen by 200 mg/100 ml in 24 hours, both estimations would be repeated before the latest was reported: on the other hand, if it were known that haemodialysis had been performed in the interval the result would have been an expected one and time, money and worry would have been saved. In this example "post-haemodialysis" would be more informative, and take no longer to write in the "Clinical Details" space than "chronic renal failure".

PATIENT IDENTIFICATION

Accurate information about the patient, including *surname* and *first names* correctly and consistently spelt, and legibly written, *age or date of birth* and *hospital case number* are essential for comparing current with previous results on the same patient. If the laboratory uses "cumulative" reporting, the results on each patient on successive days are entered on one form (Fig. 37): this type of form enables the clinician to see the progress of the patient more easily than he can when looking at a single result and, in addition, the laboratory can detect sudden changes, so that the cause can be sought. For the system to work successfully, accurate patient identification is essential: a surprising number of patients have the same names, even when these are apparently uncommon; it is less likely that they will also have the same age in years, and even less probable, the same date of birth; they will not have the same hospital number. Any of these items may be written inaccurately on the form, and unless there is complete agreement with previous details results can be entered on the wrong patient's record: this can lead to confusion, and even danger to the patient. Some large departments are beginning to use computers to report results: computers cannot think, telephone the ward, or make intelligent guesses, and if the information fed into them is inaccurate it may either be rejected or, worse still, results may be reported as belonging to another patient.

LOCATION OF THE PATIENT AND CLINICIAN

It is obvious that if the *ward or department* is not stated it may take time and trouble to find out where results should be sent. The Consultant's *name*, and the *signature of the doctor requesting the test* are desirable if urgent or alarming results are to be notified rapidly, and advice given about treatment.

DEPT. OF CHEMICAL PATHOLOGY, W.M.S. Tel. 2440

Clinical details:—

Thyrotoxicosis with vomiting

Case No. 12345   Consultant Dʳ X

Surname B····   Ward A.2

First Names E····   Sex F

Date of Birth 10.10.44

SERUM	H = Haemolysed	I = Insufficient	U = Unsuitable	* Duplicated Result
Lab. No.	A73 V8 A9 A95	A9V A95	A01 L8X A8T OX7	V34 X26 JS2
Date	4/2/69 6/2/69	21/2/69 24/2/69	24/2/69 3/3/69 6/3/69 7/3/69	14/3/69 13/4/69 12/7/69
Ca (mg/100ml)	13.8+ 13.2	9.2* 8.8	9.4 10.6 12.6+ 12.6	11.4 9.0 9.8
PO₄ (as P) (mg/100ml)	3.6 3.4	2.9 1.8	4.0 4.7 3.3 2.3	4.0 3.2 3.3
Alk. phos. (K.A. units)	1 19	15 14	16 14 15 1	1 20 22
T. Protein (g/100ml)	7.7 7.9	6.5 6.3	7.2 7.2 8.3 7.9	8.1 7.5 7.5
Urea (mg/100ml)	50 47	26 19	20 27 59 59	26 27 27
Corrected Calcium mg/100ml	13.3 12.7	9.7 9.6	9.4 10.6 11.8 12.1	10.7 8.7 9.5
Signature				

Annotations across the chart: STEROID SUPPRESSION TEST STARTED 17.2.66 — STEROIDS STOPPED 27/2/69 — VOMITING AGAIN — CARBIMAZOLE STARTED

FIG. 37.—A sample of cumulative reporting of the calcium group of tests on a patient with hypercalcaemia, showing the effect of steroids and carbimazole.

In some hospitals all types of result are reported on the same sheet.

C.C.

14

The forms designed by pathology departments ask only for information essential to ensure the most efficient possible service to the clinician and the patient. All pathologists have met the form containing as the only information "Smith"; sometimes not even the investigations requested are stated. Unless the pathologist is endowed with psychical powers it is difficult for him to help the clinician under these circumstances.

Addressograph Systems

Some hospitals are now using "Addressograph" labels. All the required information (except clinical details) can be printed on a set of these labels when the patient is admitted, and one label can be attached to each request form and another to its accompanying specimen. With this system the possibility of error is much reduced.

COLLECTION OF SPECIMENS
Collection of Blood

If the laboratory obtains a clinically improbable result on a specimen, it will usually check this on that specimen. If, as is usual, the second result agrees well with the first, a fresh specimen should be obtained. Before doing this it is essential to try to find out why the first one gave a false answer (if it was false). Contamination of the syringe, needle or tube into which the specimen was collected, although an obvious possibility, is relatively rare in these days of disposable apparatus. It should not be accepted as the cause until other more common ones have been excluded.

The errors to be discussed below, and which arise outside the laboratory are, in our experience, relatively common. Any examples given are genuine ones.

Effect on Results of Procedures Prior to Venepuncture

(a) **Oral medication.**—Specimens should not be taken to measure a substance just after a large oral dose of the same substance has been given. For example, in the presence of iron deficiency, plasma iron concentration may rise to normal, or even high, levels for a few hours after a large dose of oral iron.

(b) **Interfering substances.**—Previous administration of a substance may affect serum levels for some time. For instance, administration of iodide in cough medicines, ointment or, even more seriously, in radiological contrast media, will result in apparently raised protein bound iodine levels for some days, weeks or even months. Iodine, of course, not only affects blood levels, but will cause a falsely low thyroid uptake of radio-iodine (p. 163).

(c) **Massage of prostate.**—The prostate contains tartrate labile acid phosphatase and the serum concentration of this enzyme is used as an index of spread of carcinoma of the gland (p. 292). However, massage of a non-malignant prostate may release relatively large amounts of this enzyme into the blood stream. These false levels may persist for several days after rectal examination, passage of a catheter, of even after straining at stool. For example, a specimen was received by the department from a patient who had had a rectal examination a few hours previously. The tartrate labile acid phosphatase level was 2·4 K.A. units (the upper normal for this laboratory is 0·9 K.A. units). Three days later a further specimen gave a level of 1·5 K.A. units— still raised. At eight days after the examination, however, the concentration was only 0·2 K.A. units.

Any marginally raised tartrate labile acid phosphatase level should be checked on a specimen taken a few days later. If possible, blood for this estimation should be withdrawn before performing a rectal examination. If, as is often the case, the result of such an examination suggests the need for the estimation it is best, if possible, to wait a week before taking blood. To save time, the specimen may be taken immediately and *a note made on the request form to the effect that rectal examination has been performed.* If the result is normal no further action is required and time has been saved: if it is not, another specimen will be requested.

Effect on Results of Technique of Venesection

(a) **Venous stasis.**—When blood is taken a tourniquet is usually applied proximally to the site of puncture to ensure that the vein "stands out", and is easier to enter with the needle. If this occlusion is maintained for more than a short time, the combined effect of raised intravenous pressure and anoxia of the vein wall results in passage of water and small molecules from the lumen into the surrounding extracellular fluid. Large molecules, such as protein, and erythrocytes and other cells cannot pass through the vein wall: their concentration therefore rises. It should be remembered that there will not only be a rise in total protein levels but also in all protein fractions, and day to day variations in these can often be attributed to this factor.

Many plasma constituents are, at least partially, bound to protein in the blood stream. Prolonged stasis can falsely raise calcium concentrations (Fig. 38), possibly to high or equivocal levels. If such levels are found it is important to take another specimen, without stasis, for analysis.

Prolonged stasis, with associated local anoxia, may also cause such intracellular constituents as potassium to leak from the local cells into the plasma, causing falsely high potassium results.

Many patients have "bad veins", difficult to enter without stasis. Under such circumstances a tourniquet may be applied until the needle is in the vein lumen; if it is now released, and a few seconds allowed before removal of blood, a suitable specimen will be obtained.

(b) **Site of venepuncture.**—Many patients requiring chemical pathological investigations are receiving intravenous infusions. In veins in the same limb, whether proximal or distal to the infusion site, the drip fluid has not mixed with the whole of the blood volume; local concentrations will therefore be unrepresentative of that circulating in the rest of the patient. Blood taken from the opposite arm will, however, give valid results.

The following example illustrates the point well. The clinical details were given as "post-op". On the previous day the electrolytes had been normal, the plasma urea 100 mg/100 ml, and the plasma total protein 6·7 g/100 ml. The relevant results on the day in question were as follows:

Plasma sodium	65 mEq/litre
Plasma potassium	2·2 mEq/litre
Plasma bicarbonate	11 mEq/litre
Plasma protein	5·2 g/100 ml
Plasma urea	52 mg/100 ml

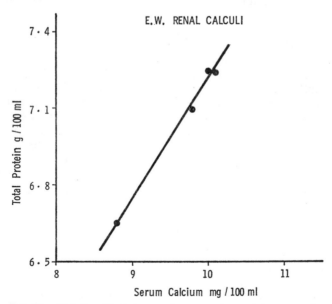

FIG. 38.—Relationship between plasma total protein and calcium concentrations.

The patient was "doing well". As all measured constituents were diluted it was assumed that dextrose was being infused. A plasma sugar of 900 mg/100 ml supported this view. A call to the ward confirmed that the specimen had been taken from the arm into which a dextrose infusion was flowing. Analysis of blood taken from the opposite arm gave results almost identical with those of the previous day.

Such an extreme example as this is easily detected and, although time has been wasted and the patient subjected to two venepunctures, no serious harm is done. If, for example, physiologically normal saline is being infused, electrolyte results might *appear* to be correct. Under such circumstances the wrong therapy might be applied.

If no veins are available in another limb a suitable sample can be obtained by stopping the infusion, disconnecting the tubing from the needle, aspirating 20–30 ml of blood through this needle and discarding before taking the specimen for analysis.

Containers for Blood

Many hospital laboratories issue a list of the types of container required for each specimen, and this will vary slightly from hospital to hospital. For instance, most departments require that fluoride be added to blood taken for glucose estimation: this inhibits glycolysis, which would otherwise continue in the presence of erythrocytes.

To ensure accuracy of results laboratories will only accept blood in the correct containers. However, errors can arise if blood is decanted from one container to another. Oxalate and sequestrene (ethylene-diamine tetracetate, EDTA) act as anticoagulants by removing or chelating calcium. Estimation of the latter is therefore invalidated by the presence of these chemicals. The potassium salt of sequestrene is usually used and this will invalidate potassium estimation: sodium oxalate (and sodium heparin instead of lithium heparin) would, of course, upset sodium estimations.

As an example blood was received from the out-patient department apparently in the correct tube. Clinical details were "uretero-sigmoidostomy". A calcium value of 1·6 mg/100 ml was obtained. The plasma potassium was 7·5 mEq/litre in spite of the fact that the patient felt very well. Enquiry confirmed that blood had been taken, at the same time, into a sequestrene bottle (for haematological investigations), and that to bring the blood level in the tube "to the mark" some had been tipped into that for chemical pathology.

Effects of Storage and Haemolysis of Blood

Erythrocytes contain very different concentrations of many substances from those of the surrounding plasma (for instance the potassium concentrations are about 25 times as high). If haemolysis occurs the contents will "leak out" and false answers will be obtained on plasma. Plasma from haemolyzed blood is red and this will be detected by the laboratory. To minimize the chance of haemolysis blood should be treated gently. The plunger of the syringe should not be drawn back too fast, and there should be an easy flow of blood. The needle should be removed from the syringe before the specimen is expelled *gently* into the correct container.

The maintenance of differential concentrations across the red cell wall requires energy, which is supplied by glycolysis. In whole blood outside the body the erythrocytes will soon use up available glucose (hence the need for fluoride in blood glucose specimens), after which no energy source remains: concentrations in erythrocytes and plasma will tend to equalize by passive diffusion across cell membranes. If blood is left unseparated for more than an hour or two the effect on plasma levels will, therefore, be the same as that of haemolysis, with the important difference that, to the naked eye, the plasma looks normal. If the container is undated, or wrongly dated, the error may not be detected. It is important to separate plasma from red cells before storing (even in the refrigerator) overnight.

COLLECTION OF URINE

Many urine estimations are carried out on timed specimens. Because of large diurnal variations in excretion only qualitative tests, or those for tubular concentrating ability, are performed on random collections. Results are expressed as units/time (for example, g/24 hours), and to calculate this figure the concentration (for example, g/ml) is multiplied by the total volume collected. Clearance estimations, too, depend on comparing the amount of, for example, urea excreted per minute with its concentration in the blood (p. 16). In both these examples the accuracy of the final answer depends largely on that of the urine collection: this latter is surprisingly difficult to ensure. In some cases the difficulty is insurmountable unless a catheter is inserted, and this is undesirable because of the risk of urinary infection: for instance, the patient may be incontinent or, because of prostatic hypertrophy or neurological lesions, be incapable of complete bladder emptying. However, more often errors arise because of a misunderstanding on the part of the nurse, doctor or patient collecting the specimen.

Let us suppose that a 24-hour collection is required between 8 a.m. on Monday and 8 a.m. on Tuesday. The volume *secreted by the kidneys* during this time is the crucial one: urine already in the bladder at the start of the test and secreted some time before should not be included; that in the bladder at the end of the test and secreted between the relevant times *should* be included. The procedure is therefore as follows:

8 a.m. on Monday—Empty bladder completely. Discard specimen.
Collect all urine passed until:
    8 a.m. on Tuesday—Empty bladder completely. *Add this to the collection.*

The error of not carrying out this procedure is very great for short (for example, hourly) collections of urine.

A preservative must usually be added to the urine to prevent bacterial growth and destruction of the substance being estimated. Before starting the collection the bottle containing the correct preservative should be obtained from the laboratory.

COLLECTION OF FAECES

Rectal emptying is much more erratic than bladder emptying, and cannot usually be performed to order. Estimations of 24-hourly faecal content of, say, fat may vary by several hundred per cent from day to day. If the collection were continued for long enough the *mean* 24-hourly output would be very close to the true daily loss from the body (which includes that in faeces in the rectum at any time). There must be a reasonable compromise on time, and most laboratories collect for between 3 and 5 days. Provided that the patient is not constipated the mean daily loss is usually reasonably representative: if no stool is passed during this period, excess faecal loss of any kind is most unlikely, and the test probably unnecessary. To render the collection more accurate many departments use coloured "markers" (see Appendix to Chapter IX).

Faecal estimations and collections are time consuming and unpleasant for all concerned. It is important that *every* specimen passed during the time of collection is sent to the laboratory if a worthwhile answer is to be obtained. Administration of purgatives or enemas during the test alters conditions and invalidates the answer.

LABELLING SPECIMENS

It is important to label a specimen accurately to correspond with the accompanying form in all particulars. The date, and sometimes the time of taking the specimen should be included, and should be written *at the time* of collection. If it is done in advance the clinician may change his mind, and the information will be incorrect; there is also the danger of using a container with one patient's name on it for another patient's specimen.

Blood Specimens

Specimens in wrongly labelled tubes may cause danger to one or more patients. The date of the specimen is important, both from the

TABLE XXVI
Some Extra-laboratory Factors Leading to False Results

Cause of error	Consequence
Keeping blood overnight before sending to laboratory.	High serum K, total acid phosphatase, LDH, SHBD, amino-transferases.
Haemolysis of blood.	As above.
Prolonged venous stasis during vene-section.	High serum Ca, total protein and all protein fractions.
Taking blood from arm with infusion running into it.	Electrolyte and sugar results approaching composition of drip fluid. Dilution of everything else.
Putting blood into "wrong" bottle or tipping it from this into Chemical Pathology tube.	e.g. EDTA or oxalate cause low Ca, with high Na or K.
Blood for sugar not put into fluoride tube.	Low sugar (fluoride inhibits glycolysis by erythrocytes).
Massage of prostate by P.R., passage of catheter, enema, etc., in last few days.	High tartrate labile acid phosphatase.
Inaccurately timed urine collection.	False timed urinary excretion values (e.g. per 24 hours). False and erratic renal clearance values.
Loss of stools during faecal fat collection. Failure to collect for long period between markers.	False faecal fat result.
Therapy with iodine, IVP, angiogram, etc.	Falsely low radio-iodine result. Falsely high PBI result.
Therapy with antithyroid drugs.	False radio-iodine result.
Patient with pyrexia, oedema, malignancy.	"False" BMR result.

clinical point of view, and as discussed on p. 395, to assess the suitability of the specimen for the estimation requested. It is important to state the time when a specimen was taken, particularly if the concentration of the substance being measured varies during the day: for instance blood glucose varies according to the time since the last meal.

If more than one specimen is sent for the same estimation on one day *each must be timed* so that it is known in which order they were taken.

Urine and Faecal Specimens

Timed urine specimens should be labelled with the date and time of starting and completing the collection, so that the volume per unit time is known. Faecal collections are best labelled, not only with date and time, but with the specimen number in the series of 5-day collections, so that the absence of a specimen is immediately obvious.

SENDING THE SPECIMEN TO THE LABORATORY

If, in an emergency, a result is needed quickly, many types of estimations can be carried out in a short time. However, it is more economical in staff, reagents and time, as well as easier to organize, if estimations are batched as far as possible. For this reason most laboratories like to receive non-urgent specimens early in the morning. A constant "trickle" of specimens may cause delay in reporting the whole batch, and possibly in noticing a result requiring urgent treatment.

If a patient is seen for the first time later in the day and the results are not required urgently, the specimen should be sent to the laboratory with a note to that effect. Plasma can then be separated from cells and stored overnight.

In cases of true clinical emergency, the department should be notified. The clinical details warranting urgency may be given on the form, but preferably the laboratory should be warned before the specimen is taken, so that it may be prepared to deal with it quickly. Usually a specimen not known to require urgent attention, and certainly one accompanied by no information about clinical details, will be assumed to be non-urgent. It is the clinician's responsibility to indicate the degree of urgency.

Table XXVI summarizes some of the errors which have been discussed in this chapter.

SUMMARY

The clinician's responsibility for maintaining accuracy and speed of reporting of results includes:

Taking a suitable specimen
    (*a*) At a time when a previous procedure will not interfere with the result (p. 392).
    (*b*) From a suitable vein (p. 394).
    (*c*) With as little stasis as possible (p. 393).
    (*d*) With precautions to avoid haemolysis (p. 395).

Putting the specimen in the correct container (p. 395).

Labelling the specimen accurately (p. 397).

Completing the form accurately, including *relevant* clinical details (p. 389).

Ensuring that the specimen reaches the laboratory without delay, and that plasma is separated from cells before storing the specimen (p. 395).

In the case of urine and faeces, collecting accurate and complete timed specimens (p. 396).

Chapter XXIII

INTERPRETING RESULTS

BEFORE considering diagnosis or therapy based on a result received from the laboratory the clinician should ask himself three questions:

1. If it is the first estimation performed on this patient, is it normal or abnormal?

2. If it is abnormal, is the abnormality of diagnostic value or is it a non-specific finding?

3. If it is one of a series of results, has there been a change, and if so is this change clinically significant?

IS THE RESULT NORMAL?

NORMAL RANGES

The normal range of, for example, blood urea is often quoted as between 20 and 40 mg/100 ml. It is clearly ridiculous to assume that a result of 39 mg/100 ml is normal, while one of 41 mg/100 ml is not. Just as there is no clear-cut demarcation between "normal" and "abnormal" for body weight and height, the same applies to any other measurement which may be made.

The majority of a normal population will have a value for any constituent near the mean value for the population as a whole, and all the values will be distributed around this mean, the frequency with which any one occurs decreasing as the distance from the mean increases. There will be a range of values where "normals" and "abnormals" overlap (Fig. 39): all that can be said with certainty is that the *probability* that a value is abnormal increases the further it is from the mean until, eventually, this probability approaches 100 per cent. For instance, there is no reasonable doubt that a blood urea value of 300 mg/100 ml is abnormal, whereas at 45 mg/100 ml it is possible that it is normal for the individual concerned.

To stress this uncertainty on the borders of the normal values it is better to quote limits between which values for 90 and 95 per cent of the "normal" population fall, than to give a "normal range". Statistically the 95 per cent limits are two standard deviations from the mean. Although the probability is high that a value outside these limits is abnormal, obviously 2·5 per cent of the "normal" population may have such a value at either end. The range of variation for a single subject is usually less than that for the population as a whole.

In assessing a result one can only take all factors, including the clinical picture, into account, and reach some estimate of the probability of its being normal.

PHYSIOLOGICAL DIFFERENCES

Certain physiological factors affect interpretation of results. For instance, the "normal" levels of plasma uric acid or iron vary with *sex*, being higher in males than in females (pp. 303 and 311); the blood

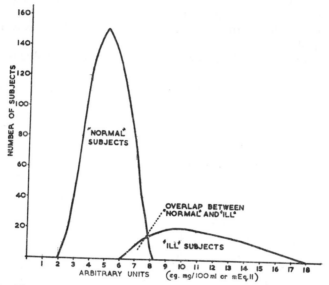

FIG. 39.—Theoretical distributions of values for "normal" and "ill" subjects, showing overlap at upper end of "normal range".

urea concentration tends to rise with *age* especially in male subjects, and normal values in children are often different from those in adults; in different parts of the world mean values of many parameters are different, either because of *racial* or *regional* factors.

It is clear, therefore, that we are not so much expressing "normal" values as the most usual ones for a given population. A blood urea level remaining at 45 mg/100 ml at the age of 20 suggests mild renal impairment, which may progress to clinically severe damage in later life: the same value at the age of 70 suggests the same degree of renal impairment, but usually the subject will die of some other disease before this becomes severe. In other words, this rising mean value of urea with age is not strictly normal and probably does reflect disease. Note that we are talking of *mean* values for a population of a certain age: in an individual there may be no change with advancing years.

DIFFERENCES BETWEEN LABORATORIES

From the above discussion will be seen that, even if the same method is used in the same laboratory, it is difficult to define a normal range clearly. With some constituents interpretation becomes even more difficult if results obtained in different laboratories are compared, because different analytical methods may be used. For most estimations agreement between reliable laboratories is close. However, with certain constituents, such as serum proteins and especially albumin, different methods, even in the best hands, give different results: this reflects the fact that different techniques measure different properties of protein, and that different methods of fractionation do not necessarily separate exactly the same fractions. If reproducibility is acceptable, one method is often no better than another for clinical purposes, provided that the results are compared with the "normals" for the laboratory in which the estimation was performed and provided that serial estimations are carried out by the same method.

IS THE ABNORMALITY OF DIAGNOSTIC VALUE?

Serum or plasma values express extracellular concentrations. Moreover, some abnormalities are non-specific and of no diagnostic or therapeutic import.

RELATIONSHIP BETWEEN PLASMA AND CELLULAR LEVELS

Intracellular constituents are not easily estimated, and plasma levels do not always reflect the situation in the body as a whole; this is particularly true for such constituents as potassium, which have very high intracellular concentrations compared with those in the surrounding fluid. A normal, or even high, plasma potassium concentration may be associated with cellular depletion, if conditions are such that the equilibrium across cell membranes is disturbed (for instance, in acidosis and dehydration).

RELATIONSHIP BETWEEN EXTRACELLULAR CONCENTRATIONS AND TOTAL BODY CONTENT

The numerical value of a concentration depends not only on what we are measuring, but also on the amount of water in which it is dissolved (for instance, mEq/litre). A low plasma sodium is not necessarily (or even usually) due to sodium depletion: it is more often due to water excess. Under such circumstances there may even be excess of sodium in the body (p. 47). Conversely, hypernatraemia is more often due to water deficit than sodium excess (p. 41). It is very important to recognize this fact and adapt therapy accordingly. It has already been noted that protein concentrations can be affected by stasis during venesection, but if this factor is eliminated, significant day to day variations of protein concentration over a short period of time can be used to assess changes of hydration of the patient (in other words, the amount of protein is not, but that of water is, changing significantly).

NON-SPECIFIC ABNORMALITIES

Serum albumin, calcium and iron levels, for example, vary considerably in diseases unrelated to a primary defect in metabolism. Albumin concentrations can fall to below normal during quite minor illnesses, acute or chronic. Routine laboratory methods for calcium measure the total protein bound + ionized concentrations: changes in albumin levels are associated with changes in those of the calcium bound to it, without an alteration of the physiologically important ionized fraction, and this can occur either artefactually, as discussed on p. 191, or with true changes in albumin. It is most important not to attempt to raise the total calcium level to normal in the presence of significant hypoalbuminaemia. Plasma iron is very labile, and levels can fall in the presence of anaemia other than that of iron deficiency: giving iron, especially by parenteral routes, to patients with anaemia and a low plasma iron can be dangerous unless other, more reliable, evidence of iron deficiency is present (p. 316).

HAS THERE BEEN A CLINICALLY SIGNIFICANT CHANGE?

To interpret day to day changes in results, and to decide whether the patient's biochemical state has altered, one must know the degree of variation to be expected in results from a normal population.

REPRODUCIBILITY OF LABORATORY ESTIMATIONS

In reliable laboratories most estimations should give results reproducible to well within 5 per cent: some (such as calcium) should be even more reproducible. Changes of less than the reproducibility of the method are probably clinically insignificant.

PHYSIOLOGICAL VARIATIONS

Physiological variations occur in both plasma levels and urinary excretion rates of many substances and false impressions may be gained from results of several types of investigation if this fact is not taken into account.

Physiological variations may be regular or random.

1. **Regular variations.**—Regular changes occur throughout the 24-hour period (diurnal or circadian rhythms, like that of body temperature), or the month: there may be seasonal variations. The causes of these are often obscure. There is a marked diurnal variation in the urinary excretion of, for example, electrolytes, steroids, phosphate and water. For this reason estimates of loss carried out on accurate 24-hour collections are more valuable than measurements of concentration of random specimens. In interpreting such results the effect of diet and of fluid intake should be remembered: because of these effects it is difficult to give "normal" values for many urinary constituents (for example, of electrolytes).

Blood sugar concentration varies with the time after a meal, and plasma protein concentration varies with posture (it is lower in the supine than in the erect position). Serum iron shows very marked diurnal variation, apparently unrelated to meals or other activity: it may fall by 50 per cent between morning and evening. The diurnal variation of plasma cortisol is of diagnostic importance (p. 97), and it should be remembered that superimposed on this regular variation "stress" will cause acute rises. To eliminate the unwanted effect of diurnal variation blood should, ideally, always be taken at the same time of day (preferably in the early morning, with the patient fasting). This is not always possible, so that these variations should be borne in mind when interpreting results. Correct interpretation of blood glucose levels requires an estimation on blood taken with the patient fasting, or at a set time after a known dose of glucose (p. 137).

Some constituents show monthly cycles, especially in women (again, compare body temperature). These can be very marked in the case of serum iron, which may fall to very low levels just before the onset of menstruation (p. 311). There are also, probably, seasonal variations in some constituents: study of these is in the very early stages.

Although some of these changes, such as those of blood sugar related to meals, have obvious causes, many of them appear to be regulated by a so-called "biological clock", which may be, but often is not, affected by the alternation of light and dark.

2. **Random variations.**—Day to day variations in, for instance, serum iron levels are very large, and may swamp regular changes (p. 311). The causes of these are not clear, but they should be allowed for when interpreting serial results. The effect of "stress" on plasma cortisol levels has already been mentioned.

CONSULTATION WITH THE LABORATORY STAFF

The object of citing the examples given in this, and in the preceding chapter, is not to confuse the clinician, but to stress the pitfalls of interpretation of a figure taken in isolation. On most occasions, if care has been exercised while taking the specimen, a diagnosis can be made and therapy instituted by relating the result to the clinical state of the patient. However, if there is any doubt about the correct type of specimen required, or about the interpretation of a result, consultation between the clinician and chemical pathologist or biochemist can be helpful to both sides.

Laboratory errors do, inevitably, occur in the best-regulated departments. However, a discrepant result should not be assumed to be due to this. Consultation may help to find the cause. The estimation may already have been checked, and if it has not the laboratory is usually willing to do so in case of doubt. If it has already been checked, a fresh specimen should be sent to the laboratory after consultation to determine why the first specimen was unsuitable. If the result is still the same every effort must be made to find the cause.

Laboratory staff of all grades often take an active interest in patients whom they are investigating. On their side they often take trouble to keep the clinician informed of changes requiring urgent action, and they may suggest further useful tests: the clinician should reciprocate by giving the pathologist information relevant to the interpretation of a result, and of the clinical outcome of an "interesting" problem. Such exchange of ideas and information is in the best interests of the patient.

SUMMARY

In interpreting results the following facts should be borne in mind:

1. The "normal range" only indicates the *probability* of a result being normal (p. 401).

2. There are physiological differences in normal ranges (p. 402) and physiological variations from day to day (p. 404).

3. There are small day to day variations in results due to technical factors (p. 403) and "normal ranges" may vary with the laboratory technique employed (p. 403).

4. Using plasma or serum, extracellular concentrations are being measured. These depend on the amount of water in the extracellular compartment, as well as that of the constituent measured, and may be a very poor reflection of intracellular levels (p. 403).

5. Changes in a given constituent may be non-specific, and unrelated to a primary defect in the metabolism of that constituent (p. 404).

Finally, when in doubt, two heads are better than one. Pathologists and clinicians tend to see things from slightly different angles and full consultation between the two is in the patient's best interest.

APPENDIX A

ANALOGIES

In this book chemical pathology has been discussed in systems. However, many principles of physiology are general to several systems, and learning is helped if these principles are recognized. It is easier to learn something once than several times, and it is easier to learn with understanding than by rote.

I. Some Tests Based on Similar Principles

1. Tests for minor degrees of dysfunction, necessary only if basal investigations are normal and disease is still suspected.

    Glucose tolerance test (p. 138).
    Renal clearance tests (p. 16).
    Bromsulphthalein retention test (p. 270).
    Stimulation tests
        TSH (p. 164).
        ACTH or Synacthen (p. 100).
    Suppression tests
        T_3 (p. 164).
        Dexamethasone (p. 97).

2. Stimulation tests based on direct stimulation of an endocrine gland by a pituitary hormone.

    TSH (thyroid) (p. 164).
    ACTH or Synacthen (Adrenal) (p. 100).

Note that in both these tests primary disease of the gland is associated with failure to respond, and response is not increased by a second dose of the stimulating substance: if the disease is secondary to pituitary failure response may be stepwise.

3. Suppression tests based on pituitary or hypothalamic feed-back, and distinguishing autonomous overaction of a gland from that due to stimulation by pituitary or hypothalamic hormones.

    T_3 (thyroid) (p. 164).
    Dexamethasone (adrenal) (p. 97).

4. Tests based on stimulation of the hypothalamic stress centre by hypoglycaemia.

    Insulin stimulation of gastric secretion (p. 221).
    Insulin stimulation of cortisol secretion (p. 103).
    Insulin stimulation of growth hormone secretion (p. 123).

II. Some Analogies between Intestinal and Renal Tubular Transport

1. Group transport mechanisms, e.g. for amino-acids, are often the same (p. 338).

2. Both transfer substances *through* cells. Other cells transport them in the same direction on all sides of the cell.

3. Analogous *reabsorption* in the proximal renal tubule and small intestine with isosmotic reabsorption of water.

4. *Exchanges* and final adjustment in distal renal tubule and colon.

III. Some Effects Due to Substances Slowly Transported into Cells

These produce osmotic effects with:

1. Osmotic diuresis in the kidney (p. 7).
   Mannitol.
   Urea, sodium, sugar, etc., to lesser extent.

2. Diarrhoea and abdominal discomfort in the intestine.
   Lactose or other disaccharide intolerance (p. 218).
   "Dumping syndrome" (p. 214).
   Large oral dose of xylose (p. 224).

3. Changes in cellular hydration which may be dangerous if blood levels are altered rapidly. Such substances can be *used* to treat cellular overhydration.
   Urea.
   Sodium.
   Sugar.

4. Rapid changes in ionized calcium produce changes in neuromuscular activity.

IV. Substances Carried Bound to Protein

Total concentrations of the substance may be affected by changes in that of the relevant protein without any change in the physiologically important fraction, or in body content.

	Bound to	*Altered in*
Calcium	Albumin	Hypoalbuminaemia
		Changes in hydration
		Stasis during venesection
Cortisol	Cortisol binding globulin	⎫ Pregnancy and oral
Thyroxine	Thyroxine binding globulin	⎬ contraceptive therapy
Iron	Transferrin	⎭ Hypoproteinaemic states

Note that in alkalosis and acidosis the physiologically important ionized calcium fraction is altered without a change in total plasma calcium concentration (p. 176).

V. Substances of which Plasma Concentrations are Affected under the Same Circumstances

1. Substances which diffuse slowly, if at all, into cells, and whose concentration in plasma is affected by the amount of water, even if the total amount stays constant.
   Sodium.
   Chloride.
   Protein and protein bound substances, especially calcium.
   Haemoglobin and haematocrit.

Note that hydration affects plasma urea concentrations not so much by direct dilution or concentration of ECF, but mainly by changing GFR.

Concentrations of substances which diffuse easily into cells, or which are predominantly intracellular tend to remain stable during changes of hydration.

2. Substances which are intracellular or stored, and of which plasma levels are a poor reflection of total body amount.

Intracellular—These can diffuse out of cells *in vitro* (p. 395).

Potassium.
Phosphate.
Stored.
Iron.

3. Substances of which plasma concentrations are increased by tissue breakdown.

Urea.
Potassium.
Hydrogen ion.
Urate.

VI. Analogous Effects in Bicarbonate Metabolism

H_2CO_3 is formed from CO_2 and water, catalyzed by carbonic anhydrase.

1. In the erythrocyte. The H^+ is buffered by haemoglobin and HCO_3^- moves into the ECF (in exchange for chloride).

2. In the renal tubular cell. The H^+ is secreted into the urine in exchange for sodium and HCO_3^- moves into the ECF.

In both cases disposal of H^+ is linked with extracellular HCO_3^- repletion.
In both cases K^+ "competes" with H^+.

VII. Relatively Insoluble Substances which may Precipitate in the Kidney or Renal Tract and Cause Renal Damage or Calculi

Calcium (p. 178)   More soluble in acid urine.

Urate (p. 303)
Cystine (p. 339)   } More soluble in alkaline urine.

VIII. Conditions in which Patchy Damage to an Organ results in "Overaction" of the Normal Areas

Pulmonary disease with low arterial P_{O_2} (failure) and low P_{CO_2} (p. 85).

Chronic renal failure, with high plasma urea level (failure) and polyuria (p. 14).

INDEX

INDEX

The main page references are in **bold** type

Abetalipoproteinaemia, 261
Acetazolamide and acidosis, 73
Acetest, 154
Acetoacetate, 132
Acetone, 132
Acetyl cholinesterase, 295
Acetyl CoA, 127
  fatty acid metabolism and, 131, 132
  ketone production and, 131, 132
  pantothenic acid and, 358
  thiamine and, 356
Achlorhydria, 220
Acid, definition, 60
  gastric, 219
  strong and weak, 60
Acidosis, Addison's disease and, 93
  bicarbonate depletion and, 75
  calcium, ionized and, 176
  causes, **69**
  diabetes and, 141
  effects, 69, 73
  glomerular filtration rate and, 9, 67
  glycogen storage disease and, 148
  hyperchloraemic, 68
  "mixed", 75
  potassium excess and, 79
  potassium, plasma level, effect on, 76
  renal failure and, 71
  renal tubular, 72
  respiratory, 73
  tubular damage and, 12
Acromegaly, **116**
  BMR and, 170
  diabetes and, 130
  lactation and, 117
ACTH (*see* Adrenocorticotrophic
  hormone), 101, **117**
ACTH stimulation test, **109**
  Addison's disease and, 100
  corticosteroid therapy and, 104
  Cushing's syndrome and, 98
  hypopituitarism and, 103, 122
Active transport, 2
Acute tubular necrosis, 13
  treatment, 18
Addison's disease, **93**
  ACTH in, 94, 118
  causes, 99
  congenital adrenal hyperplasia and,
   106
  diagnosis, 99
  pseudo, 43
  sodium depletion and, 43

Adenohypophysis, **112**
ADH (*see* Antidiuretic hormone), 4, 36
Adipolytic lipase, 256
Adipose tissue, metabolism of, 255
Adrenal hypofunction, primary, **93**
  causes, 99
  diagnosis, 99
Adrenal hypofunction, secondary, **100**
Adrenaline, **374**
  glycogen and, 129
  hyperglycaemia and, 132
  stimulation of secretion, 129
  stress and, 129, 132
Adrenocorticotrophic hormone, 101, **117**
  Addison's disease and, 94, 100
  adrenal steroid synthesis and, 94
  congenital adrenal hyperplasia and,
   106
  Cushing's syndrome and, 96
  ectopic production, 96, **380**
  excess, 117
  hypopituitarism and, 101, 121
  secondary adrenal hypofunction and,
   101, 121
Agammaglobulinaemia, 245
ALA (*see* δ-Aminolaevulinic acid), 323
Alanine aminotransferase, **287**
  liver disease and, 272
ALA synthetase, 323, 329
Albinism, 343
Albumin, **232**
  bilirubin, plasma and, 232, 264
  calcium, plasma and, 176, 188, 191
  flocculation tests and, 229, 271
  nephrotic syndrome and, 11
  oedema and, 33, 46
  thyroxine binding and, 159
  water distribution and, 32
Alcohol, hypoglycaemia and, 145
Aldolase, 292, 296
Aldosterone, **34, 91**
  congenital adrenal hyperplasia and,
   104
  control of, 34
  hypopituitarism and, 101
  renin-angiotensin and, 35
  secondary adrenal hypofunction and,
   101
  sodium, urinary and, 48
  synthesis of, 94
Aldosteronism, primary, **45**
Aldosteronism, secondary, **46**
Alkali, definition of, 60

Alkalosis, 77
  aldosteronism, primary and, 46
  calcium, ionized and, 52, **176**
  causes, 77
  Cushing's syndrome and, 93
  glomerular filtration rate and, 67
  milk-alkali syndrome and, 186
  potassium depletion and, 49, **79**
  pyloric stenosis and, 77
  respiratory, 79
  tetany and, 52, 176
Alkaptonuria, 150, **343**
Allopurinol, 304
Amenorrhoea, 120
Ametazole hydrochloride, 221
Amino-acids, absorption, 207
  gluconeogenesis and, 127
  insulin secretion and, 129
  liver disease and, 276
  reabsorption in kidney, 2
    in tubular damage, 12
Aminoaciduria, **338**
  cystinosis and, 339
  cystinuria and, 338
  Fanconi syndrome and, 338
  galactosaemia and, 344
  glycine iminoaciduria and, 338
  Hartnup disease and, 339
  maple syrup urine disease and, 340
  overflow, 338, 340
  renal, 338
  tubular damage and, 12
  Wilson's disease and, 345
δ-Aminolaevulinic acid, 323
  acquired cutaneous hepatic porphyria
    and, 328
  acute intermittent porphyria and, 326
  hereditary coproporphyria and, 328
  lead poisoning and, 329
  porphyria variegata and, 327
  porphyrin synthesis and, 323
Aminotransferase, alanine, **287**
  in liver disease, 272
Aminotransferase, aspartate, **287**
  in liver disease, 272
Ammonia, buffering and, 66
  glutaminase and, 66
  intestinal production, 263
  ureteric transplantation and, 76
  urinary, 66
Ammonium chloride loading test, 88
Amylase, **289**
  acute pancreatitis and, 215
  carbohydrate digestion and, 126, 206
  pancreatic function and, 215
  renal failure and, 215
  salivary, 206
Amyloidosis in myelomatosis, 241
Anaemia, investigation of, 315
  iron absorption and, 309

Anaemia, "iron deficiency without", 315
  iron overload and, 316, 320
  iron, plasma and, 312
  malabsorption and, 214
  megaloblastic, 359
  myelomatosis and, 241
  pyridoxine responsive, 312, 358
  renal failure and, 17
  scurvy and, 362
  sideroblastic, 312, 315
Analbuminaemia, 232
Androgens, 91
  Addison's disease and, 93, 94
  congenital adrenal hyperplasia and,
    104
  Cushing's syndrome and, 93
  ovary and, 119
  synthesis in adrenal, 94
  testis and, 92
Aneurine, **355**
Angiotensin, 35
Anoxia and acidosis, 69
Antibiotics, jaundice and, 278
  macrocytic anaemia and, 216
  steatorrhoea and, 216
Antidiuretic hormone, 4, **36**
  control of, 36
  "inappropriate" secretion, 43, **379**
  osmolarity, plasma and, 36
  osmolarity, urine and, 4
  sodium, plasma concentration and, 36
  specific gravity, urinary and, 36
  synthesis of, 114
  water depletion and, 38
Apoferritin, 309
Argentaffinoma, 373
Arginine, insulin, secretion and, 129
  cystinuria and, 338
Ariboflavinosis, 357
Ascorbic acid, **360**
Ascorbic acid saturation test, 362, **364**
Aspartate aminotransferase, **287**
  in liver disease, 272
Astrup analysis, 82

Bantu siderosis, 320
Basal metabolic rate, **168**
  acromegaly and, 116
  hypopituitarism and, 121
  interpretation, 169
  oral contraceptives and, 368
Base, definition of, 60
Bence-Jones protein, **239**
  macroglobulinaemia and, 243
  myelomatosis and, 241
  tests for, 248
Benedict's test, 149, **153**
  alkaptonuria and, 343
  galactosaemia and, 344
Beri-beri, **356**

Bicarbonate, depletion and acidosis, 75
  duodenal and pancreatic function,
    215
  kidney and, 3, **65**
Bicarbonate, blood, acid-base balance
    and, 80
  actual, 84
  buffering and, 61, **66**
  erythrocyte and, 64
  ketosis and, 141
  primary aldosteronism and, 45
  pyloric stenosis and, 77
  renal glomerular insufficiency and, 9
  renal tubular disease and, 12
  standard, 84
Bile acids, **279**
  bile salts, formation from, 206
Bile formation, 279
Bile pigments, **264**
Bile salts, **279**
  cholesterol and, 206, 264
  enterohepatic circulation, 206, 279
  lipid absorption and, 205
  metabolism, 206
  micelle formation and, 205
Biliary atresia and jaundice, 269
Biliary calculi, **279**
Biliary cirrhosis and jaundice, 269
Biliary obstruction, **275**
  differential diagnosis, 275
  liver cell damage and, 268
  steatorrhoea and, 216
  urinary urobilinogen in, 270
Biliary secretion, potassium content, 48
  sodium content, 38
Bilirubin, 264
  albumin binding, 232, 264
  breakdown products, 264
  conjugated, 264
  direct, 265
  formation, 264
  indirect, 265
  metabolism, 264
  unconjugated, 264
  urinary, 270, **283**
Biotin, 358
Bisalbuminaemia, 232
"Blind loop syndrome", 216
Blood gases, **84**
Blood glucose, diabetes mellitus and,
    135
  fasting and, 132
  fasting level, 137
  growth hormone and, 129, 130
  insulin and, 115, 129, 130
  maintenance of level, 130
  measurement of level, 133
  oral contraceptives and, 367
  post-prandial (2 hours), 138
  pregnancy and, 367

Blood transfusion and iron overload,
    317, 320
Blood urea nitrogen (see Urea)
BMR (see Basal metabolic rate), **168**
Bone marrow, investigation of anaemia
    and, 315
  iron overload and, 317
  macroglobulinaemia and, 243
  myelomatosis and, 241, **243**
Bradshaw's test, 248
Bradykinin, 373
Brain, metabolism of, 128
Bromsulphthalein retention test, 270, **283**
Buffer anions, 67
Buffering, ammonia and, 66
  bicarbonate and, 61, 65, **66**
  definition, 60
  haemoglobin and, 64, **65**
  phosphate and, 66
  proteins and, 62, 64
BUN (see Urea)
Butanol extractable iodine, 166

Caeruloplasmin, 345
  oral contraceptives and, 368
  pregnancy and, 368
  Wilson's disease and, 345
Calciferol (see Vitamin D), **178**, 354
Calcitonin, 156, **177**
Calcium, deficiency, **180**, **183**
  intake, 175
  intestinal absorption of, 175, 208
  loss, 177
  metabolism, **177**
  parathyroid hormone and, 176
  renal failure and, **183**
  thyroid hormone and, 178
  vitamin D and, 178
Calcium, ionized, **176**
  excess, effects of, **178**
  hyperparathyroidism, primary and,
    181
  hyperparathyroidism, secondary and,
    182
  lowered, **179**, 191
  parathyroid hormone secretion and,
    177
  pH and, 176
  raised, 188
  reduced, effects of, **179**
Calcium, plasma, accuracy of estimation,
    176
  acidosis and, 176
  acute pancreatitis and, 184, 216
  alkalosis and, 52, 176
  control, 176
  ectopic parathyroid hormone and,
    182, **378**
  EDTA, cause of misleading results,
    395

Calcium, plasma, excess, effects of, 178
    familial hypophosphataemia and, 187
    hyperparathyroidism, primary and,
        181
    hyperparathyroidism, secondary and,
        182
    hyperparathyroidism, tertiary and,
        182
    hypoparathyroidism and, 184
    malignant disease and, 182, 186, 378
    "milk-alkali syndrome" and, 186
    nephrotic syndrome and, 12
    osteoporosis and, 186
    Paget's disease and, 187
    pseudohypoparathyroidism and, 184
    renal calculi and, 19
    renal failure and, 13, 178
    "resistant rickets" and, 187
    sarcoidosis and, 185
    steatorrhoea and, 212
    venous stasis and, 393
    vitamin D and, 178, 183, 185, 208
Calcium preparations, 200
Calcium, protein bound, 176
    raised, 188
    reduced, 191
Calcium pyrophosphate and pseudo gout,
    306
Calcium, urinary, factors affecting, 176
    hypercalcaemia, differential diagnosis
        of and, 189
    renal calculi and, 19
    renal function and, 178
Calculi, biliary, 279
Calculi, renal, 18
    composition of, 19
    cystinuria and, 339
    formation of, 19
    hypercalcaemia and, 178
    hyperparathyroidism and, 181
    treatment of, 20
    xanthine and, 21
Carbohydrate, absorption of, 126, 206
    adrenocortical hormones and, 91, 129
    chemistry of, 125
    digestion of, 126, 206
    growth hormone and, 115
    oral contraceptives and, 367
    pregnancy and, 367
Carbon dioxide, bicarbonate and, 3, 65
    erythrocytes and, 64
    kidney and, 3, 65
    lungs and, 73
Carbonic anhydrase, erythrocyte and,
    64
    kidney and, 3, 65
Carcinoid syndrome, 371
    carcinoma of the bronchus and, 382
    malabsorption and, 211, 372
    nicotinamide deficiency in, 358

Cardiac failure, enzymes in, 286
    oedema in, 46
    renal circulation in, 11
Carotenes, 352
Casts, renal, 15
Catecholamines, 374
Cephalin cholesterol test, 271
Cerebrospinal fluid, 384
    chloride, 388
    examination, 384
    formation, 384
    glucose, 387
    protein, 386
Chiari-Frommel syndrome, 117
Chloride, absorption of, 208
    acid-base balance and, 67
    CSF, 388
    depletion, 68
    kidney and, 3
    pyloric stenosis and, 77
    ureteric transplantation and, 76
Chlorpromazine and jaundice, 269, 278
Cholangiolytic hepatitis, 269
Cholestasis, 268, 269
    urobilinogen, urinary in, 270
Cholesterol, 251
    absorption, 206
    bile salt circulation and, 206
    liver and, 263
    metabolism, 257
Cholesterol, plasma, diet and, 257
    liver disease and, 269, 273
    malabsorption and, 213
    nephrotic syndrome and, 11
    oral contraceptives and, 368
    pregnancy and, 368
    raised, 259
    thyroid disease and, 170
Cholinesterase, 295
    liver disease and, 271
Chromaffin cells, 374
Chylomicrons, 253
    lipid absorption and, 206, 254
    plasma turbidity and, 261
Circadian rhythms, cortisol, 97, 405
    iron, 311, 405
Cirrhosis, 276
    electrophoretic pattern in, 236
    iron, plasma and, 319
    liver cell destruction in, 268
    Wilson's disease and, 345
Cirrhosis, biliary, and jaundice, 269
Clearance, 16
    creatinine, 17
    EDTA, 17
    inulin, 16
    urea, 17
    vitamin B_{12}, 17

Clinistix,
Clinitest, 149, 153
    alkaptonuria and, 345
    galactosaemia and, 344
Coagulation factors in liver disease, 272
Coeliac disease, 210
Colchicine, 304
Collecting ducts, 8
    ADH and, 4
Colloid osmotic pressure, 31
Congenital adrenal hyperplasia, 104
Congenital hyperbilirubinaemia, 277
Conn's syndrome, 45
Copper in Wilson's disease, 345
Corticosterone, 91
    synthesis, 94
Corticotrophin releasing factor, 101
Cortisol, glucose, blood and, 129
    physiology of, 91
    stress and, 132
    synthesis of, 94
Cortisol binding globulin, 91
    nephrotic syndrome and, 11
    oral contraceptives and, 368
    pregnancy and, 368
"Cortisol", plasma, 96, 109
    collection of blood for, 109
    congenital adrenal hyperplasia and, 104
    corticosteroid releasing factor &, 101
    corticosteroid therapy and, 104
    Cushing's syndrome and, 97
    nephrotic syndrome and, 11
    oral contraceptives and, 368
    pregnancy and, 368
Cortisol secretion rate, 97
Cortisol, urinary, 96
    Cushing's syndrome and, 97
Cortisone, 91
    congenital adrenal hyperplasia, treatment of and, 106
    glucose tolerance test, 140
Countercurrent multiplication, 5
    tubular damage and, 12
CPK, 289, 296
Creatine and muscle disease, 296
Creatine phosphokinase, 289
    muscle disease and, 296
    myocardial infarction and, 293
Creatinine, clearance, 17
    excretion, 296
    kidney and, 4
    metabolism of, 15
    muscle disease and, 296
    renal disease and, 15
CRF, 101
Crigler-Najjar syndrome, 266, 277
Cryoglobulinaemia, 243
    in myelomatosis, 242

CSF (see Cerebrospinal fluid), 384
Cushing's syndrome, 92
    ACTH in, 117
    causes, 96
    chemical abnormalities in, 92
    diagnosis, 96
Cystic fibrosis, 211
Cystine and renal calculi, 21, 339
Cystinosis, 339
Cystinuria, 338
Cytochromes, 307

Desferrioxamine, 319
Dexamethasone, congenital adrenal hyperplasia and, 106
Dexamethasone suppression test, 97, 110
Dextrose, cerebral oedema, treatment of, 32
Diabetes insipidus, 40
    hereditary nephrogenic, 40
    unconscious patient and, 41
Diabetes mellitus, 133
    asymptomatic, 135
    cholesterol in, 260
    hyperosmolar coma in, 142
    insulin levels in, 134
    juvenile onset, 134
    ketosis and, 140
    latent, 135, 140
    maturity onset, 134
    pancreatic damage and, 142
    potential, 135
    primary, 134
    secondary, 142
    treatment, 142
    triglycerides in, 260
Dialysis, haemo-, 18
    peritoneal, 18
Diarrhoea stool, potassium content, 48
    sodium content, 38
Dibucaine number, 295
Dihydroxyphenylalanine, 343, 374
Dihydroxyphenylethylamine, 374
Di-iodotyrosine, 158
Disaccharidases, 126, 206
    deficiency, 217
Diuretics, potassium loss and, 48
    urate retention and, 306
Diurnal rhythms, cortisol, 97, 405
    iron, 311, 405
DOPA, 343, 374
DOPamine, 374
"Drip", intravenous, cause of misleading results, 394
Dubin-Johnson syndrome, 277
"Dumping" syndrome, 214
Duodenal aspirate, 215
Dwarfism, pituitary, 122
Dyshormonogenesis, thyroid

Ectopic hormone secretion, 376
EDTA, calcium, plasma effect *in vitro*, 395
  clearance, 17
  potassium, plasma, effect *in vitro*, 395
Electrocardiogram and plasma potassium, 52
Electrolytes, sweat, 38, 48
  fibrocystic disease and, 211
Electrophoresis, immuno, 231
  isoenzyme, 288
  lipoprotein, 251
  zone, 230
  of CSF, 386
Ellsworth-Howard test, 193, **198**
Embden-Meyerhof pathway, 127
Endocrine adenomatosis, multiple, 220
Endogenous triglycerides, 256
  plasma turbidity and, 261
Enterohepatic circulation of bile salts, 206, 279
Enteropathy, protein losing, 218
Enzymes, duodenal and pancreatic function, 215
Enzyme units, 285
Epinephrine (*see* Adrenaline) **374**
Erythrocyte sedimentation rate, 229
Erythropoietin, 1
  renal carcinoma and, 381
ESR, 229
Essential fructosuria, 150
Essential paraproteinaemia, 244
Ethylene diamine tetraacetate,
  calcium, plasma, effect *in vitro*, 395
  clearance, 17
  potassium, plasma, effect *in vitro*, 395
Exophthalmos, 160
Extracellular fluid compartment, 29

Faecal fat, 202, **211**
  collection, **223**
  split and unsplit, 213
Familial hypophosphataemia, 187
Fanconi syndrome, 12, **338**
  cystinosis and, 339
  galactosaemia and, 344
  rickets and, 187
  Wilson's disease and, 345
Fat absorption, **205**
Fat metabolism, **253**
  diabetes mellitus and, 134
  growth hormone and, 129
  insulin and, 129
Fatty acids, **250**
  calcium absorption and, 175, 183
  free plasma, 250
    diabetes mellitus and, 134, 256
    fasting and, 131, 256
    glycogen storage disease and, 148

Fatty acids, free plasma, growth hormone and, 129
    insulin and, 129
    ketones and, 131, 132
Feedback centre and cortisol, 101
Ferric chloride test, **154**
  phenylketonuria and, 342
Ferritin, 307
Ferrocyanide, potassium and iron, 307, 315
FFA (*see* Free fatty acids), **250**
Fibrinogen, electrophoresis and, 230
  ESR and, 229
  liver disease and, 272
Fibrocystic disease of the pancreas, 211
Fistula fluid, electrolytes in, 28
Flavoproteins and riboflavin, 357
Flocculation tests, 229, **271**
  acute hepatitis and, 236
  liver function tests and, **271**
Fluid balance, assessment of, 27
  normal, 26
Fluoride number, 295
Foeto-placental monitoring, 365
Folic acid, **359**
  oral contraceptives and, 368
  pregnancy and, 368
Folic acid antagonists, 299
Follicle stimulating hormone, **118**
  menstrual cycle and, 119
Franklin's disease, 243
Free fatty acids, **250**
  diabetes mellitus and, 134, 256
  fasting and, 131, 256
  glycogen storage disease and, 148
  growth hormone and, 129
  insulin and, 129
Free thyroxine index, **168**
Froin's syndrome, 385
Fructose, 125, 127
  urinary, 150
  von Gierke's disease and, 149
Fructose intolerance, hereditary, 150
Fructosuria, essential, 150
FSH (*see* Follicle stimulating hormone), **118**
Functional hypoglycaemia, **144**

Galactosaemia, **343**
  hypoglycaemia and, 147
Galactose, 125, 127
  urinary, 150
  von Gierke's disease and, 149
Galactose-1-phosphate uridyl transferase, 343
Gallstones, **279**
Gastrectomy, "dumping syndrome" and, 214
  malabsorption and, 211, 214
Gastric analysis, 220, **225**

Gastric juice, **219**
  hypersecretion, 219, 225
  hyposecretion, 220, 225
  potassium content, 48
  pyloric stenosis, 77
  sodium content, 38
Gastrin, **219**
Gastro-intestinal secretions, potassium
    content, 48
  sodium content, 38
Gerhardt's test, **154**
GFR (*see* Glomerular filtration rate)
Gigantism, **116**
Gilbert's disease, 266, **277**
Globulins, α, **233**
  ESR and, 229
Globulins, β, **234**
  biliary obstruction and, 275
Globulins, γ, **234**
  CSF, 386
  ESR and, 229
  flocculation tests and, 229, 271
  raised, 234
  reduced, 234
Glomerular filtration rate, acid-base
    balance and, **67**
  Addison's disease and, 93
  measurement of, **16**
  reduced, effect of, **9**
    acidosis and, 9
    causes of, 10
    creatinine and, 9
    findings in, 9
    oliguria and, 9
    phosphate and, 9
    potassium and, 10
    sodium, urinary and, 10
    specific gravity, urinary and, 10
    urate and, 10
    urea and, 9
Glomerulonephritis, **11**
Glomerulus, renal, disease of, **9**
  nephrotic syndrome and, **11**
Glucagon, **129**
  insulin secretion and, 129, 130
Glucagon test, **146**
  von Gierke's disease and, 149
Glucocorticoids, **91**
  Addison's disease and, 94
  Cushing's syndrome and, 92
  glucose, blood and, 129
  hypoadrenalism, secondary and, 101
Gluconeogenesis, **127**
  amino-acids and, 127
  Cushing's syndrome and, 92
  glucocorticoids and, 129
Glucose, cell hydration and, 32
  fasting and, 131
  kidney and, 2
  metabolism, **126**

Glucose, osmotic diuresis and, 8
  tubular damage and, 12
Glucose, blood, fasting and, 131
  fluoride, *in vitro* effect on, 395
  growth hormone and, 129
  insulin and, 129
  measurement of, 133
Glucose, CSF, 387
Glucose oxidase, 133
  Clinistix and. 149
Glucose-6-phosphatase, **127**
Glucose-6-phosphate, **127**
  glycogenolysis and, 127
  von Gierke's disease and, 148
Glucose-6-phosphate dehydrogenase, **128**
  haemolytic anaemia and, **344**
Glucose tolerance test, 130, **138**, 154
  acromegaly and, 116
  Addison's disease and, 94
  cortisone, 140
  Cushing's syndrome and, 92
  diabetic, 139
  disaccharidase deficiency and, 218
  factors affecting, 138
  flat, 140
  indications for, 138
  intravenous, 140
  lag storage, 139
  malabsorption and, 213
  "normal", 139
  oral contraceptives and, 367
  pregnancy and, 367
  reactive hypoglycaemia and, 144
  thyrotoxicosis and, 170
  types of curves, **138**
Glucose, "true", 133
Glucuronates in urine, 150
Glutamate oxaloacetate transaminase,
    287
  liver disease and, 272
Glutamate pyruvate transaminase, **287**
  liver disease and, 272
Glutaminase, 66
Gluten, 210
Glycine, iminoaciduria, 338
  purines and, 300
Glycogen, 125
  liver and, 127
Glycogenesis, 127
Glycogenolysis, 127
Glycogen storage disease, 148
Glycolysis, 127
Glycoproteins, 233
Glycosuria, **132**, **149**
  Cushing's syndrome and, 92
  diabetes mellitus and, 136, 140
  glomerular filtration rate and, 137
    141
  phaeochromocytoma and, 132, 375
  stress and, 132

Glycosuria, tests for, 153
  tubular damage and, 12
Glycosuria, renal, 132, **150**
  glucose tolerance test and, **140**
  pregnancy and, 150, 367
Goitre, euthyroid, 161
  Graves' disease and, 160
  thyroid dyshormonogenesis and, 161
Gonadotrophin, chorionic, malignant
    disease and, 381
Gonadotrophins, pituitary, **118**
Gonadotrophin, urinary, amenorrhoea
    and, 120
  oral contraceptives and, 369
  ovarian failure and, 120
  pituitary insufficiency and, 120, 122
Gout, **303**
  treatment, 304
Graves' disease, **160**
Growth hormone, **115**
  acromegaly and, 116
  children and, 123
  control, 115
  diabetes mellitus and, 134
  effects, 115
  excess, 116
  fasting, 131
  glucose, blood and, 129
  glucose ingestion and, 130
  hypopituitarism and, 121
  measurement of, 115
  pituitary dwarfism and, 122
GTT (*see* Glucose tolerance test), 130,
    138, 154
Guthrie test, 342
Gynaecomastia in malignant disease, 381

Haematocrit, haemoconcentration and
    dilution and, 27
Haemochromatosis, **317**
Haemoconcentration, **27**, 34
  Addison's disease and, 93
  calcium, plasma and, 188
Haemodialysis, 18
Haemodilution, **27**, 34
  calcium, plasma and, 191
Haemoglobin
  breakdown of, 264
  haemoconcentration and dilution
    and, 27
  iron and, 307
  oxygen saturation and, 85
Haemolysis, anaemia and, 312
  effects on results *in vitro*, 395
  enzymes, plasma and, 295
  G-6-PD deficiency and, 344
  gallstones and, 280
  iron, plasma and, 312
  jaundice and, 266, **276**
  pyruvate kinase deficiency and, 344

Haemosiderin, 307
  urinary, in haemochromatosis, 319
Haemosiderosis, **317**
Halothane and jaundice, 278
Hartnup disease, **339**
  nicotinamide and, 358
Hashimoto's disease, 161
HBD, **289**, 293, 294
Heavy chain disease, 243
Henderson-Hasselbalch equation, **61**
  Astrup analysis and, 82
  derivation, 61
Henle, loop of, 4, 8
  countercurrent multiplication and, 5
Heparin, clearing effect of, 254
Hepatitis, acute, **273**
  electrophoretic pattern and, 236
  extrahepatic obstruction, diagnosis
    from, 275
  iron, plasma and, 312
  liver cell destruction in, 275
Hepatocellular failure, 276
Hepatolenticular degeneration, 345
Hepatotoxins, **278**
Hereditary fructose intolerance, 150
  hypoglycaemia and, 145
Hereditary nephrogenic diabetes
    insipidus, 40
Hexose monophosphate shunt, 127
5 HIAA, **371**
  oat cell carcinoma of bronchus and,
    382
Hirsutism, Cushing's syndrome and,
    93
  steroids, urinary and, 97
"Histalog", 221
  "Test meal", **225**
Histamine, carcinoid syndrome and, 373
  gastric secretion and, 221
HMMA, **375,** 376
Homogentisic acid, **343**
  urinary, 150
5HT, **371**
  oat cell carcinoma of bronchus and,
    382
5HTP, **371, 373**
  oat cell carcinoma of bronchus
    and. 382
Hydrogen ion, bicarbonate and in
    kidney, 3, 65
  buffering of, **60**, 62
  fate in body, 62
  GFR and, 67
  kidney and, 3, 65
  metabolic production, 59
  potassium and, 3, 67
  sodium and, **3,** 67
  tubular damage and, 72
  water and, 62
β Hydroxybutyrate, 132

Hydroxybutyrate dehydrogenase, 289, 293, 294
11-Hydroxycorticosteroids, 96
  Cushing's syndrome and, 97
17-Hydroxycorticosteroids, 96
  (see 17-oxogenic steroids, total)
5-Hydroxyindole acetic acid, 371
  oat cell carcinoma of bronchus and, 382
4-Hydroxy-3-methoxymandelic acid, 375
Hydroxyproline, 338
Hydroxypyrazolopyrimidine, 304
17-Hydroxysteroids
  (see 17-oxogenic steroids, total) 96
5-Hydroxytryptamine, 371
  oat cell carcinoma of bronchus and, 382
5-Hydroxytryptophane, 371
  oat cell carcinoma of bronchus and, 382
Hyperbilirubinaemia, congenital, 277
Hypercalcaemia, differential diagnosis of, 187
  ectopic parathyroid hormone and, 182, 378
  effects of, 178
  hyperparathyroidism, primary and, 181
  hyperparathyroidism, tertiary and, 182
  idiopathic of infancy, 185
  malignant disease and, 182, 186, 378
  phosphate excretion tests and, 189
  renal calculi and, 19, 178
  sarcoidosis and, 185
  steroid suppression test and, 189, 198
  thyrotoxicosis and, 170, 185
  treatment of, 193, 199
  urinary calcium and, 189
  vitamin D and, 185
Hypercalcaemia, idiopathic of infancy, 185
Hypercalcuria, idiopathic, 19, 189
  renal calculi and, 19
Hyperchloraemic acidosis, 68
Hyperchlorhydria, 219, 225
Hypercholesterolaemia, 259
Hyperglycaemia, 133
  phaeochromocytoma and, 132, 375
  stress and, 132
Hyperinsulinism, 146
Hyperlipaemia, 258
Hyperosmolar coma, 142
Hyperoxaluria, primary, 20
Hyperparathyroidism, primary, 181
  diagnosis, 187
  steroid suppression test and, 189, 198
Hyperparathyroidism, secondary, 182
Hyperparathyroidism, tertiary, 182
  steroid suppression test and, 189

Hypertension, congenital adrenal hyperplasia and, 106
  Cushing's syndrome and, 92
  metabolic causes, 376
  phaeochromocytoma and, 375
Hyperthyroidism, 159
  calcium in, 185
  ectopic TSH production and, 381
Hypogammaglobulinaemia, 245
Hypoglycaemia, 143
  Addison's disease and, 94
  alcohol induced, 145
  brain and, 128, 143
  causes, 143
  CSF glucose and, 387
  diagnosis, 146
  "dumping syndrome" and, 214
  fasting, 143
  functional, 144
  galactosaemia and, 145, 343
  glycogen storage disease and, 148
  growth hormone and, 129
  hepatic disease and, 144
  hereditary fructose intolerance and, 145
  hyperinsulinism and, 146
  leucine sensitivity and, 145
  malignant disease and, 144, 381
  reactive, 144
  secondary adrenal hypofunction and, 101, 121
Hypolipoproteinaemia, 261
Hypoparathyroidism, 184
  Ellsworth-Howard test and, 193, 198
Hypophosphataemia, familial, 187
Hypopituitarism, 100, 120
  acromegaly and, 116
  diagnosis of, 122
  investigation of, 103
  stress and, 101
Hypoproteinaemia, protein-losing enteropathy and, 218
Hypothalamic-pituitary-adrenal axis, 101
  ACTH stimulation test and, 103
  corticosteroid therapy and, 104
  disorders of, 101
Hypothalamus, ADH and, 36
  adrenal cortex and, 101
  corticotrophin releasing factor and, 101
  thirst and, 36
Hypothyroidism, 160
  secondary, 161
Hypouricaemia, 306
Hypoxanthine, 301

ICSH, 118
Idiopathic haemochromatosis, 317
  diagnosis, 319

Idiopathic hypercalcaemia of infancy, 185
Idiopathic hypercalcuria, 19, 189
IgA, 239
  myelomatosis and, 242
IgD, 239
IgE, 239
IgG, 239
  myelomatosis and, 242
IgM, 239
  macroglobulinaemia and, 243
Ileal secretion, potassium content, 48
  sodium content, 38
Immunoelectrophoresis, 231
Immunoglobulins, 236
  classification, 237
  physiology, 238
  structure, 237
"Inappropriate" hormone secretion, 43, 180, 379
Indoles in Hartnup disease, 340
Inheritance, modes of, 335
"Insensible loss", 27
Insorption, 202
Insulin, 129
  acromegaly and, 116
  antagonists, 135
  antiketogenic action, 129
  arginine and, 129
  control, 129
  diabetes mellitus and, 133
  fasting and, 131
  free fatty acids and, 129, 134
  glucose, blood and, 129
  glucose ingestion and, 130
  glucose metabolism and, 129
  glycogen and, 129
  leucine and, 129, 145
  malignant disease and, 381
Insulin hypoglycaemia, adrenal
    hypofunction and, 103, 110, 122
  gastric secretion and, 221, 225
  growth hormone and, 123
  pituitary dwarfism and, 123
Insulinoma, 146
Insulin "test meal", 225
Interstitial cell stimulating hormone, 118
Intestinal secretion, acidosis and, 76
  potassium content, 48
  sodium content, 38
Intestinal villi, 204
Intravenous infusions, cause of
    misleading results, 394
Intrinsic factor, 207, 217, 360
  antibodies and, 220
  pernicious anaemia and, 217, 220, 360
  Schilling test and, 217
Inulin clearance, 16

Iodine, deficiency and goitre, 161
  and neck uptake, 164
  excess and neck uptake, 163, 174
  and protein bound iodine, 166, 174
Iodine metabolism, 156
Iron, absorption, 209, 309
  anaemia and, 315
  distribution in body, 307
    in Bantu siderosis, 317, 320
    in cirrhosis, 317
    in haemochromatosis, 317, 318
    in haemosiderosis, 317, 318
  excretion, 308
  haemochromatosis and, 317
  storage, 307
  transport, 309
  urinary, in haemochromatosis, 319
Iron binding capacity, 312
  anaemia and, 313
  congenital transferrin deficiency and, 317
  haemochromatosis and, 318
  iron deficiency and, 313, 314
  nephrotic syndrome and, 313
  oral contraceptives and, 368
  percentage saturation, 313
  pregnancy and, 368
Iron overload, 316
Iron, plasma, anaemia and, 313
  factors affecting, 311, 405
  haemochromatosis and, 318
  nephrotic syndrome and, 313
Iron therapy, 316
  iron overload and, 316, 321
Islet cell hyperplasia, 144
Isocitrate dehydrogenase, 293
  liver disease and, 272
Isoenzymes, 285
  alkaline phosphatase, 290
  lactate dehydrogenase, 288
Isoleucine and maple syrup urine disease, 340
Isoniazid and pyridoxine deficiency, 358

Jaundice, classification, 266
  drug induced, 278
  haemolytic, 266, 276
  neonatal, 266, 279
  "physiological", 266, 279
  pregnancy, 269, 369

Kallikrein, 373
Kernicterus, 277
Ketoacidosis, 140
Ketonaemia, 132
Ketones, 132
  tests for, 153
Ketonuria, 132
  tests for, 153

Ketosis, 132
  acidosis and, 69
  causes, 132
  diabetic, 140
    treatment, 142
  fasting, 132
  glycogen storage disease and, 148
  salicylate poisoning and, 80
17-Ketosteroids (*see* 17-oxosteroids), **96**
Ketostix, 154
Krebs cycle, 127

Lactase, 206
  deficiency, 218
Lactate dehydrogenase, **288**
  isoenzymes of, 288
  liver disease and, 273
  myocardial infarction and, 293
Lactic acidosis, 59, **69,** 127
  glycogen storage disease and, 148
Lactogenic hormone, 112, **117**
Lactose, 125
  lactation and, 150
  pregnancy and, 150
  urinary, 150
"Lag storage curve", 139
Lange colloidal gold reaction, 387
LATS in Graves' disease, 160
LDH, 288
  isoenzymes of, 288
  liver disease and, 293
Lead poisoning, porphyrin metabolism
  and, 329
Lecithin, 251
Lesch-Nyhan syndrome, 304
Leucine, hypoglycaemia and, **145**
  insulin secretion and, 129
  maple syrup urine disease and, 340
  sensitivity, 145
Leucine aminopeptidase, liver disease
  and, 273
LH, 118
  menstrual cycle and, 119
Light chain, 237
  Bence-Jones protein and, 240
Lipase, 205
Lipase, adipolytic, 256
Lipase, lipoprotein, 254
Lipase, plasma, pancreatic function and,
  215
Lipid, absorption, **205,** 254
  metabolism in liver, 256, 258, 263
Lipids, plasma, analysis, 249, 251
  classification, **249**
  glycogen storage disease and, 148
  nephrotic syndrome and, 11
  oral contraceptives and, 368
  pregnancy and, 368
Lipoprotein, 251
Lipoprotein lipase, 254

Liver, detoxication and, 263
  functions, 263
  lipid metabolism and, 258, 263
Liver disease, acquired cutaneous
  hepatic porphyria and, 328
  bile pigments and, 266
  BSP retention and, 270
  enzymes, plasma, and, 272, **294**
  flocculation tests and, 271
  hypoalbuminaemia and, 232
  iron, plasma and, 312
  porphyrins, urinary and, 328
  proteins, plasma and, 271
  prothrombin time and, 272
  vitamin K and, 272
Liver function tests, **269,** 273
  oral contraceptives and, 369
  pregnancy and, 369
Long-acting thyroid stimulator, in
  Graves' disease, 160
Loop of Henle, 4, 8
  countercurrent multiplication and, 5
Luteinizing hormone, **118**
  menstrual cycle and, 119
Lysine in cystinuria, 338
Lysine vasopressin, secondary adrenal
  hypofunction and, 104

Macroamylasaemia, 290
Macroglobulinaemia, 243
  Sia test and, 248
Magnesium, intestinal absorption, 208
  metabolism, **195**
  plasma, 195
Malabsorption, anaemia in 214
  calcium and, 183
  causes, **209**
  differential diagnosis, **213, 216**
  results, **211**
Malignancy, ectopic hormone
  production and, **376**
  enzymes, plasma in, 294
Maltase, 206
  deficiency, 218
Maltose, 125
Mannitol, osmotic diuresis and, 7
Maple syrup urine disease, 340
Megaloblastic anaemia, **359**
  enzymes, plasma in, 288, 294
  iron, plasma in, 312
  malabsorption and, 214
  pernicious anaemia and, 217
Melanin, albinism and, 343
Melanocyte stimulating hormone,
  Addison's disease and, 94
Menstrual cycle, **119**
  iron, plasma and, 311
Methaemoglobinaemia, 345
Methaemoglobin reductases, 345

Methylene blue, methaemoglobinaemia and, 345
Methyltestosterone, jaundice and, 269, 278
Metyrapone (metopyrone) test, 110
  hypopituitarism and, 103, 122
  17-oxogenic steroids and, 103
Micelles, 205
"Milk-alkali syndrome" 186
Mineralocorticoids, 91
  Addison's disease and, 93
  Cushing's syndrome and, 93
Monoamine oxidases, 371
Monoclonal gammopathy, 240
Monoiodotyrosine, 158
MSH in Addison's disease, 94
Mucoprotein, 233
"Mucosal block" and iron absorption, 309
Mucoviscidosis, 211
Multiple endocrine adenomatosis, 220
Multiple myeloma (see myelomatosis), 241
Muscular dystrophy, 296
Myelomatosis, 241
  alkaline phosphatase and, 186, 242
  IgA and, 239
Myocardial infarction, plasma enzymes in, 293
Myoglobin, 307
Myopathies, 296
Myxoedema, 160

Natriuretic hormone, 35
  aldosteronism, primary and, 45
  aldosteronism, secondary and, 47
Neck uptake tests, 162
  factors affecting, 163, 174
  interpretation, 163
NEFA (see Free fatty acids), 250
Neonatal period, enzyme levels in, 286
  hypoglycaemia in, 147
  jaundice in, 277, 279
Nephrogenic diabetes insipidus, 40
Nephrotic syndrome, 11
  electrophoretic pattern in, 236
  hypoalbuminaemia and, 232
  iron and, 313
Neuroblastoma, 376
Neurohypophysis, 112
Neutral fat, 250, 253
Nicotinamide, 357
  in Hartnup disease, 339
Non-esterified fatty acids (see Free fatty acids), 250
Nonne-Apelt reaction, 386
Noradrenaline, 374
Norepinephrine, 374
Novobiocin and jaundice, 266, 278
Nucleic acid and uric acid, 299

5′ Nucleotidase, 291
  liver disease and, 273, 294

Obesity, BMR in, 169
  Cushing's syndrome and, 92, 93
  urinary steroids in, 97
Ochronosis, 343
Oedema, aldosteronism, secondary and, 46
  hypoalbuminaemia and, 232
  water excess and, 34
Oestriol, 119
  pregnancy and, 366
Oestrogens, 119
17-OHCS (see 17-oxogenic steroids, total), 96
Oliguria, acute tubular necrosis and, 13
  chronic renal failure and, 14
  diagnosis, 15
  GFR and, 9
  water depletion and, 40
Oliguric renal failure, acute, 13
  chronic, 14
  treatment, 18
Oncotic pressure, 31
Opsin, 352
Oral contraceptives, carbohydrate metabolism and, 367
  carrier proteins and, 367
  folate and, 368
  gonadotrophin levels and, 369
  iron, plasma and, 312, 368
  jaundice and, 278, 369
  metabolic effects, 366
  TIBC and, 313, 368
Ornithine in cystinuria, 338
Osmolarity, 31
  ADH, inappropriate and urinary, 44 379, 380
  distal tubule and, 4
  kidney and, 4
  loop of Henle and, 7
  osmotic diuresis and, 7
  plasma, 4
  proximal tubule and, 4
  sodium and plasma, 32, 33
  urinary, 7
  water depletion and plasma, 39
Osmotic diuresis, 7, 36
  chronic renal failure and, 14
  glucose and, 8
  mannitol and, 7
  sodium reabsorption and, 7, 36
  urea and, 8
Osmotic pressure, 31
Osteoblasts and alkaline phosphatase, 179
Osteomalacia, 180
  malabsorption and, 212
  renal tubular disorders and, 187

Osteoporosis, 186
  Cushing's syndrome and, 92, 93
  myelomatosis and, 241
  scurvy and, 362
Ovarian hormones, **119**
Oxalate and renal calculi, 20
Oxidative phosphorylation and acid-base balance, 62
17-Oxogenic steroids, total, **96**
  congenital adrenal hyperplasia and, 106
  Cushing's syndrome and, 98
  hypopituitarism and, 121
  hypothyroidism and, 172
17-Oxosteroids, 96
  congenital adrenal hyperplasia and, 106
  Cushing's syndrome and, 98
  hypopituitarism and, 121
  hypothyroidism and, 172
Oxygen, 84
  alveolar exchange, 84
  haemoglobin, saturation with, 85
  water solubility, 85
11-Oxygenation index, 106
Oxytocin, 113
  synthesis, 114

Paget's disease, 187
Palmitic acid, 250
Pancreas, cystic fibrosis, 211
  gastrin secretion and, 219
Pancreatic function, tests of, **214**
Pancreatic secretion, iron absorption and, 209, 214, 309
  potassium content of, 48
  sodium content of, 38
Pancreatitis, acute, **215**
  hypocalcaemia and, 184
  triglycerides and, 260
Pancreatitis, chronic, 211, 215
Pancreozymin, 215
Pandy reaction, 386
Panhypopituitarism, 120
  diagnosis, 122
Pantothenic acid, 358
Paraproteinaemia, 236, **240**
  assessment, 244
  benign, 244
  essential, 244
Parathyroid hormone, **177**
  ectopic production, 182, **378**
  excess, effects of, 179
  "inappropriate" secretion, 180, **378**
  osteomalacia and, 183
  rickets and, 183
  vitamin D and, 178
Passive transport, 2
P_{CO_2}, acid-base balance assessment and, 71, **82**

P_{CO_2}, airways obstruction and, 86
  collapse of lung and, 85
  pneumonia and, 85
  pulmonary fibrosis and, 85
  pulmonary oedema and, 85
Pellagra, 357
Penicillamine, cystinuria and, 339
  Wilson's disease and, 346
Pentagastrin, 221
  "test meal", **225**
Pentoses, 125
  urinary, 150
Pentose shunt, 127
Pentosuria, alimentary, 150
  essential, 150
Pepsin, 203, 207
Peptide absorption, 207, 340
Perchlorate, thyroid iodine uptake and, 158
Pernicious anaemia, **217**
  gastric secretion and, 220
  vitamin B_{12} and, 360
Peritoneal dialysis, 18
pH, definition, 60
  estimation in blood, 82
pH, urinary, ammonium chloride loading and, 88
  renal calculi and, 19
  tubular damage and, 12
Phaeochromocytoma, 375
  basal metabolic rate in, 169
  hyperglycaemia in, 132
Phenistix, 342
Phenylalanine, blood, 342
Phenylalanine hydroxylase, 342
Phenylketonuria, 340
Phenylpyruvic acid, 342
Phosphatase, acid, **292**
  prostatic massage and, 393
Phosphatase, alkaline, **290**
  bony secondaries and, 182, 186
  cirrhosis and, 276
  childhood and, 286
  familial hypophosphataemia and, 187
  heat stable, 366
  hypercalcaemia and, 179, **188**
  hyperparathyroidism, primary and, 181
  hyperparathyroidism, secondary and, 182
  hyperparathyroidism, tertiary and, 182
  hypocalcaemia, diagnosis of and, 191
  hypocalcaemia, treatment of and, 191, 194
  liver disease and, 273
  malabsorption and, 212
  myelomatosis and, 186, 242
  5'-nucleotidase and, 291
  osteomalacia and, 180

Phosphatase, alkaline (*cont.*)
  Paget's disease and, 187
  parathyroid hormone excess and, 179
  pregnancy and, 286, **366**
  renal failure and, 17, 183
  "resistant rickets" and, 187
  rickets and, 180
Phosphate, acromegaly and, 116
  buffering and, 66
  calcium absorption and, 175, **193**
  Fanconi syndrome and, 12
  GFR and, 9
  hypercalcaemia, treatment of and, 193, **199**
  kidney and, 3
  osteoporosis and, 186
  parathyroid hormone and, 177, 181
  renal failure and, 9, 17, **183**
  "resistant rickets" and, 187
  tubular damage and, 12
  vitamin D and, 178, 185
Phosphate clearance tests, 189
Phosphaturia, "resistant rickets" and, 187
  tubular damage and, 12
Phospholipids, 251
  fat absorption and, 205
  metabolism, **258**
Phosphoribosyl pyrophosphate, in purine metabolism, 299
Physiological variations, 404
  iron and, 311
Pigmentation, ACTH and, 118
  Addison's disease and, 94
  hypopituitarism and, 121
Pitressin test, 23
Pituitary dwarfism, **122**
Placenta, alkaline phosphatase and, 290, 366
  oestriol and, 365
  pregnanediol and, 366
  progesterone and, 366
Plasma cell myeloma, **241**
  alkaline phosphatase and, 186, 242
P$_{O_2}$, 84
  airways obstruction and, 86
  collapse of lung and, 85
  pneumonia and, 85
  pulmonary fibrosis and, 85
  pulmonary oedema and, 85
Polycythaemia, & renal carcinoma, 381
Polyuria, chronic renal failure and, 14
  hypercalcaemia and, 178
  osmotic diuresis and, 7, 36
  tubular damage and, 12
Polyvinyl pyrrolidone, 219
Porphobilinogen, 323
  acquired cutaneous hepatic porphyria and, 328
  acute intermittent porphyria and, 326

Porphobilinogen, hereditary coproporphyria and, 328
  lead poisoning and, 329
  porphyria variegata and, 327
  production of, 323
  tests for, **332**
Porphyria, acquired cutaneous hepatic, 327
  acute intermittent, 326
  cutanea tarda, 327
  erythropoietic, **328**
  hepatic, **326**
  screening tests for, 325
  Swedish genetic, 326
  variegata, 327
Potassium, acid base balance and, **67**
  acidosis and, 76
  Addison's disease and, 93
  aldosteronism, primary and, 45
  aldosteronism, secondary and, 47
  alkalosis, extracellular and, 52, **79**
  body content, 26, 29, 30, 48
  body fluid, concentration, 48
  cellular, **29,** 48
  Cushing's syndrome and, 93
  depletion, causes, 48
  distribution of, 29
  EDTA, *in vitro* effect, 395
  effect of keeping blood on, 395
  GFR and, 9
  haemolysis *in vitro* and, 395
  hydrogen ion and, 3
  intestinal absorption of, 208
  kidney and, 3
  preparations containing, **55**
  sodium ion and, 3
  treatment of disturbances, 53
  tubular damage and, 12
Potassium ferrocyanide, iron and, 307, 315
Prednisolone test, 276, **283**
Pregnancy, carbohydrate metabolism and, 367
  carrier proteins and, 367
  cholestasis and, 269, 369
  enzymes, plasma and, 286
  folate, plasma and, 368
  iron, plasma and, 312, 368
  monitoring of, **365**
  reducing substances, urinary and, 150
  TIBC and, 313, 368
Pregnanediol, 119
  pregnancy and, 366
Pregnanetriol in congenital adrenal hyperplasia, 106
Probenecid, 304
Progesterone, 119
  menstrual cycle and, 119
  placenta and, 366
Prolactin, 117

Proline, 338
Protein bound iodine, 165
    interfering substances and, 166, **174**
    nephrotic syndrome and, 168
    newborn infant and, 168
    oral contraceptives and, 167, **367**
    pregnancy and, 167, **367**
Protein, Bence-Jones, **239**
Protein, CSF, 386
Protein-losing enteropathy, **218**
    hypoalbuminaemia and, 232, 236
Proteins, adrenocortical hormones and,
        91, 129
    buffering and, 62, 64
    Cushing's syndrome and, 92
    growth hormone and, 129
    insulin and, 129
    liver and, 263
Proteins, plasma, aldosteronism,
        secondary and, 46
    cirrhosis and, 276
    control of, 228
    fractionation of, **230**
    functions of, 227
    hydration and, 27, 228
    liver disease and, 271
    nephrotic syndrome and, 11
    sources of, 227
    total, value of, 228
    venous stasis and, 229
    water, distribution of, 32, 227
Proteinuria, nephrotic syndrome and, 11
    tubular disease and, 15
Prothrombin time, liver disease and, 272
    malabsorption and, 212
Prussian blue reaction, 307
Pseudo Addison's disease, 42
Pseudocholinesterase, **295**
    liver disease and, 271
Pseudogout, 306
Pseudohermaphroditism, 106
Pseudohypoparathyroidism, 184
    Ellsworth-Howard test and, 193, **198**
Pulmonary embolism, enzyme changes
        in, 293
Purine, fate of, 301
    folic acid and, 360
    gout and, 303
    metabolism of, **299**
    synthesis of, 299
PVP, 219
Pyelonephritis, 14
Pyloric stenosis, **77**
Pyrexia and water loss, 41
Pyridoxine, 358
    iron, plasma and, 312
    responsive anaemia, 312, 358
Pyruvate, 127
    thiamine and, 356
Pyruvate kinase, 344

Radioiodine therapy, myxoedema and,
        161
Radioiodine uptake tests, **162**
    factors affecting, 163, **174**
    interpretation, 163
Reducing substances in urine, **149**
    alkaptonuria and, 343
    galactosaemia and, 150
    tests for, 153
Releasing factors, 114
Renal circulatory insufficiency, 10
    Addison's disease and, 93
    tubular damage and, 13
Renal concentration tests, 16, **23**
Renal failure, acidosis and, 71
    acute, **13**
    anaemia and, 312
    calcium and, 178, 181, 183
    chronic, **14**
    enzymes, plasma and, 289
    hyperuricaemia and, 303
    iron, plasma and, 312
    phosphate and, 177, 183
"Renal threshold", 2, 132
Renal tubular acidosis, **72**
    potassium levels and, 76
Renal tubule, acidosis and, 12, 16, 72
    ADH and, 4
    amino-acids and, 2
    bicarbonate and, 3
    casts and 12, 15
    chloride and, 3
    creatinine and, 4
    damage, effects of, 12
        causes of, 13
    familial hypophosphataemia &, 187
    GFR and, 13
    glucose and, 2
    hypokalaemia and, 12
    hypophosphataemia and, 12
    pH, urinary and, 12
    phosphate and, 3
    polyuria and, 12
    potassium and, 3
    proteinuria and, 12
    sodium and, 3, 12
    sodium, urinary and, 12
    specific gravity, urinary and, 12
    urea and, 3
    urea, urinary and, 12
    water and, 4
Renin, **35**
    aldosteronism and, 46
    renal blood flow and, 35
    stimulus to, 35
Resin uptake tests, **166**
    nephrotic syndrome and, 168
    oral contraceptives and, 167
    pregnancy and, 167, **367**
"Resistant rickets", 187

Rhodopsin, 352
Riboflavin, 356
Rickets, 180
    renal tubular disorders and, 187
Rickets, "resistant", 187
Rothera's test, 153

S units, 238
Salicylates, acid base balance and, 80
    Gerhardt's test and, 154
    uric acid excretion and, 304
"Salt losing" syndrome, 106
Sarcoidosis, calcium in, 185
    proteins in, 234
Schilling test, 217
Scurvy, 361
Secretin, 215
Sequestrene, calcium, plasma, effect on
        in vitro, 395
    clearance, 17
    potassium, plasma, effect on in vitro,
        395
Seromucoid, 233
Serotonin, 371
S_f units, 252
SGOT, 287
    liver disease and, 272
SGPT, 287
    liver disease and, 272
SHBD, 289
Sia test, 243, 248
Sideroblastic anaemia, 312, 315
Siderophilin (see TIBC) 312
Siderosis, Bantu, 320
Small intestinal secretion, potassium
        content, 48
    sodium content, 38
Sodium, absorption of, 208
    acid-base balance and, 67
    Addison's disease and, 93
    ADH and, 36
    aldosterone and, 35
    aldosteronism, primary and, 45
    aldosteronism, secondary and, 47
    balance, assessment of, 28
    blood volume and, 35
    body content, 26, 28
    cell hydration and, 32
    concentration in body fluids, 38
    concentration changes, 33
    Cushing's syndrome and, 93
    depletion, 41
    distribution of, 29
    effect of change in concentration, 32
    excess, 45
    faecal, 26
    GFR and urinary, 9, 35
    hydrogen ion and, 3, 9, 67
    hypopituitarism and, 101, 121
    kidney and, 3

Sodium, natriuretic hormone and, 35
    osmolarity, plasma and, 32, 33
    osmotic diuresis and, 7
    potassium ion and, 3, 9
    preparations containing, 56
    treatment of disturbances, 52
    tubular damage and, 12
    urinary, 26, 34, 48
    water metabolism and, 32, 33, 52
Sphingomyelin, 251
Sprue, 210
Starch, 125
Stearic acid, 250
Steatorrhoea, 209, 216
    abetalipoproteinaemia and, 261
    causes of, 209
    diagnosis, 216
    effects of, 206
Stercobilin, 264
Stercobilinogen, 264
Steroid suppression test, 189, 198
Steroid therapy, 104
Stones, renal (see calculi, renal), 18
Stress, cortisol and, 97
    glucose and, 132
Stress centre, adrenal function and, 101
Succinyl choline sensitivity, 295
Sucrase, 206
    deficiency, 218
Sucrose, 125
Svedberg flotation units, 252
Svedberg units, 238
Sweat, potassium content, 48
    sodium content, 38
    water loss, 26, 41
Synacthen stimulation test, 100, 109
    Addison's disease and, 100

Tangier disease, 262
TCA cycle, 127
Testosterone, 92
Thalassaemia, plasma iron and, 312
Thiamine, 356
Thiocyanate and thyroidal radioiodine
        uptake, 158, 174
Thiouracil and iodine binding, 158, 174
"Third factor", 35
Thirst, control of, 36
    water depletion, 38
Thymol flocculation, 271
Thymol turbidity test, 271
Thyrocalcitonin, 156, 177
Thyroglobulin, 158
Thyroid adenoma and thyrotoxicosis,
        159
Thyroid antibodies, 172
Thyroid dyshormonogenesis,
    hypothyroidism and, 161
Thyroid function tests, 162
    interfering substances, 174

Thyroid hormones, action, 159
  bone, action on, 178
  circulating, **158**
  control, 158
  ingestion, and hyperthyroidism, 160
  synthesis, 156
Thyroiditis, 161
Thyroid stimulating hormone (*see*
    TSH), **118**
Thyrotoxicosis, **159**
  hypercalcaemia and, 185
Thyrotrophic hormone (*see* TSH), **118**
Thyrotrophin releasing factor, 118
Thyroxine, **158**
  circulating, 158
  synthesis, 158
Thyroxine binding globulin, **159**
  congenital deficiency, 168
  drugs and, 168
  nephrotic syndrome and, 11
  oral contraceptives and, 367
  pregnancy and, 367
  protein bound iodine and, **167**
  resin uptake tests and, **167**
Thyroxine, free, **159**
  control of TSH and, 159
  index, 168
Thyroxine, total plasma, **159**
  nephrotic syndrome and, 11
  oral contraceptive therapy and, 367
  pregnancy and, 367
TIBC, 312
  anaemia and, 313
  congenital transferrin deficiency and,
    317
  haemochromatosis and, 318
  iron deficiency and, 313
  nephrotic syndrome and, 11, 313
  oral contraceptives and, 313, **368**
  percentage saturation of, **313**
  pregnancy and, 313, **368**
T_m, 3
Tocopherols, 355
Tolbutamide test, 146, **154**
Tophi, gouty, 303
Total iron binding capacity (*see*
    TIBC), **312**
Transaminases, 287
  liver disease and, 272, 294
  myocardial infarction and, 293
Transferrin (*see* TIBC), **312**
Transplantation of the ureters, acidosis
    and, 76
Transport, active, 2
Transport, passive, 2
Tricarboxylic acid cycle, 127
Triglycerides, 250
  absorption, **205,** 254
  endogenous, 256
  exogenous, 256

Triglycerides, glycogen storage disease
    and, 148, 260
  hypothyroidism and, 170, 260
  oral contraceptives and, 260, **368**
  pregnancy and, 260, **368**
Tri-iodothyronine, 156
  circulating, 158
  synthesis of, 156
Tri-iodothyronine suppression test, 164
Tropical sprue, 210
Trypsin, 207
  faecal, pancreatic function and, **215**
Tryptophane, Hartnup disease and,
    339
  nicotinamide synthesis and, 357
TSH, 118
  ectopic production, 381
  hypopituitarism and, 121
  thyroid hormone synthesis and, 158
TSH stimulation test, **164**
  hypopituitarism and, 122
T_3 suppression test, **164**
Tyrosinase, 343
Tyrosine, 340

UDP glucuronyl transferase, 264, 277
    279
Ultracentrifugation, 238
  lipoproteins and, 252
Uraemia, glomerular disease and, 9
  iron, plasma and, 312
  tubular disease, 12
  water deficiency and, 34
Urate, excretion of, 301
  GFR and, 9
  metabolism of, **299**
  purines and, 301
  renal calculi and, 20
  renal failure and, 9
Urea, Addison's disease and, 93
  ADH, inappropriate and, 380
  cell hydration and, 32
  cerebral oedema and, 32
  clearance, **16**
  GFR and, **9**
  kidney and, 3
  liver disease and, 276
  metabolism, **14**
  osmotic diuresis and, 8, 36
  phosphate and, 177, **183**
  renal disease and, **14**
  tubular damage and, **12**
Ureteric transplantation, acidosis and
    76
Uricolysis, 301
Uricosuric drugs, 304
Uridyl diphosphate glucuronyl
    transferase, 264, 277, 279
Urine concentration test, 16, **23**
Urine, timed collection of, 396

Urobilin, 264
  urinary, 270, 284
Urobilinogen, 264
  urinary, 270, 283

Valine and maple syrup urine disease,
    340
Van den Bergh reaction, 265
Vanillyl mandelic acid, 375
Vasa recta, countercurrent
    multiplication and, 5, 7
Vasopressin, lysine, hypopituitarism and,
    104
Villi, intestinal, 204
  idiopathic steatorrhoea and, 210
Virilization, congenital adrenal
    hyperplasia and, 106
  Cushing's syndrome and, 93
Visual purple, 352
Vitamin A, 352
  steatorrhoea and, 353
Vitamin B_1, 356
Vitamin B_2, 356
Vitamin B_6, 358
Vitamin B_{12}, 359
  absorption, 207
  clearance, 17
  intestinal disease and, 216, 217
  liver and, 263
  pernicious anaemia and, 217
Vitamin C, 360
Vitamin D, 178, 354
  calcium absorption and, 175, 183
  deficiency, causes of, 183
    effects of, 180
  excess, effects of, 185
  hypocalcaemia, therapy of, 194
  idiopathic hypercalcaemia of infancy
    and, 185
  liver and, 263
  renal failure and, 183
  "resistant rickets" and, 187
  sarcoidosis and, 185
  steatorrhoea and, 206
Vitamin E, 355
Vitamin K, 355
  liver disease and, 272
  malabsorption and, 212
Vitamins, fat soluble, 351
  absorption of, 206

Vitamins, water soluble, 355
  absorption of, 208
VMA, 375
Von Gierke's disease, 148

Waldenström's macroglobulinaemia, 243
  Sia test and, 248
Water, absorption of, 208
  Addison's disease and, 93
  ADH and, 4, 36
  balance, 26
  body content of, 26
  Cushing's syndrome and, 93
  depletion, effects of, 34
  distribution of, 30
  disturbances of metabolism, 33, 38
    treatment, 52
  excess, 34, 43
  expired air and, 26, 41
  faecal, 26
  kidney and, 4, 26
  osmotic diuresis and, 7, 36, 41
  sodium and, 37
  sweat and, 26
  tubular damage and, 12
  urine and, 26
Water load test, 94
Weight, body, assessing hydration and,
    28
Wilson's disease, 345

Xanthine, 301
  renal calculi and, 21
  xanthinuria and, 306
Xanthine oxidase, 301
  allopurinol and, 304
  uric acid and, 301
  xanthinuria and, 306
Xanthinuria, 306
Xanthochromia, 385
Xanthomatosis, 258
Xerophthalmia, 353
Xerosis conjunctivae, 353
Xylose absorption, 214, 224

Zinc sulphate turbidity test, 271
Zollinger-Ellison syndrome, 219
  acid secretion and, 225
Zone electrophoresis, 230